DATE DUE

Modern Corn Production

Samuel R. Aldrich, Walter O. Scott and Earl R. Leng

Second Edition

i

Contents

Explanation of THE METRIC SYSTEM vi

Section 1. HOW THE CORN PLANT GROWS 1

Composition of the corn kernel 1

Germination and early growth 2

Growth of the stalk and leaves 5

Formation of the tassel and ear 7

Pollen shed, silking, and fertilization .. 8

Kernel development to maturity 13

The ear after maturity 14

Section 2. CORN IN YOUR FARMING SYSTEM 19

The best climate for corn 20

Geographically advantaged areas 24

Advantages of growing one or two crops 25

Insect and disease problems 26

Is continuous corn most profitable? ... 27

Can soils stand continuous row crops? 28

Narrow strips on steep land 29

Advantages of crop rotation 29

Crop diversity and yield stability 31

Double cropping 31

Livestock vs. cash grain farming 32

The importance of high yields 33

Section 3. HYBRID SELECTION 35

Selecting the proper maturity 35

Factors that influence standability 37

Resistance to disease 38

History of Race T leaf blight 39

Adaptability to a wide range of conditions 40

How hybrids are produced 41

Help in choosing hybrids 44

Corn for special purposes: white; waxy; amylomaize; high lysine, high oil; high sugar; dwarf corn; popcorn 45

Section 4. SEEDBED PREPARATION 53

Needs of a seedbed 53

Weed control in seedbed preparation . 54

Maintaining proper tilth 55

Overfitting 56

Primary tillage 57

Leaving residues on the surface 58

Moldboard, chisel and disk plows .. 58

Fall vs. spring plowing 58

Lister and subsurface tillers 60

Rotary tillers 62

Chisels, subsoilers and pan-breakers 62

Secondary tillage 64

Disk 64

Spring-tooth harrow and field cultivator 64

Cultipacker..................... 65

Minimum tillage 67

Strip tillage 73

Sod planting, zero tillage 73

Section 5. PLANTING FOR HIGH YIELDS.................................... 77

When to plant..................... 78
Planting by soil temperature......... 79
Depth to plant..................... 80
"Calendarized" planting............ 80
Optimum plant population......... 81
Hill-drop or drill?................ 83
Row width...................... 84

New types of planters.............. 85
Calibrating the corn planter........ 87
No-till, zero-till 89
Ridge planting.................... 92
Aerial planting.................... 92
Orienting the kernels.............. 93
Applying water through the planter... 93

Section 6. FERTILIZING FOR TOP PROFIT 95

Fertilizer labels 96
Physial forms: gas, liquid, solid, slurry 99
Elements necessary for growth....... 104
"Natural" vs. chemical fertilizers..... 105
"Organic" or "natural" foods....... 105
Nitrogen....................... 106
    Kinds of nitrogen fertilizers 108
    Fertilizer reactions in the soil...... 110
    Movement through the soil........ 113
    Biological changes in nitrogen 115
Phosphorus..................... 123
    Uptake by corn 123
    Kinds of fertilizers.............. 124
    Phosphorus reactions in soil 128
    Factors that influence availability... 132
    Soil tests..................... 132
    Placement of P fertilizers 133
    Effect on zinc and manganese 133
Potassium...................... 134
    Uptake by corn 134
    Kinds of fertilizers.............. 135
    Reactions in the soil 136
    Time and placement 137
    Soil tests..................... 138
Secondary and Micronutrients 140
    Conditions favoring deficiencies.... 140

    Formulations 143
    Methods of application 143
Soils differ in fertility needs 145
Maintaining organic matter 149
Soil tests as guides to fertilizing...... 151
Nutrients soils can furnish 157
Farm manure................... 159
Crop residues and green manure..... 160
Placement of row fertilizer 164
Fertilizer burn 168
Broadcast fertilizer............... 169
Bulk blending 173
Leaf feeding.................... 174
Best times to supply fertilizer........ 174
Influence of fertilizer on maturity and lodging.................... 177
Costs and returns from fertilizer 178
Liming acid soils................. 180
Watching the crop through the season 183
How to spot fertility "quacks" 184
Importance of combining good practices....................... 185
Municipal wastes, sludge 185

Section 7. WATER MANAGEMENT **189**

Water needs................... 189

How to stretch the water supply 194

Plant population and water needs 197

Early planting and available moisture. 198

Chemical and plastic covers........ 200

Water movement in soils 200

Tile drainage 203

Land smoothing.................. 203

Irrigation 207

Soil conservation and water
management..................... 217

The Universal Soil Loss Equation 219

Section 8. WEED CONTROL **223**

The importance of early control...... 224

Pre-emergence control............. 226

Herbicide - fertilizer mixtures 229

Crop rotation effects 230

Cultivation when weeds aren't present 233

Control in no-till corn............. 234

Miscellaneous methods 234

Herbicide injury.................. 236

Section 9. COMBATING CORN TROUBLES **238**

Pesticide needs of high yield systems.. 239

A key to troubles through the season . 241

Pictures and descriptions of corn
troubles with suggested treatments.... 246

Before emergence 246

Emergence to knee-high 250

Knee-high to tasseling........... 259

Silking to maturity.............. 273

Mature to harvest 290

In storage..................... 292

Check list for spotting troubles 297

Plant tissue tests 298

Deciding whether to replant poor
stands.......................... 300

Section 10. HARVESTING AND STORING HIGH QUALITY SILAGE........... **303**

Feeding to control spoilage 309

Nitrates in silage 309

Silo gas....................... 314

Time to harvest.................. 303

Preservatives.................... 305

Frosted corn.................... 307

Section 11. HARVESTING, STORING, AND MARKETING GRAIN CORN **317**

When to harvest grain 317

Moisture levels for safe storage 318

Preservatives.................... 319

Moldy corn 321

Market discounts for high moisture... 322

Harvesting, drying and storing
systems......................... 323

Using solar energy................ 328

Corn topping 328

Temperature at which frost occurs.... 330

Handling soft corn 330

Changes in the corn market........ 331

Deciding when to sell............. 333

Cash and futures markets.......... 335

Section 12. ENVIRONMENTAL PROTECTION AND IMPROVEMENT......... **339**

Historical perspective 339

Nature of pollution from agriculture.. 341

Sediment 342

Nitrates...................... 343

Phosphorus..................... 346

Pesticides 348

Impact of technology 350

Agriculture: victim of pollution 351

Section 13. EFFICIENT USE OF ENERGY..................... **353**

Agriculture uses and captures energy . 353

Energy in food production 355

Energy for corn.................. 356

Tips for high prices, short supplies ... 358

Section 14. A LOOK INTO THE FUTURE..................... **361**

Changes in corn growing methods.... 361

The ultimate limiting factors 364

    Light....................... 364

Available water 364

Carbon dioxide 365

How to grow contest-winning yields .. 365

REFERENCE TABLES.................................... **368**

1. Plant nutrients in crops 368

2. Grain shrinkage 369

3. Amount of corn at different
    moisture to equal 1 bushel 369

4. Dry test weight from wet weight... 370

5. Kernel spacing for various stands.. 370

6. Capacity of silos 371

7. Amino acids in grain 371

INDEX **371**

CREDITS for photographs and charts **378**

The Metric System

Most of the world uses the metric system of weights and measures. There is much talk about using it in the United States, Canada, Great Britan and other countries where the English system is now used. Most scientific journals have already converted to metric.

We decided to put all weights, measures and yields in both the English and Metric systems in Modern Corn Production, second edition. The use of both systems is somewhat awkward. When we show amounts of phosphorus and potassium on both the elemental and oxide bases and in the English and Metric systems it is really cumbersome.

We are aware of the major problems and considerable cost involved in changing everything to the metric system. But the dual system in Modern Corn Production will help to prepare U.S. and many other readers for the anticipated change. It will make it easier for those who read both scientific and non-scientific literature. Finally, it will greatly increase readability for our many readers throughout the world who are already on the metric system.

In simplest terms, the metric system for weights and measures begins with a unit of measure and then increases to the larger units by multiplying by 10 or 100 or 1000.

For example:

10 millimeters = 1 centimeter
100 centimeters = 1 meter
1000 meters = 1 kilometer

We have intentionally written out the full metric words in some cases and abbreviated in others.

We had to chose between using kilograms or quintals as the unit for yields. We chose quintals because quintals per acre will look much more like bushels per acre than will kilos (short for kilograms). For example, 100 bushels of corn per acre equals 62.76 quintals per hectare. Those who prefer kilos to quintals, need only to move the decimal two places to the right: 62.76 quintals per hectare equals 6276 kilos.

The only trouble with using quintals is that in some Spanish speaking countries the quintal is a different sized unit than the standard metric unit. In those countries a quintal is 100 pounds rather than 100 kilograms (220.5 pounds).

The conversion from English to Metric and vice versa is given on the opposite page. Because of our inexperience in dealing with the metric system, we expect to find some errors in conversions in this book. Hopefully they are few.

English — Metric System Comparisons

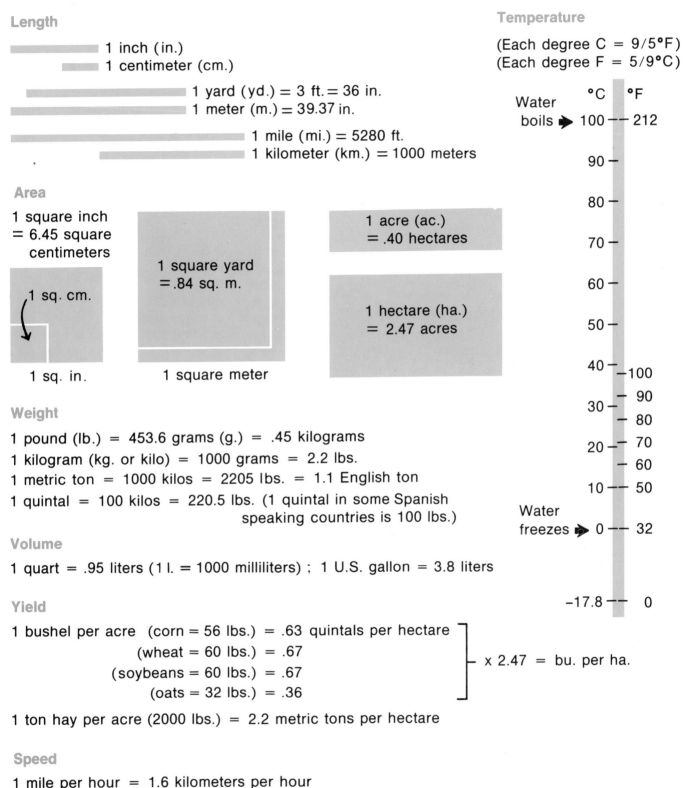

Length

1 inch (in.)
1 centimeter (cm.)

1 yard (yd.) = 3 ft. = 36 in.
1 meter (m.) = 39.37 in.

1 mile (mi.) = 5280 ft.
1 kilometer (km.) = 1000 meters

Area

1 square inch = 6.45 square centimeters

1 sq. cm.

1 sq. in.

1 square yard = .84 sq. m.

1 square meter

1 acre (ac.) = .40 hectares

1 hectare (ha.) = 2.47 acres

Temperature

(Each degree C = 9/5°F)
(Each degree F = 5/9°C)

	°C	°F
Water boils ➤	100	212
	90	
	80	
	70	
	60	
	50	
	40	100
	30	90
		80
	20	70
		60
	10	50
Water freezes ➤	0	32
	-17.8	0

Weight

1 pound (lb.) = 453.6 grams (g.) = .45 kilograms
1 kilogram (kg. or kilo) = 1000 grams = 2.2 lbs.
1 metric ton = 1000 kilos = 2205 lbs. = 1.1 English ton
1 quintal = 100 kilos = 220.5 lbs. (1 quintal in some Spanish speaking countries is 100 lbs.)

Volume

1 quart = .95 liters (1 l. = 1000 milliliters) ; 1 U.S. gallon = 3.8 liters

Yield

1 bushel per acre (corn = 56 lbs.) = .63 quintals per hectare
(wheat = 60 lbs.) = .67
(soybeans = 60 lbs.) = .67
(oats = 32 lbs.) = .36
⎤ x 2.47 = bu. per ha.

1 ton hay per acre (2000 lbs.) = 2.2 metric tons per hectare

Speed

1 mile per hour = 1.6 kilometers per hour

Rate of Application

1 pound per acre = 1.12 kilograms (kg., kilos) per hectare = .45 kilos per ac.
1 gallon per acre = 3.8 liters per acre = 9.4 liters per hectare

Samuel R. Aldrich,

Assistant Director, Agricultural Experiment Station and Professor of Soil Fertility in Extension, University of Illinois

Samuel R. Aldrich has been on the Illinois staff since 1957. Born in Michigan, he completed his undergraduate training at Michigan State University in 1938 and received his graduate degree from Ohio State University in 1942. In 1952 he went to Cornell University as an extension specialist and remained there 15 years, serving for several years as leader in agronomy extension. He has conducted fertility research and during the 1950s, Professor Aldrich was involved in pioneer research and field trials on minimum tillage.

Dr. Aldrich is co-author, with E. L. Worthen, of *Farm Soils, Their Fertilization and Management,* is co-editor of *Advances in Corn Production,* and co-author with Walter O. Scott of *Modern Soybean Production.* He has been widely published in leading farm magazines; his articles have dealt with fertility programs, minimum tillage, and crop rotation. In recent years he has been involved in environmental matters and served two years on the Illinois Pollution Control Board.

Walter O. Scott,

Professor of Crops Extension, University of Illinois

Walter O. Scott, a native Kansan, has been on the staff of the University of Illinois since 1946. He did his undergraduate work at Kansas State University, received his masters from the University of Illinois, and his Ph.D. degree from Purdue University. He has served as coordinator of agronomy extension for several years. It is for his active part in the Association of Official Seed Certifying Agencies that Dr. Scott has received widespread credit for service to Agriculture. He is an outspoken advocate of the use of high quality planting seed in farming. Dr. Scott is co-author with Samuel R. Aldrich of *Modern Soybean Production.* He is an authority on corn and soybean production in the midwest and has authored many articles dealing with the production of these crops.

Earl R. Leng,

Professor of Plant Breeding and Genetics, University of Illinois

Earl Leng grew up on a farm near Williamsfield, Illinois. He graduated from the University of Illinois College of Agriculture in 1941, and has served on the staff there since that time, with interruptions only for military service. From 1955 to 1964 Professor Leng was in charge of Illinois corn performance tests. He is an authority on corn problems, the growth and development of the corn plant, and practical breeding programs. Professor Leng is also well versed in the problems of foreign corn production; he has served with USAID as Advisor on Agricultural Research and has been a Fulbright Senior Research Fellow.

1

How the Corn Plant Grows

The corn plant is one of Nature's most amazing energy-storing devices. From a seed which weighs little more than one-hundredth of an ounce, a plant 7 to 10 feet tall (2⅓ to 3⅓ meters) develops in about nine weeks. In the following two months, this plant produces 600 to 1000 seeds similar to the one from which it started. For perspective, the corn plant's achievement can be compared with that of small grains: wheat produces a 50-fold yield per seed planted.

How does the corn plant get this job done? First, by producing a large, efficient energy factory—the plant with its roots, leaves, stalks and flowering parts; then by storing huge amounts of energy in a concentrated product — the corn grain.

Seed and Embryo

The mature corn kernel is made up of three main parts, the seed coat or *pericarp*, the starchy *endosperm*, and the *embryo* (often called "germ") which will develop into a new plant. Each of these parts has a different hereditary makeup—the *pericarp* is all tissue from the mother plant, which produced the seed; the *endosperm* inherits two-thirds from the mother plant and one-third from the male; the *embryo* has an equal contribution from the male and female parents. Usually,

these differences in heredity are not important to the commercial corn grower because all the pollinations that make hybrid seed are controlled by the seed grower. In growing special types, however, such as waxy maize, popcorn and even white corn, the hereditary makeup of the kernel part can be important

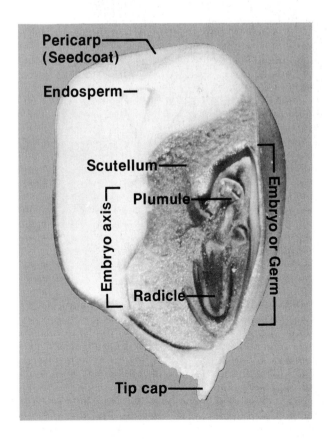

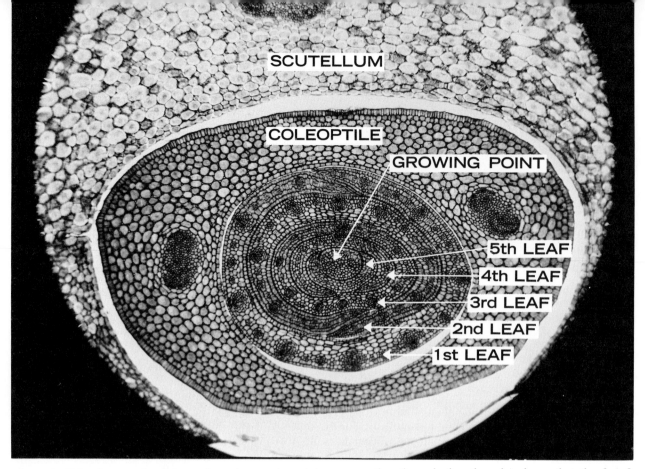

Figure 1. This photograph of the embryonic corn kernel (a cross section through the plumule) shows that the first 5 leaves of the young corn seedling are already present in the seed when it is planted. The leaves are the concentric partial rings imbedded within the coleoptile which in turn is surrounded by the scutellum.

because foreign pollen can change endosperm composition from the desired type to an undesirable or unacceptable form.

Each of the three parts of the kernel has a definite role to play. The *pericarp* protects the seed both before and after planting—limiting or preventing the entry of fungi or bacteria which would invade the kernel. If the pericarp is damaged, germination of the seed may be slowed; disease organisms can invade the germinating kernel and use up the stored food before the seedling is established. Thus, sound seed with little or no seed coat damage is important for seedling vigor and the establishment of good stands.

The *endosperm* is the main energy reserve of the kernel. In most dent corn, this part makes up about four-fifths of the whole kernel by weight. It is about 90 per cent starch and 7 percent protein, with small amounts of oils, minerals and other chemical constituents. The chief function of the en-

dosperm is to provide food energy for the young plant until its roots are well established and its own leaves are able to manufacture enough energy-producing substances (carbohydrates) to meet requirements for life and growth. The protein in corn endosperm is a horny network in which starch granules are imbedded.

The *embryo* of the corn kernel is made up of two main parts, the *embryo axis* or new plant, and the *scutellum*, which is a rich storehouse of food for the developing seedling. In the mature kernel, the embryo axis consists of a *plumule* (leafy part) in which 5 to 6 embryonic leaves and a *radicle* or root-like portion are already formed in miniature (figure 1). Thus, the parts which will first develop into a new seedling are already formed in the resting seed, and the nature of the early seedling is already determined to a considerable extent when the seed of the previous crop is fully developed. The *scutellum* (*cotyledon* in botanical terms) is high in oil (35 to 40 percent in scutellums of ordinary corn kernels) and contains many substances which are active and important in the very early stages of germination and growth.

Germination and Seedling Establishment

When the corn kernel is planted, it usually is placed in soil moist and warm enough to allow germination to begin promptly. If the seed is in contact with moisture, water is absorbed through the seed coat and the kernel begins to swell. Chemical changes activate growth in the embryo axis and if conditions continue to be favorable, the radicle elongates and emerges from the seed coat within 2 or 3 days (figure 2). Shortly thereafter, the plumule also begins to elongate and additional leaves begin to form inside this part of the developing seedling (called the *coleoptile* after it breaks out of the seed).

The first seedling root is soon followed by several other *seminal* or seed roots (figure 3), which serve to anchor the developing seedling and play a role in water and nutrient uptake. However, these do not build a permanent root system — the main root system originates later from the *crown* of the developing plant *above* the first root system.

Between the point of attachment to the seed and the crown is a tubular, white, stemlike part, the *mesocotyl* (first internode) (figure 3). Elongation of this structure is very important to emergence of the seedling. With an average planting depth of 2 to 3 inches (5 to 7.5 centimeters), the mesocotyl will ordinarily elongate about half the distance to the surface. Lengthening of the coleoptile brings the leafy parts the rest of the way above ground. When growing conditions are favorable the mesocotyl can, if necessary, elongate two or three times this far (figure 6, page). However, most Corn Belt dent strains have a limit somewhere around 5 or 6 inches (12.5 to 15 centimeters) planting

Figure 2. The kernel has swelled and the radicle (root) has just broken through the seed coat. The plumule (shoot that will become the stalk) has not yet emerged but its presence is indicated by the ridge under the seedcoat.

Coleoptile ➞

Figure 3. The plumule (shoot) breaks through the seed coat one or two days after the radicle (figure 2). It is enclosed in the coleoptile which protects the leaves as the shoot pushes upward through the soil. The coleoptile in this seedling has ruptured and two leaves have begun to unfold. Two seminal roots have been added to the first root (radicle) and the total number may increase to 6 or 7 before this early root system has fulfilled its purpose and is supplanted by the main root system (figure 5).

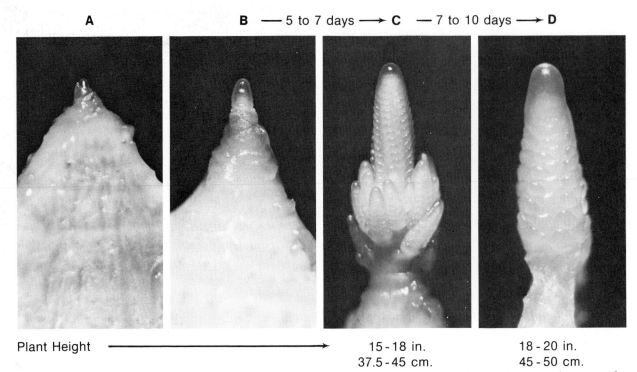

Plant Height ———————————————————→   15 - 18 in.   18 - 20 in.
                                                              37.5 - 45 cm.   45 - 50 cm.

Figure 4. Appearance of the internal growing point of the corn plant, 56 times natural size. A. Vegetative stage, first 4 or 5 weeks after germination. All of the leaves have already started in miniature. B. Transition stage. The main shoot is beginning to lengthen just before the tassel and ear shoots start forming. The plants are still only 15 to 18 inches tall. C. The young tassel showing the tip and branches. It will not emerge from the leaf whorl for another 4 to 5 weeks. D. The miniature ear, less than 1/16 inch in length, is borne on the tip of a side branch (figure 12).

depth, beyond which the mesocotyl and coleoptile cannot elongate enough to bring the leafy parts above ground. A few rare corn types have the capacity to produce mesocotyls 8 inches (20 cm) to a foot (⅓ meter) long: these strains were selected by Indian tribes of the Southwest for their capacity to emerge from deep planting in dry soils. They are of little or no value as commercial corns in the Corn Belt. When corn is planted too deep, or when growing conditions are unfavorable, elongation of the mesocotyl may stop; in other cases the seedling loses orientation and grows in a corkscrew fashion, failing to emerge (see "Corn Troubles," page 248).

The coleoptile is pointed and quite stiff. It can push its way through normal soil. But when it ruptures an inch or more below the ground, the leaf that is exposed is quite wide — no longer pointed or rigid. It cannot push its way to the soil surface, but instead spreads out, stays yellow and twisted, and soon dies.

The coleoptile usually emerges 6 to 10 days after planting but may be delayed by cool temperatures or dry soil. As soon as this part reaches the light, it splits at the tip and two true leaves unfold in rapid succession. The next few leaves come out of the whorl and unfold at the rate of about one leaf every 3 days under good growing conditions. Seven days after emergence, the new seedling should be well established, with 2 leaves fully expanded and with its primary root system developed to the extent that it no longer depends on the nearly-exhausted food supply in the kernel.

Germination and seedling establishment are the first critical times in the life of the corn plant. Once the seed coat is broken, the food-rich tissues of the kernel are open to attack by disease organisms unless the seed has been protected by treatment. *If the soil is too cold, too wet, or too dry, germination may be slow or the young seedling may die before it becomes established.* Nutrient shortages are not critical in the first few days, but as the roots begin to take over the job of nourishing the young plant, shortages of major elements, especially phosphorus, can seriously slow growth and development. Many of the troubles which can occur at this stage (see "Corn Troubles," page 239) including frost need not have a permanent effect on growth or yield if they are corrected in time. The young plant is flexible in its requirements and has a high capacity to recover from early setbacks. This stage when the growing point is still below ground, is most susceptible to damage by flooding, especially if temperature is high (see page 251). For maximum and most economical yields, it is best if early growing conditions are made as favorable as possible.

Vegetative Development

Once the seedling is established, the corn plant begins to create the root system and leaf structure which will be used later to support ear and grain formation. Under normal Corn Belt conditions, all the leaves which a plant will ever have are formed during the first 4 to 5 weeks of the plant's development.

The new leaves are produced by a single *growing point*, at the tip of the stem (A in figure 4). This region actually is underground or near ground level for much of the first 3 to 4 weeks after planting. As the plant develops, you may observe "new" leaves appearing until shortly before tasseling time; yet all these leaves were formed inside the plant during the "vegetative" period of growth. Starting with about 5 embroynic leaves in the seed, a normal corn plant develops 20 to 23 foliage leaves. All of these are started in the growing point before development of the tassel can begin (C in figure 4). The first 5 to 7 leaves never get very large. They break off and are likely to be overlooked as the base of the corn stalk enlarges.

The root system develops rapidly during this stage of growth. The seminal roots

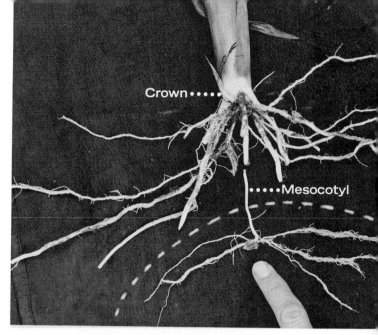

Figure 5. The circled area includes the early root system (radicle and seminal roots). Note that the main root system arises from the "crown" above the first roots.

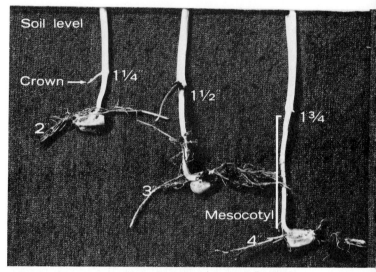

Figure 6. These seeds were planted 2, 3 and 4 inches deep, but the "crown" from which the main root system will develop is at 1¼, 1½ and 1¾ inches. Increasing the depth of planting from 2 to 4 inches resulted in the crown being only ½ inch deeper. The section between the seed and the "crown" is called the mesocotyl (see text). The deeper the planting, the longer the mesocotyl becomes.

quickly lose their importance (figure 5) and the young plant is supported and nourished by the permanent root system which begins to develop from the crown. Depth of planting has only a slight influence on the depth at which the main root system originates (figure 6). The main root system continues

Figure 7. After tasseling, brace roots emerge from the lower nodes and penetrate the soil surface where they branch extensively. It appears that they not only support the plant in the late stages of growth but also absorb nutrients (see text).

Figure 8. The growing point of this knee-high corn plant is only about one inch (2.5 cm) above the secondary roots which means that it is about at ground level.

to grow downward and to branch, and additional roots are produced in successive whorls from stem nodes above the crown. These joints from which roots develop just below the soil surface correspond to the joints above ground from which leaves arise. By the time the corn plant has 8 leaves fully emerged or is about knee-high, the roots have reached the middle of the corn rows and penetrated to a depth of about 18 inches (45 centimeters). There are still few roots in the surface soil layer. But as the plants become larger, the entire plow layer becomes filled with a mass of roots which feed on the fertility that is concentrated there in productive soil. To avoid root pruning, cultivation should have been completed before this occurs.

Later, usually after tasseling, whorls of brace roots thrust out from the lower joints and enter the soil (figure 7). Until recently it was believed their only function was to

support the plant. Research at Purdue University reveals that they can effectively absorb phosphorus and perhaps other nutrients. Brace roots branch profusely in the surface soil and thus provide feeding roots in a soil zone that may have relatively few other active roots late in the season.

Depending chiefly on temperature — but also to some extent on nutrient and moisture supply — the average Corn Belt hybrid can require as little as 18 to 20 days or as many as 40 days from planting to reach the stage of development at which the miniature tassel is developed. Cool temperatures slow down the rate of growth and development; warm temperatures speed up these processes.

Although good growth is desirable, the vegetative development stage is not usually so critical in determining the yield as earlier or later developmental stages. The most important effect of this stage is its bearing on when the plant will mature. *Differences be-*

6

tween varieties, or those resulting from temperature and other environmental effects, influence the length of this developmental period more than they do any other stage of growth and development. If early development is slow, tasseling, silking and grain maturing will be delayed.

Several nutrient deficiency symptoms, especially phosphorus, potassium and zinc, are most likely to be seen during the vegetative development stage. Insects, wet weather, hail and other hazards also have their effect. However, the corn plant has an amazing capacity to recover from apparent injury during this stage, provided that later conditions are favorable. If, however, the plant is broken below the growing point, it cannot recover.

Tassel and Ear Initiation

A sudden and dramatic change in the function of the growing point takes place when the plant has formed its full number of leaves, many of which are not yet visible. Under normal Corn Belt conditions, this occurs about 30 days after planting. At this time, the corn plant is about knee-high. The growing point is at the soil surface (figure 8). Eight to ten leaves can be seen externally if none have died or been broken off. With early to mid-May planting, this point usually is reached between June 2 and June 20.

The growing point, which has been rounded or hemispherical until now, (figure 4, A) elongates into a round-tipped cylinder (B). This transition, which lasts only 2 or 3 days, is followed by the appearance of tiny bumps on the sides of the growing point. Within a few more days, the embryonic tassel has developed far enough to be recognizable (C). At this time, the lower stalk joints (internodes) begin to elongate rapidly. The plant then enters a stage of extremely rapid vertical growth, placing heavy requirements on the root system to supply water and nutrients. The roots grow rapidly during this time, and soon fill most of the available space in the rooting zone.

The miniature ears begin to form on the side of the growing point shortly after the tassel has been initiated but they develop little for 2 to 3 weeks. The main corn ear (figure 12, page 10) is borne at the tip of a side branch which arises from about the sixth to eighth node below the tassel. In fact, five to seven nodes below the main ear-node produce rudimentary ears and the first one below the main ear often produces a cob and grain where the stand is thin, but only rarely in thick stands. In prolific strains grown in southern states, ears may develop at several nodes.

From the beginning of tassel initiation, the corn plant normally requires 5 to 6 weeks to reach the stage of pollen-shedding and silking. During this period, which usually is in the hottest weather of the year, solar energy is high (see page 363) and plant size increases at a tremendous rate. Tassel initiation occurs when the plant is about 15 to 18 inches (37.5 to 45 centimeters) tall. All leaves have begun to form by this time, but the main growth in size of stalk, leaves and flowering parts occurs while the flowering organs (tassel and ear) are developing inside the plant. All of the life processes must be operating at full speed and efficiency if maximum yield is to be obtained. The leaves conduct photosynthesis (capturing the sun's energy and producing sugars) at a high rate, roots take up water and nutrients rapidly, and the various enzymes which control metabolic processes are at a high rate of activity.

By the time the tassel emerges and the tip of the ear shoot can be seen, the plant is beginning to slow its rate of vegetative growth and is in the final stages of preparation for pollen shed and kernel set. All of the internodes except the top two or three have fully elongated about a week before pollen shed begins and the plant has reached its full height. The last few days of the period before pollen shed and silking are a time when the plant spends most of its energy to produce the mature pollen, and to form the cob and ear structures. These two processes create a very high requirement for proteins in which young tissues are especially rich. If growing conditions have been unfavorable, especially if nitrogen metabolism in protein formation has been deficient, the size of the developing ear is decreased. Apparently within the control mechanism of the plant, tassel and pollen formation take priority over ear and silk formation at this stage, so the tassel function and pollen shedding are much less likely to be damaged by unfavorable conditions than are ear formation and silk development. A few days before pollen shed begins, the top internodes elongate rapidly and thrust the tassel out of the leaf whorl.

The size of the ear is determined over about a three week period starting about 6 weeks after the plant emerges. First the number of rows of ovules (kernels) is determined. Then the maximum number of kernels per row is fixed by the ovules which develop silks. Drought or nutrient deficiency stress at this stage, especially 10 days to 2 weeks prior to silking and pollen shed, can greatly reduce the number of kernels that develop.

This stage, which includes pollination, is the most critical period in the development of the corn plant. The high requirements for nutrients, water and the "building block" products of metabolism make any shortages or defects in function at this stage especially serious. Moreover, damage to pollen or to ear structure at this time is likely to be permanent, and has little chance of being overcome by favorable conditions later. This is the stage at which shortages of nutrients (especially nitrogen), drouth, serious injury from insects, and overcrowding have their greatest effect. Often, however, the damage is hidden within the plant and you cannot see the results until later when it is, of course, too late. If you have an irrigation system, be sure that the crop has plenty of water during this period.

Flowering
(Pollen Shed and Silking)

If we could fantasize and say that the corn plant itself is "interested" in its functions, it would be clear that its major objective is to produce grain — seeds — in order to assure the next generation. For this reason, after its preparation for flowering is complete, the corn plant directs most of its energies and functions toward the main job of producing kernels on an ear. The first of the final steps in this process is *flowering* — the functional stage for which tassel and ear shoot were developed.

Pollen shed and silking of the corn plant usually take place during the hottest days of the growing season — mid-July to early August in the central Corn Belt. By this time, all major vegetative growth of the plant has taken place. The leaves and stalks have reached their full size, and metabolic activity of the plant tissues is normally at a peak level. Without delay, the flowering parts emerge, fertilization of the silk is completed by pollen, and kernel development starts while all activities of the plant are at their maximum rate and capacity.

The *tassel* (figure 9) is the male flowering structure of the corn plant. Unlike all other major grain crops, the corn plant has separate male and female flowering parts. The only function of the tassel is to produce ample quantities of pollen to fertilize the female structures (ears). No one can give a completely accurate figure for the number of pollen grains produced by a vigorous corn tassel, but it is probably somewhere between 2 million and 5 million for each normal-sized tassel. This means that there are 2,000 to 5,000 pollen grains produced for *each* silk. In its evolution, the corn plant has developed pollination habits insuring that there is nearly always pollen for every exposed silk.

Pollen shed does not begin when the tassel first emerges from the leaf whorl in most types of corn. Ordinarily, the tip of the tassel

Figure 10. The anthers open at the tip, usually in early to mid-morning and the pollen grains pour out.

Figure 9. The tassel normally emerges a week or ten days before the first silks, but pollen shedding is delayed until 2 or 3 days before the first silks. From 20,000 to 50,000 pollen grains are produced in the anthers of a tassel. Pollen shedding usually continues 5 to 8 days.

can be seen a week to ten days before any silks appear. The tassel stretches out from the enclosing leaves and usually becomes fully spread before any pollen is shed. The pollen grains are borne in *anthers* (figure 10), each of which contains a large number of pollen grains. These anthers emerge from enclosing *glumes,* usually in early to mid-morning after the dew has dried off the tassel.

The anthers split open at the bottom and shed their pollen into the wind. The pollen is light, and is often carried a considerable distance on the wind but most of it settles within 20 to 50 feet (6 to 15 meters). One full-shedding plant can provide enough pollen for several ears, if the timing and spread of pollen are right.

Pollen shed continues for several days — 5 to 8 is usual — with the peak production coming about the third day. Pollen shed begins from the middle of the central spike of the tassel, spreads out over the whole tassel in succeeding days, and ends with shed from the tips and bases of the lower branches.

Pollen shed is not a continuous process. It stops when the tassel is too wet or too

Figure 11. See text. **Figure 13.** See text.

Figure 12. The corn ear is borne on the tip of a side branch. The ear of a typical Corn Belt hybrid has 750 to 1000 ovules (potential kernels), each of which must be pollinated through an attached silk that is exposed from the husks at the tip of the ear.

dry and begins again when temperature and moisture conditions are favorable. On a typical midsummer day, the peak shedding is between 9:00 and 11:00 a.m.

Pollen is not subject to being washed off the tassel during a rain because none is being shed. Shedding will not start again until sometime after the rain stops. Neither is pollen especially vulnerable to being washed off after it lands on a silk. The pollen grain germinates and starts the pollen tube down the silk within a few minutes after coming in contact with the silk, figure 11. Under favorable conditions pollen will remain viable for only 18 to 24 hours. However, this is probably not a major reason for poor pollination.

Shortage of pollen rarely is a problem in corn production, except under conditions of extreme heat or drouth, which may damage a high percentage of plant tops, or in the case where planned genetic sterility prevents pollen formation. Usually, poor seed set is caused by some interference with silk formation or ear development. This may be the result of silks emerging after pollen has been shed. The *amount* of pollen produced is almost never a limiting factor in grain yield.

The corn *ear,* or female flowering structure, is a unique organ in the plant kingdom. No other major crop produces grain on a *side branch* or branches as corn does (figure 12). The ear itself is a central cob with a cylindrical group of female flowers (figure 13), each capable of producing a kernel if pollinated at the proper time. On a well-developed ear, there are 750 to 1000 potential kernels — "ovules" — arranged in an even number of rows around the cob.

In normal Corn Belt hybrids, there are 16, 18 or 20 *rows* of potential kernels per ear, and about 50 potential *kernels* per row. Each of these *ovules* produce a long slender tube — the *silk* — which receives the pollen and conducts the contents of the pollen grain down to the female flower on the cob.

Ordinarily, the first silks (figure 14) pro-

Figure 14. Silks usually begin to emerge from the ear husks 2 to 3 days after pollen shedding begins. Each silk is a long, slender tube attached to an ovule (potential kernel) on the ear. Pollen grains fall on the silk and are held by tiny hairs and a sticky surface. They germinate and send a pollen tube down the silk to the ovule where the pollen nucleus fertilizes the egg and the new kernel begins to develop.

11

Figure 15. Artificial shade structures placed over corn plants showed that the first few days after pollination are critical in determining whether kernels develop or abort.

duced on a plant emerge from the enclosing husks one or three days after pollen has begun to shed on the plant. The silks from near the base of the ear emerge first, and those from the tip appear last. Under favorable growing conditions, all silks will emerge and be ready for pollination within 3 to 5 days; thus there is time for all silks to be pollinated before the tassel stops shedding pollen. Yet, despite this overlap in the timing of pollen shed and silking, the pollen of a given plant rarely fertilizes silks of the same plant. Under field conditions, 97 percent or more of the kernels produced by each plant are pollinated by other plants in the field.

When the pollen grains fall on corn silks, they are trapped by small hairs and by the moist, sticky nature of the surface. The pollen grain germinates rapidly, producing a *pollen tube* which grows down the silk channel and enters the female flower. The pollen tube grows the length of the silk in 12 to 28 hours. Usually, the first tube to reach the

female *egg sac* causes fertilization, and a new kernel begins to develop from this union.

Pollination is an extremely critical stage in the life of the corn plant. Failures or troubles at this stage have drastic effects on the yield produced, since a kernel which does not begin developing at this stage cannot start later, and an ear shoot which is not well-formed and fully-pollinated can never become a full-sized ear at maturity. Silks dry rapidly under hot dry conditions and may not contain enough moisture to support pollen germination and growth of the pollen tube to the ovary.

Hot dry weather conditions are much more likely to interfere with pollination than is wet weather. It's doubtful that rainy weather has any detrimental effect on kernel set.

Perhaps the most critical matter at this stage is the heavy demand for water and nutrients, especially nitrogen, which is set up by the tremendous physiological activity of the flowering plant. This is complicated by the fact, mentioned above, that flowering often is a time of moisture shortage.

Actually, many of the difficulties at the flowering stage may have resulted from problems that arose during the preceding development stage. One of the most important of these is poor timing ("nicking") of pollen shed with silk emergence. *Nearly always, this results from delayed silking,* which in turn may be traced to faulty ear shoot development. Extreme shortage of moisture is likely the most common cause of delayed silking. As we have said actual pollen shortage is rare; silking after the pollen has shed is much more common.

The first few days after fertilization is a very critical period. If proteins and sugars are in short supply because of drouth, nutrient deficiencies, very cloudy weather or shading from too high plant population, kernels in the upper part of the ear which are at the end of the assembly line abort and even though fertilized they fail to develop. Illinois researcher Earley found that 90 percent shade, figure 15, for three days reduced yield of one hybrid by 25 percent. Six days of shade reduced yield 71 percent. A more shade-tolerant hybrid was reduced 16 to 44 percent.

Kernel Development and Maturation

The union of the male sperm nuclei from the pollen tube with the female egg and polar nuclei gives the embryonic corn kernel its start. These unions, which are called *fertilization* and are of a double nature (embryo and endosperm) in each female structure, produce two parts of the developing kernel, as we have already seen. The embryo ("germ") will become the new plant; the starch *endosperm* serves as a food reserve. Both are enclosed in a *pericarp* (seed coat) formed entirely from tissue of the mother plant.

For the first few days, no visible change takes place in the fertilized ear shoot, except that the silks wilt and turn brown. The cob continues to grow. By the time the developing kernels appear as watery blisters, the cob has reached its full length and diameter. The blister stage is reached about 1½ weeks after fertilization takes place. Within the next two weeks, the kernels grow very rapidly, the developing embryo takes shape within them. At this stage, most of the plant's physiological activity is directed toward food storage in the kernels. By the end of the third week after pollination, the kernels are filled with a milky, almost fluid substance, high in sugars but containing the beginnings of starch and protein-forming bodies. This is the "roasting ear" stage.

From this time until about the end of the fifth week, the contents of the kernel undergo a marked change. Sugars rapidly disappear, and are replaced first by gummy dextrins and shortly thereafter by drier starch. The top, or *crown*, of the kernel is the first area where hardened, dry starch is deposited, and by the 40th day after fertilization, a definite band can be seen across the kernel, fig. 19, page 16, separating the maturing starchy area from the lower milky region where food storage deposit continues. Dry matter is increasing with a corresponding loss of moisture. By the end of the seventh week of kernel development, the embryo has nearly reached its full size, food storage slows, and the kernel nears maturity.

Under normal conditions, this stage is less critical in its effects on yield than the two preceding stages of development. The number of ears and kernels per ear have previously been fixed. Yet, serious moisture shortages, lack of nutrients, disease attack, or other severely adverse conditions will reduce kernel fill and determine whether tip kernels will fill at all, even though they are pollinated. In extreme cases of stress, the plant dies prematurely before the grain has reached full size. On the other hand, exceptionally favorable conditions of moisture and fertility result in better-than-usual kernel fill, and thus lead to

Distribution of Dry Weight in the Corn Plant (Iowa)

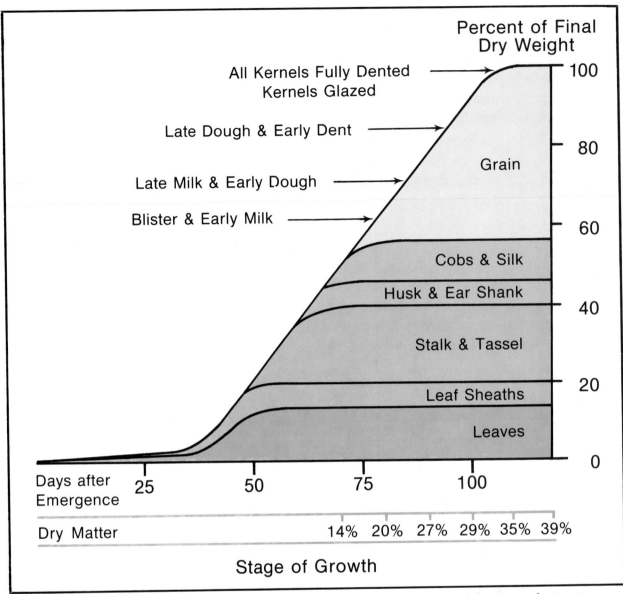

Figure 16. Per cent of total dry weight at various stages of growth and distribution of weight among plant parts.

higher grain yield than was expected. Conditions during this period, then, determine kernel size, whereas conditions in earlier growth stages mainly determined the number of ears and kernels.

Maturity and Drying

By the end of the eighth week after pollination, the corn kernel usually has reached the greatest *dry weight* it will have, and can be considered *physiologically* mature. The plant also has now reached its maximum total dry weight (figure 16). After pollination,

dent hybrids grown in the Corn Belt need about 50 to 60 days to reach maturity; this may vary in other areas and with flint corns or other less-common types. The difference in length of growing seasons between early and late hybrids is more in the number of days from planting to silking, than in the days from silking to maturity! If frost or plant diseases kill the plant before physiological maturity is reached, kernel-fill is stopped, resulting in chaffy kernels of "soft corn"; when this happens the entire maturation and drying process is interrupted.

14

Up until this point, the kernel has been increasing in dry matter weight, as a result of the starch storage process which has been steadily at work since the "roasting ear" stage. As starch deposit is completed, the kernel becomes harder, passing from a "soft dough" stage through a "hard dough" stage and on to a mature, fully-dented appearance as the moisture content decreases.

When is corn mature? The grain does not reach maximum dry weight until the moisture level is below 35 percent — probably around 30 percent in most Corn Belt hybrids (figure 17) and perhaps as low as 28 percent in some. This is the stage of physiological maturity, and maximum yield is not produced until it is reached.

The "black layer" (figure 18) is another indicator of maturity in corn. This is an area near the tip of all mature kernels that appears dark to the naked eye. It is easily observed by either cutting the mature kernel lengthwise in half or by breaking the tip of the kernel off with your thumb nail.

The appearance of the black layer signals that the transport of photosynthate into the kernel has stopped. When this occurs, the kernel has reached its maximum dry weight. The black layer is caused by the collapse and compression of several layers of cells near the tip of the kernel. The collapse of these cells closes off the conducting tubes and translocation stops.

The black layer appears first in kernels at the tip of the ear and last in the large kernels at the butt of the ear. The black layer appears relatively early in tip kernels under unfavorable conditions as if the corn plant had decided that it could not completely fill all of the kernels that were set.

An individual ear can be considered to be essentially mature when at least 75 percent of the kernels in the central part of the ear have black layers.

From this time on, "maturity" of the corn ear and grain is entirely a matter of moisture loss. Unless suitable drying and storage fa-

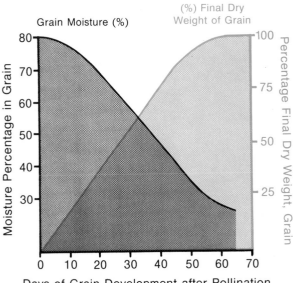

Figure 17. The percentage of maximum grain yield at different percentages of moisture in the grain related to the number of days after pollination. The yield curve is based on a two-year harvest of ten hybrids at two locations picked every four days. It represents over 4000 ears.

In the soft dough stage, about 55 percent of the kernels are starting to dent; in the hard dough stage, more than 90 percent are dented. In the mature stage, there is no milk in the base of the kernels on the side opposite the germ, figure 19.

Figure 18. The black layer indicates maturity.

15

Figure 19. One of the best ways to tell whether corn is mature is to break a few ears and examine the kernel opposite the germ face. When the kernels have reached full size there will be no milk at the base of the kernels.

cilities are available, the grain is not ready for harvest, and has not completed its maturity from a biological point of view. At this moisture content, it is still subject to spoilage, and must become much drier for safe storage. Thus, the last few days that the ear is on the stalk are devoted to drying while the grain goes into an inactive stage.

The rate of moisture loss after physiological maturity depends more on the weather than any other factor. Differences between hybrids also are important, since some types tend to give up moisture more slowly than others. If the ear has reached full dry matter content, frost-kill of the plant, followed by warm, dry weather leads to the most rapid moisture loss of all.

The corn kernel itself dries from the crown downward not through the cob, so that the part nearest the cob is highest in moisture during most of the drying period. The cob has a higher moisture content than the grain during most of the time the kernel is maturing and drying on the plant. As a result, whole ear moisture percentage is higher than grain moisture until both cob and kernel have dried to below 20 percent. This means that safe moisture levels in the grain for ear corn storage are lower than might be expected. (See page 313).

Shortly after the grain begins to dry and shrink, the ear becomes "twisty" and will not firm up until later when the cob dries and shrinks.

From the time the corn kernel reaches full dry weight, the acre yield cannot be changed either up or down by outside conditions. Thus, the period of maturity is not critical for overall yield. Yet, from a practical point of view, the corn crop is not safe until it is harvested and dried to a safe moisture content. Delayed harvest means risk of loss from stalk breakage, ear rot and reduced machine efficiency, hence the modern trend is toward the use of dryers to permit harvest as soon as possible after the grain matures. As the cost of energy increases, each farmer will have to balance the cost of drying verses the possible extra field losses if harvesting is delayed.

The appearance of corn ears when 50, 95 and 100 percent of the dry weight has been reached. Note that slight kernel denting occurs when only one-half of the final weight is attained. At 95 percent of final weight there is considerable variation in kernel development on an ear because of differences in date of fertilization of the ovules.

Maximum weight occurs only after all kernels are fully dented and glazed. The best way to tell when the grain is physiologically mature is to break and check the ear as in figure 19, or to ascertain that the black layer has developed, figure 18.

2

Corn in Your Farming System

Corn is the great American crop. Several American civilizations have been built with it as their staple food: the Mayan, the Aztec, the Incan, and to a great degree, our own. Corn has always been America's most efficient major crop for converting the sun's energy into food; in this century, hybrids and tremendous advances in fertilizing and machinery use, weed control and harvesting and storage methods have combined to give it a leading role in revolutionizing our agriculture.

Corn can be grown in every state (except Alaska) and ranks second to wheat in acreage among field crops in the world (figure 20). Corn on your farm competes with

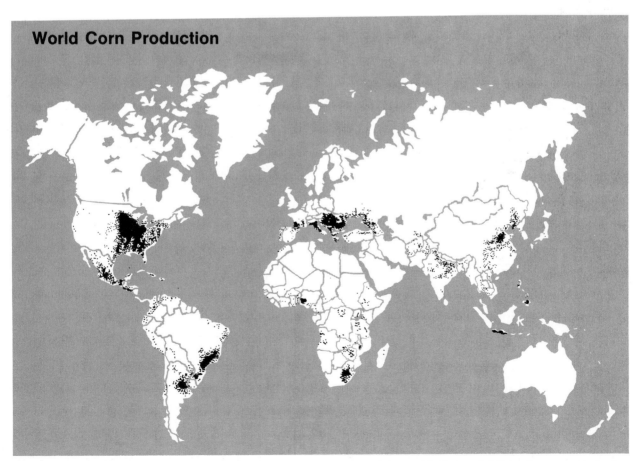

World Corn Production

Figure 20. Corn is grown throughout the temperate and tropical zones of the world where rainfall is adequate or irrigation water can be provided.

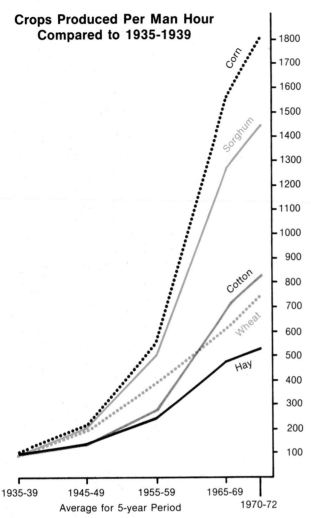

Crops Produced Per Man Hour Compared to 1935-1939

Corn

Sorghum

Cotton

Wheat

Hay

1800
1700
1600
1500
1400
1300
1200
1100
1000
900
800
700
600
500
400
300
200
100

1935-39   1945-49   1955-59   1965-69
Average for 5-year Period   1970-72

Figure 21. The relative amount of crop grown for each man-hour of labor compared with the amount grown in 1940 to 1944. Efficiency in growing corn has increased faster than for the other crops.

Table 1.
Effect of night temperatures 52 nights following pollination on corn yield at Urbana, Illinois. D.B. Peters.

| Treatment | Average night temperature | | Grain Yield | |
	°F	°C	Bushels per acre	Quintals per hectare
Natural air	65	18	168	105
Cooled	62	17	162	102
Heated	85	29	100	63

What Is the Best Climate for Corn?

Corn is a fast-growing crop that yields best with moderate temperatures and a plentiful supply of water.

The ideal temperature is cooler than many people think — 75 to 86° F. (24 to 30° C.) (figure 22) unless moisture supply is plentiful at all times. By this standard, the central Corn Belt is often too hot, but overall its temperatures are the most favorable of any region in the United States and about as favorable as anywhere in the world. In the Corn Belt, above normal temperatures are advantageous from planting to about mid-June; slightly below normal temperatures are better from mid-June to early September This generalization would not hold if there was always plenty of moisture.

When the temperature reaches 100° F. (38° C.) it is difficult to maintain adequate moisture even under irrigation as farmers in Kansas and Colorado learned in 1974.

The general effect of temperature for the season can be shown as "growing degree days" or "heat units" (see page 36) using 50° F. (10° C.) as the starting point, since corn grows hardly at all at lower temperature. The mean growing degree days are shown for the United States in figure 23.

Most farmers believe that corn grows best when the nights are hot. The reverse is true: corn burns up too much energy in cell respiration on warm nights (table 1). Both the

corn grown throughout the United States, and to an increasing extent with that grown in other countries. It is important, therefore, that you have a proper perspective on how favorable your situation is for corn.

A partial list of corn's attributes as a grain crop include the following: it is ideally suited to mechanization from planting to harvest; it responds well to heavy fertilization; it finds a ready market as cash grain or livestock feed in the form of grain, ear-corn silage or whole-plant silage; it has a high acre value among the major field crops; and efficiency of production per hour of labor is increasing faster than for most field crops, figure 21.

The Relation of Temperature to Rate of Growth

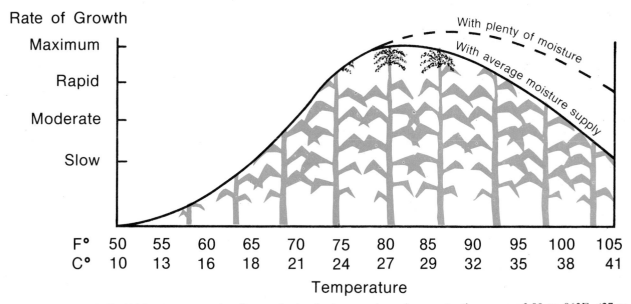

Figure 22. At 50° F. 10°C. corn grows hardly at all. As the temperature rises up to the range of 80 to 86°F. (27 to 32°C.), corn grows faster if moisture is adequate. When the temperature rises above 86°F. (32°C.) the roots have increasing difficulty taking in water fast enough to keep the plant cells turgid (full of water) and working at top speed. When soil moisture is short, the optimum temperature is less than 80°F. (27°C.). With perfect moisture supply the optimum temperature is likely 90 to 95°F. (35 to 38°C.).

Below. Growth involves accumulation of dry weight from photosynthesis during the day and loss by respiration at night (see also Table 1). When nights are too warm respiration loss is excessive, *lower line.*

What Happens When Nights Are Too Hot?

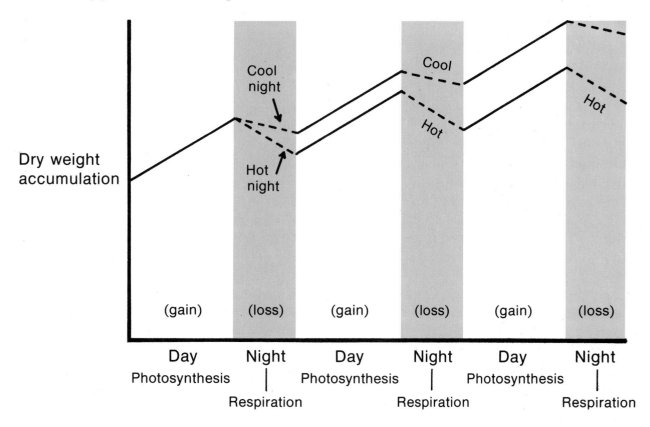

21

Figure 23. Mean number of growing degree days (GDD). In half of the years the number will be greater, and in half it will be less. A corn hybrid that requires 2800 GDD will mature before frost about 5 years in 10 on the 2800 line on the chart. Differences in elevation and nearness to large bodies of water cause local variations. In mountainous areas the differences are so great that no general lines can be drawn.

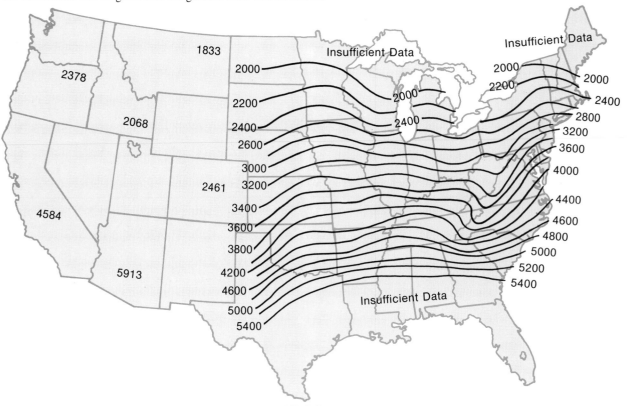

cool and hot treatments were in chambers closed at night. Cooling was by an air conditioner. Heating was with electric heaters.

The *internal leaf temperature* at night is influenced to a surprising extent by the sky condition. On a clear night, the leaf begins to radiate heat into outer space at a rapid rate. This is demonstrated by early, heavy dew on clear nights. The rate of heat loss by radiation is dependent upon the difference in temperature between the leaf and the entity that receives the radiated heat. In the case of a clear sky the receiving body is outer space which is near absolute zero. When cloud cover is present, the temperature of the receiving body is that of the cloud cover which is always far warmer than outer space. Very high humidity has much the same effect as a cloud cover. In essence, the kind of night when you feel the greatest need

for an air conditioner is a poor night for corn growth. *High yields in the Corn Belt are made in spite of, not because of, warm humid nights! The ideal is cool nights, sunny days and moderate temperatures.*

Daytime temperatures, solar radiation, and humidity have a lot to do with the effectiveness of the rainful a crop receives. When temperatures and radiation are high and relative humidity low (figure 129, page 190) more water evaporates from the soil and from corn leaves (evaporation from leaves is called transpiration). For this reason, the amount of rainfall during the growing season (figure 24) is by itself inadequate for judging how favorable the moisture supply will be for a crop. Note, for example, that the April-September rainfall is nearly equal in central Kansas and in central New York, but Kansas is considered a very dry area and New York

Figure 24.

Normal Rainfall; April-September

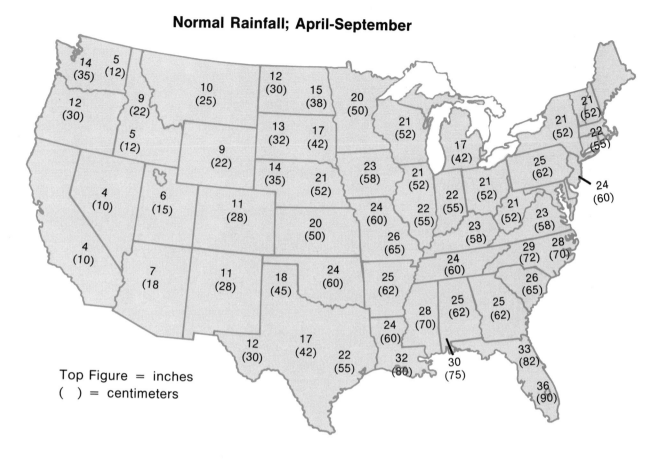

Top Figure = inches
( ) = centimeters

a relatively humid one. The "discomfort index" of corn and other plants is due to an opposite set of conditions than that for humans (or other animals). Plants show moisture stress most in very clear sunny days even though the temperature is only in the 70's F. (20's C.) because of rapid moisture loss. People suffer in humid weather because they can't lose moisture hence can't benefit from evaporative cooling.

The total water available to a corn crop is rainfall plus moisture stored in the soil. The subsoil is normally recharged with moisture in the central Corn Belt, but not in the western part. In this respect the Central Corn Belt is more favorable. When temperature and radiation become too high and the effective rainfall too low for corn, sorghums are more profitable.

The practical limits for corn as a grain

crop are a frost-free period of about 120 days (figure 25); an average of about 2100 to 2200 growing degree days (figure 23); and rainfall during the growing season of at least 12 inches (30 cm) in the northern plains and 19 to 20 inches (47.5 to 50 cm) in Oklahoma and Texas. Corn can be grown for silage about 100 to 150 miles (161 to 241 kilometers) farther north than it can as a grain crop or 400 to 800 feet (119 to 239 meters) higher where elevation is an important factor.

The Corn Belt in the United States is the largest area in the world that (1) is nearly level to only gently rolling, (2) has mainly medium-textured soils with high moisture-holding capacity, (3) has a favorable temperature, and (4) receives a generous amount of well-distributed rainfall. These factors have made it the largest area for profitable corn production.

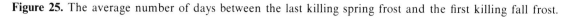

Figure 25. The average number of days between the last killing spring frost and the first killing fall frost.

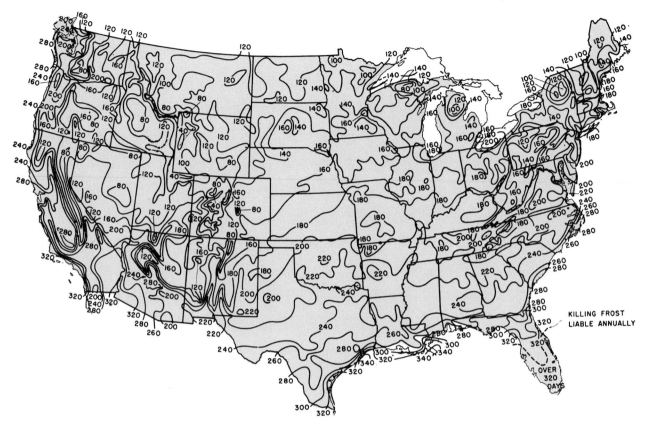

KILLING FROST
LIABLE ANNUALLY

OVER 320 DAYS

Do You Have a Competitive Advantage or Disadvantage?

In deciding the place of corn in your farming system, you need to consider whether you have a competitive price advantage or disadvantage.

Chicago, Illinois is commonly considered to be the base of comparison for the price of grain corn. Figure 26 shows the average price differential for all states for which USDA data were available for 1971 and 1972. Figures preceded by a plus indicate a higher price than at Chicago; minus signs indicate a lower price.

The figures must be used with some caution because they are averages for the state whereas there may be a considerable range in local prices from one end to another of a large state. Obviously two adjacent farms in different states will not have widely different prices. For example a farmer in Ohio on the Pennsylvania border will not receive 1 cent less than the Chicago price while a neighbor in Pennsylvania receives 24 cents above the Chicago price.

Another reason for caution is that the prices are for 1971 and 1972 when the average Chicago price was only $1.21 per bushel. The 1974 price was much higher and the differential (which was not available) may have been higher.

In spite of these deficiencies, figure 26 clearly shows the regions where farmers grow corn at a compttive disadvantage or advantage. North Dakota, South Dakota and Minnesota are clearly disadvantaged. Atlantic Coast states, and the 12 western states just as clearly have a price advantage. Texas and Oklahoma prices may have been influenced by drouth in the two-year period.

Figure 26. Difference in the price of corn (state basis) as compared to Chicago price. There are, of course, some differences within states. Average of 1971 and 1972. Chicago price was $1.21 per bushel, U.S.D.A.

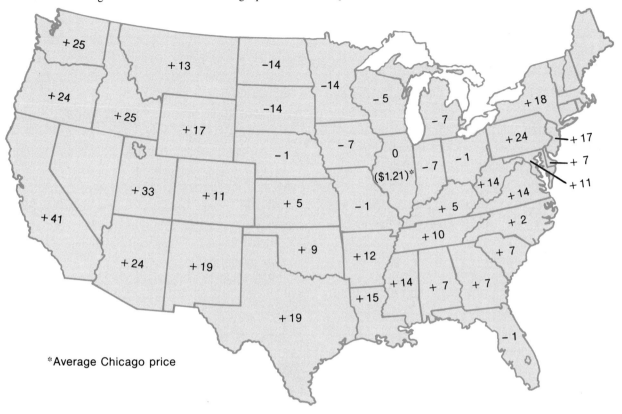

*Average Chicago price

The price differential is caused by relative surplus or deficit production of feed grains, and if surplus how far the grain must be shipped to reach the livestock that well eat it. If in the future there are major shifts in livestock numbers, as indeed there have been in recent years in feeder cattle into the southwestern states, the price differential will change.

If you have a price advantage, you can likely produce corn profitably even if you get somewhat lower yields than average Illinois farmers, or you can invest more in land, irrigation, fertilizer and other production practices. If you have a price disadvantage, you need to consider how to lower the production cost per bushel or to produce more bushels per man or both.

Price differential discussed here is, of course, not the only factor that will deter-mine your interest in growing corn. You will need to consider how corn profit compares with profit from other crops that you can grow. You may also decide to feed the corn on your farm and thus get a higher return than would be indicated by the map.

The Advantages of Growing Only One or Two Crops

The concept that corn, small grains and hay must be rotated to keep soils productive is no longer valid. With modern fertilizer practices, reduced tillage, and special conservation methods when necessary, many farmers can crop their fields intensively, even to continuous row crops if that is most profitable. Here are some advantages of restricting yourself to a few crops:

• You can become a specialist — with time to keep abreast of the latest research information, the best growing methods, and the most profitable techniques of marketing. In this age of rapid advances in crop growing methods, specilization may allow you to produce more efficiently than those who stick to general farming.

• You can tool up with the best machinery on the market for one or two crops (for example, corn and soybeans) something it may not be feasible to do if you grow a variety of crops that require different types of machinery. Specialized equipment can largely offset the seasonal peak work loads that result from growing only one or two crops.

• You have more free time. This is the other side of the coin that is listed as the first advantage of a rotation system. When you grow only one or two crops, you have to work extra long hours at key times. You must plow, plant, cultivate, spray, fertilize and harvest on time, but there are slack periods between these operations for vacation or other activities.

• If your farm is largely of one general soil type, you can grow the one or two crops for which it is best suited on your entire acreage. This partly offsets the inherent slight yield advantage of crops in rotation.

• If your farm has widely different soil types, for example rolling upland and level bottomland (figure 101, page 146), each different soil situation can be farmed intensively with the crop for which it is best suited. This may be intensive row crops on the bottom land and long-term meadow on the steeper, erosive fields. In this case, the one-crop system is applied to part rather than the whole farm. Crop specialization on individual fields or in whole regions often favors long-term soil conservation.

• Yields may be higher. Though agronomy research plots show long-term yield advantages for crops in rotation, in actual practice, farmers who specialize in a few crops often produce as high or even higher yields than they would in a rotation. This

is due to the overall impact of the advantages just described. Moreover, costs per bushel are frequently lower.

In years that have a dry fall, winter and spring, corn after corn or following another row crop will yield more than corn after meadow because the row crop stops using water at an earlier date in the fall. Late spring plowing of sod is especially undesirable in dry years because the sod continues to draw on subsoil moisture. For example, at the Morris Research Station in Minnesota, 1958 and 1960 were unusually dry seasons. In the following years, 1959 and 1961, corn after corn averaged 40 percent higher in yield than corn after alfalfa.

Whether you can or should grow continuous row crops like corn, beans and sugar beets depends on how you answer the questions on the next several pages.

Will Insects and Diseases Become Too Troublesome?

To date, *insects* that attack corn, with the exception of western corn rootworm, have not been noticeably worse in fields where corn is grown for several consecutive years. Wireworms are, in fact, a greater problem when corn follows a hay crop. Though some insects have developed genetic resistance to certain insecticides (page 348), most insects can be controlled well enough to permit growing corn repeatedly if you wish. There may be exceptions to this in certain areas; farmers should watch for the latest information from their own state experiment station and from pesticide manufacturers.

When insect resistance to a chemical develops it is the result of using the same insecticide for many years. Most of the insect population is killed but a few that have natural tolerance escape. These may increase and produce a race that cannot be controlled without a new insecticide.

Diseases have not often been a special problem in corn grown several years on the same land. Corn has been grown every year

Figure 27. Corn has been grown for 98 years on this section of the Morrow Plots at the University of Illinois. There is no indication that insects or diseases are worse than on other sections where corn has been alternated with oats and clover.

On a section where the stalks were removed but manure, lime and phosphorus were applied through the 98 years with modern rates of nitrogen, phosphorus, potassium and limestone since 1955, continuous corn has yielded about 93 percent as high as corn in the corn-oats-clover cropping system.

On another section that was untreated from 1876 to 1954, heavy fertilizer treatments beginning in 1955 are producing yields only a little over 86 percent as high as for corn that follows clover. Nearly 20 years of good treatment have not offset the effect of 79 years of mistreatment.

on one of the Morrow plots at the University of Illinois (figure 27) for 98 years without a buildup of stalk rot or other disease. Many farmers have grown corn for 5 to 10 years without trouble but the situation may, however, be different on land where the corn stalks are not turned under (see page 277). Ohio research indicates that soybeans in the rotation reduce stalk rot in some years. Based upon experience thus far, disease will not prevent intensive corn growing. Seed treatment, resistant hybrids, and early harvesting help to keep diseases within acceptable limits.

Is Intensive Corn Growing Your Most Proftable Crop System?

The first step in answering this question is to set realistic yield goals for corn and your other crops. Most State Experiment Stations have published yield guides for important soils. At first look these yields may seem low to some farmers. But remember they are ten-year average goals rather than

the expected yields in the best years. Also, they are for all of the acres of the named soil in the whole state or region rather than an especially good field or part of a field.

Farmers who have crop yield records for at least five years can use them to compare yields of corn and others crops on their farms.

The second step in deciding whether intensive corn is profitable for you is to obtain figures on costs to grow the different crops and then compare the probable margins of profit, based on the yield guides that you set for your farm. Here are approximate costs (includes a charge for the operator's labor) to grow some important field crops on highly productive soils in the central Corn Belt:

	1965		1974	
	Per acre	Per hectare	Per acre	Per hectare
Corn	$ 75	$ 185	$ 186	$ 460
Soybeans	$ 55	$ 136	$ 145	$ 358
Wheat	$ 55	$ 136	$ 125	$ 309
Oats	$ 45	$ 112	$ 114	$ 282

Third, consider the difference in machinery investment for a single crop versus several crops. Differences may turn out to be small. For example, a farmer who has his entire 400 acres in corn and soybeans can invest in large, modern equipment, but he doesn't need the grain drill, mower and baler of his neighbor who grows corn, oats and hay.

Don't overlook the possibility of hiring some custom work done, especially for jobs that require a machine only a few days each year. Custom rates vary from area to area and from year to year and so must be checked locally for realistic costs. Timeliness is your greatest concern with custom work. Fall plowing is well suited because there are several weeks over which it can be done. Planting is poorly suited because timeliness is crucial.

Can Your Soil Stand Continuous Row Crops?

Maintaining *tilth* is of prime importance on fields that have a cultivated crop every year. The more you work the seedbed and cultivate the crop, the faster you destroy the crumb structure that makes your soil porous, easy to work, and free from clods. For more information on this subject, see Section 4.

High yields of corn with the stalks left on the field actually return more organic matter than a rotation with corn, small grains, and one or two years of meadow. The fact that soil tilth doesn't always hold up is due to the extra plowing, harrowing, and cultivating that usually go with row-crop farming. A minimum tillage system and chemical weed control may make it possible for you to maintain good soil tilth while growing continuous row crops.

On sandy loams and silt loams, continuous corn with high fertility and reduced tillage will yield an average of 95 to 100 percent as high as corn that follows a hay crop in rotation. However, you harvest three corn crops as opposed to one in a rotation of corn,

small grains and hay. Optimum nitrogen rates will result in more residues from corn than under a rotation — except in warm southern areas where a forage crop can take advantage of the long growing season.

On clay loams, silty clays and straight clays, good structure or tilth is more important than on sands and silt loams but is more difficult to maintain with row crops. Continuous corn or continuous row crops are not as well suited to these heavy soils. Fertilization to produce a lot of plant residues; minimum tillage; working the soil only at the proper moisture content; and fall plowing on level fields will permit you to grow at least four or five years of row crops with high enough yields to justify this system. Production can probably be kept at about 80 to 90 percent of yields that would be obtained with a rotation in average years but may fluctuate from 70 percent in unfavorable years to over 100 percent in the best years.

Soils high in silt and clay should be watched carefully for the following warning signs under a continuous row crop system:

• The field dries slowly in the spring and plowing is delayed.

• Plowing requires more power.

• The seedbed remains cloddy even after several harrowings.

• The field dries slowly after rains; water stands between the rows in low places; cultivation is delayed.

• Yields are lower than from other fields with the same soil on which a crop rotation is grown.

These warning signs tell you that your farming methods are not maintaining soil structure. You should consider reducing your tillage and assuring optimum fertilization to produce more residues. The damage from overcropping with row crops is temporary and can be corrected unless it results in serious soil loss by erosion.

On sloping fields where erosion cannot be kept within safe limits, continuous row crops

Figure 28. Planting corn in narrow strips allows you to grow corn on land that is too steep for conventional methods.

is impractical. Research workers in Iowa suggest that corn can be grown continuously without difficulty on fields up to 1 percent slope, and safely with some special erosion control measures such as contours, terraces or strips on fields from 2 to 4 percent slope. However, the experiences of leading farmers indicate that these limits can be stretched somewhat when minimum tillage methods are practiced. The Soil Conservation Service, working with soil classification specialists from each state's Land Grant College, has set up guides to the most intensive cropping system for every soil type. (See page 219.)

Narrow Corn Strips on Steep Land

Researchers in Tennessee and Missouri have planted narrow strips of corn in sod on slopes that are too steep for regular seedbed preparation even with usual strip cropping or terraces, figure 28. Because the corn strips are only 6 rows wide with sod between, hardly any soil moves off the field. Woodruff in Missouri sprayed the sod in the corn strips with paraquat and atrazine or simazine. This set back the grass and prevented new seedlings. He moved the corn strips down slope two rows each year and had one third of the area in corn each year. There are several ways to harvest both the sod strips and corn.

Tennessee researchers harvested corn silage from the strips but harvesting was difficult on the steep slopes and losses were great partly because of the difficulty of keeping the receiving truck or wagon properly placed to catch the chopped forage.

The basic purpose of this approach is to permit farmers who have no land suited to growing corn by usual methods to compete more effectively with farmers who have land better suited to corn growing.

The Advantages of Crop Rotation

Even in today's agriculture there are reasons for alternating row crops, small grains, and hay. These can be compared with the statements made under "advantages for

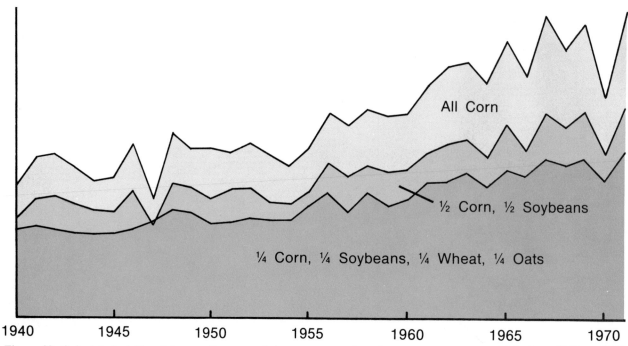

All Corn

½ Corn, ½ Soybeans

¼ Corn, ¼ Soybeans, ¼ Wheat, ¼ Oats

1940   1945   1950   1955   1960   1965   1970

Figure 29. Calculated yields of 1-crop, 2-crop, and 4-crop systems based upon state average yields from 1940 to 1971 (Illinois).

growing only one or two crops" for an appraisal of which system best fits your own situation:

• Better *distribution of labor* because the work peaks for different crops come at different times.

• Less *erosion* on sloping fields than with continuous row crops.

• Better *control of weeds.* Annual weeds, for example, start from seed each year, so when a farmer prepares a seedbed for corn, beans or sugar beets, he makes a seedbed for annual weeds. But annuals have no chance to establish in a long-term meadow. On the other hand, some tough perennial weeds like quackgrass, Canada thistle and bindweed are often most troublesome in hay fields because they can't be cultivated or sprayed effectively (see page 230).

• *Fewer insect* and *disease* problems. A crop rotation breaks the cycle of some insects and diseases that thrive on one crop. It prevents them from building to a dangerous level. As pointed out on page 26 and in figure

27, however, insects (except western corn rootworms) and diseases have not often been a problem in continuous corn in the Corn Belt. The situation could change at any time and may be different in other areas.

• The *weather risk is spread.* You don't have all your eggs in one basket. You rarely have a poor growing season for all the crops in a rotation. This point can be illustrated with a corn-oats-hay rotation. A wet spring delays oat planting but favors a large hay crop. A drouth during June hurts oats but helps you to make early-cut, high-quality hay. A drouth in late summer hurts corn but does not reduce the yield of oats. The matter of yield stability is discussed further in the next section.

• In experimental plots, *highest long-term crop yields* are produced in rotations. Differences have not been entirely overcome by extra fertilizer and excellent growing methods. On the farm, however, the situation may be somewhat different because of factors discussed previously on page 26.

Figure 30. Double-cropping after an early harvest of a small grain is increasing. Because of late planting as in this strip, soybeans are better suited than corn in the central and southern Corn Belt.

Does Lack of Crop Diversity Mean Unstable Yields?

The opinion is widespread that growing a wide variety of crops on a farm or in a community means stability of yields whereas only one or two crops leads to instability.

Ecologists who have studied natural ecosystems have concluded that diversity means stability. But it is doubtful that this principle can be transferred directly from natural to man-made systems. In natural systems the various components co-evolved over many thousands of years and natural checks and balances developed among insects, predators, diseases, and host plants. But a corn-soybeans cropping system did not go through the process of evolution with its pests, so the concept of diversity being desirable does not necessarily apply. In fact long-term state average yields in a major Corn Belt state (figure 29) show that corn yield is not noticeably more variable than a system of half corn and half soybeans, or of one fourth each corn, soybeans, wheat and oats.

Specializing in only a few crops in a geographic region permits concentration of each crop in the area to which it is best suited. This tends to reduce variability in yield of each crop from year to year. The yield of any crop is more variable in areas to which it is not well suited.

Concentrating the acreage of each crop in the geographic region to which it is best suited always produced the highest yield averages. Note in figure 29, that the grain equivalent produced by corn averages about 45 percent more than a corn-soybeans system and 70 percent more than a four-crop system. There are, of course, regions where wheat or oats outyield corn. In those regions it would be undesirable to insist on adding corn to the system.

Double Cropping

Planting corn or soybeans after an early harvest of winter wheat or barley has increased dramatically in recent years, figure 30. The main hazard for both crops is lack

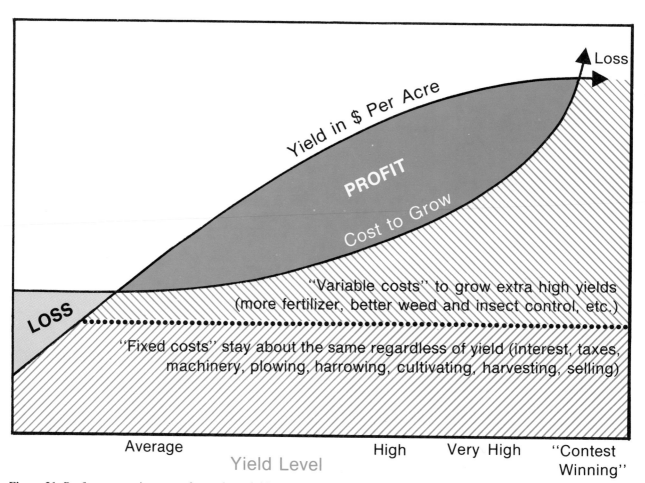

Figure 31. Profit per acre increases faster than yield per acre when you move from average to high yields. This is because there are many "fixed costs." When you aim for the absolute maximum yield, your costs increase faster than yield, and your profit per acre decreases.

of moisture at and soon after planting to assure good germination. Local experience is the most reliable guide. Enough farmers have tried it during the past ten years to provide a fairly sound basis for evaluating your chances. County extension agents and state agronomists can advise you based upon observations over a wide area.

The second hazard for corn is not enough time to mature before frost. For this reason double cropping with corn after wheat or barley harvest is limited to the area south of the main Corn Belt. Soybeans have a shorter growing season and can be double cropped to about the central Corn Belt in many years.

Early trials with double cropping involved plowing and preparing the usual seedbed. This is too costly, results in loss of precious moisture, and may cause several days delay in planting, and is not suited to as steep land as is planting directly in the stubble by no-till or zero-tillage methods.

Livestock Versus Cash Grain Farming

Whether to grow corn to sell or to feed on the farm is a very complex decision and no attempt is made here to supply the detailed information that you can get from agricultural economists at your state Land Grant College. But here are a few general considerations: livestock give you an on-the-farm market for corn which means you can keep the profit both from growing and feeding the crop. On the other hand, a livestock operation requires additional investment in equipment, buildings and the stock itself, plus knowledge of all sides of the livestock

32

business. It ties you or your hired man to the farm every day which you may consider a disadvantage but looked at another way it provides an opportunity to utilize labor in the off-season.

The livestock farmer has a by-product in manure. Average plant nutrient content is given in table 15, page 158. Livestock farmers are being required to meet increasingly stringent standards for waste handling to avoid pollution.

The Importance of High Yields

Many farmers greatly underestimate the effect of yield on profit, equating for example a 10 percent increase in yield with the same increase in profit. The real increase in profit may be 50, 100 or even 200 percent (figure 31). This is because many costs (plowing, planting, cultivating, spraying as well as interest and taxes), remain the same for all yield levels. Unless you greatly overdo on variable costs (mainly fertilizer and weed and insect control, but perhaps also in unneeded tillage operations) yield will rise faster than cost, thus giving you both more margin of profit per unit and more units to sell. Eventually, of course, you reach the upper yield limit for available water, the genetic makeup of the hybrid, and light. Further increases in fertilizer or other non-fixed costs cause a decrease in profit or even a loss.

The sections which follow contain information that you can use to develop the most profitable set of practices for growing corn in your farming operation. High acre yield is the foundation on which to build.

3

Hybrid Selection

You can't judge the performance of hybrid corn by the looks of the seed. What, then, must the modern farmer know to choose the right seed for his corn crop? Requirements today are entirely different from those in Grandpa's day, when the careful farmer took time in the fall to select the best ears from good standing stalks in the field, then carefully stored them to use for seed the next spring. Many farmers didn't bother with seed selection; they just took some ears from the crib, shelled them, and planted the grain as it came. Rarely did anyone buy seed; most farmers thought this a poor business practice.

The picture changed dramatically when hybrid seed corn became available in the 1930s. The hybrid seed corn industry has completely taken over the job of producing and processing seed corn, and local dealers are ready to deliver high-quality seed of proven hybrids to your door. No longer do neighbors each have their own variety of corn. Modern farmers can now choose from a wide range of scientifically-bred, carefully-produced hybrids. The job is to choose hybrids with the characteristics that each farmer wants. The first question is: *What do you want from a hybrid?*

Most likely the answer will be: I want the *best* hybrid. So does everyone, but *there is no one best hybrid*, even for every farm in a township or perhaps for every field on one farm. Hybrids have their own personalities and capabilities, much like people. Since they have different parents and ancestors, they differ in their ability to do specific jobs. This means that the farmer must choose hybrids that fit his special needs and desires because not all farmers desire the same characteristics.

Maturity

Whether a farmer wants to use his crop for silage or grain, the right maturity is important. A hybrid that is too early for your conditions will yield less grain or forage than your land should produce in most years and in some years it will lodge more from stalk rot than a full-season hybrid. If the hybrid is too late, you may take a yield loss from early frost, or may not be able to harvest and store your crop without serious risk of spoilage from wet corn. Actually, farmers don't have to worry much about relative maturity when they select a hybrid because commercial seed companies supply full information on their hybrids. They are as eager to have the hybrid perform well as is the farmer.

Trying to grow corn that is too late for your area won't pay. For many years, farmers who lived near the northern limit for economic production of grain corn looked with envy at the big-eared, late hybrids that were grown in the central Corn Belt. After two or three years of unusually favorable growing seasons, some of these farmers invariably shifted to later hybrids. Then a year would come with an early frost and they were stuck with soft corn.

Along the northern margin of grain corn areas, the soundest program in the long run is to select hybrids that will be mature at least 9 out of 10 years and plant them thicker than late hybrids. The plants are smaller and can stand a little more crowding. Thicker planting will largely offset the small ear size. The yield will be almost as high as with later hybrids in the best years. In years with a short growing season, yields will be higher with no danger of soft corn.

Thus, for your farm you need hybrids which will regularly reach or be near physiological maturity two to three weeks before the average date of the first killing frost. This avoids the danger of soft corn in the years of early frost and in all years takes advantage of the warmer weather that follows maturity which will aid in field drying. Field drying slows as the weather cools in the fall.

In addition to days to maturity, many companies provide the average number of "Growing Degree Days (GDD)" (figure 23, page 22) that are required for their hybrids to reach maturity. GDD are calculated for each 24-hour day and accumulated from the time the hybrid is planted until it reaches physiological maturity in the fall. The formula used in calculating GDD is:

$$\frac{T.\ Max\ +\ T.\ Min}{2}\ minus\ 50\ =\ GDD$$

T. Max is the maximum temperature during the day and T. Min is the minimum. Fifty degrees F is substituted for the minimum temperature when it falls below 50°F (10°C), and 86°F is substituted for the maximum if it goes above 86°F (30°C). The substitutions are made in the calculation because corn grows very little at 50°F or below (until about 1970 the figure used was 55°F, 12°C).

Likewise growth slows as temperatures go above 86°F unless moisture is abundant (see page 21).

You can calculate GDD for your own farm if you keep a record of the minimum and maximum temperatures or you may use those reported by your local radio or TV station. GDD is not a perfect guide to corn maturity and you will find that the GDD required to mature a hybrid varies somewhat from year to year due to factors such as moisture that influence the rate at which the corn plant develops. But GDD rating is a more precise description of relative maturity than the previous rough guide such as 100 days or 120 days.

You may find it interesting to keep a record of GDD from planting to emergence. Most hybrids require about 100 GDD to emerge regardless of whether these are accumulated in a few days or as much as 3 weeks.

Several states on the northern edge of the main corn growing area have tried to make sure that corn sold to their farmers is of proper maturity for the respective areas by passing laws requiring that every bag of seed sold must carry a tag showing the official maturity rating of the hybrid. In some of these states, hybrids are subject to official maturity trials and hybrids which prove to be later than the accepted maturity standard for a given area cannot be sold at all. Most of the rating systems used are "relative maturity" (R.M.) designations, and several different systems are used. Two examples are shown below:

Minnesota System		"AES System"
79-83 days R.M.	Earliest	100 series
80-84 days R.M.		200 series
84-88 days R.M.		300 series
89-93 days R.M.		400 series
93-97 days R.M.	to	500 series
98-102 days R.M.		600 series
103-107 days R.M.		700 series
108-112 days R.M.		800 series
112-116 days R.M.		900 series
114-118 days R.M.	Latest	

No system can show the exact number of

days from planting to maturity or harvest, and since systems differ greatly, you need a clear idea about the comparative maturity of the hybrids you are interested in growing *under your conditions.*

Your seed corn dealer is the best source of information on the maturity of the hybrids he sells. Corn performance tests conducted by many state experiment stations are a source of information which may help you compare maturity, lodging and yield of hybrids from different companies.

You may conduct your own comparisons by planting several different hybrids in strips of 8 to 16 rows across a field. On-farm tests are discussed in more detail later in this chapter.

Yield

`Why didn't we discuss yield first? Everyone wants high-yielding corn. No farmer is interested in deliberately choosing a low-yield type. The fact is, no commercial hybrid can be sold with much success year after year unless it does have high yield potential. Then why discuss yield at all? Because there are small differences which become important on a large acreage over a period of years.

Yield is not a simply-inherited, easily-predicted characteristic. The corn plant can be thought of as a factory which produces packages of energy — the corn kernels. Grain yield is the weight of the grain on each plant times the number of ear-bearing plants per acre.

The total production of grain per acre can be achieved in so many ways that no one can tell from the number of ears, size of ear, number of kernel rows, length of ear, or kernel size whether Hybrid "A" or Hybrid "B" will yield more. In other words, you can't pick a hybrid because it has big ears, many rows of kernels, big or deep kernels, or several ears per plant and automatically say it will be the highest yielder. What's more, you can't even be sure that a hybrid will always have the same yield relation to an-

Table 2.

Stalk lodging usually increases when plant population is increased. Data from an experimental Illinois corn test at Urbana in a year of severe lodging; the same trends have been shown by many other tests in average years.

	Population	
Per Acre	20,000	28,000
Per Hectare	49,420	69,160
Hybrid	**% Lodged Plants**	
(Oh7 x C103)	53	75
(Hy2 x Oh7)	86	93
(WF9 x C103)	18	19

other hybrid from one year to the next. (See the discussion of "Adaptability," page 40.)

By now you may wonder if there is any way to make a choice for yielding ability. To sum the matter up: the best procedure is for you to check performance test records for several years in your area, and observe maturity, lodging, disease, etc. on your own farm. Take advice, but check the hybrids out yourself. Grow the types which suit you best *on the average,* but don't be surprised if hybrids rank differently in yield from year to year.

Standability

Farmers have always wanted their corn to stand up well for ease of harvesting including hand picking, but until the machines took over harvesting, standability wasn't a crucial problem, even though it was easier to pick corn that stood well. Now good standability is absolutely essential. Corn combines don't scavenge for ears on the ground. Hybrids which do not stand until harvest cause yield loss, inconvenience and actual danger to the machine operator. Corn breeders are now placing major emphasis on stalk and root strength in developing new hybrids. If you aim for high yields with high populations, you must be sure that the hybrids you grow have proven standability. There are large differences among hybrids (Table 2).

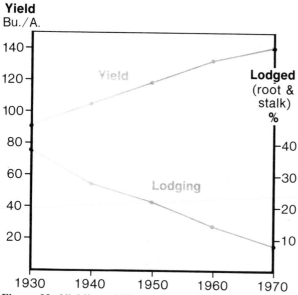

Figure 32. Yielding ability and resistance to lodging of two representative hybrids from eras 10 years apart show steady improvement. Data are the average of all hybrids grown in 1971 and 1972. (W.A. Russell, Iowa State University)

Corn breeders have made great strides in improved standability. W. A. Russell, an Iowa researcher, compared good commercial hybrids popular at 10-year intervals from 1930 to 1970. All were grown in the same field in 1971 and 1972. The results are shown in figure 32. The downward trend in lodging is dramatic.

The major causes of lodging will be discussed in more detail under "Corn Troubles" in a later section. Here is a brief rundown of the factors which lead to problems in root or stalk strength.

• *Disease.* In its various forms, and with various disease organisms as the direct cause, stalk rot is the most important factor in producing broken stalks. Many hybrids now have considerable resistance to the stalk-rot organisms, and some hybrids have such strong stalks that they can withstand severe disease or insect attack with little lodging.

• *Insect damage,* especially from the European corn borer or the Southwestern stalk borer, can also lead to serious stalk breakage. In most parts of the Corn Belt, however, European corn borer damage causes break-age *above* the ear rather than *below,* and thus does not produce harvest losses as severe as those from stalk rot. Insect damage, especially by corn rootworms, is most serious as a cause of root lodging early or in midseason. The lodging may persist until harvest time.

• *Plant population* is also important as a controlling factor in stalk breakage, and hybrids differ in their response to increased population. In table 2 note the sharp increase in stalk lodging, especially of the hybrid (Hy2 x Oh7) when the plant population was increased from 20,000 or 28,000 plants per acre (49,420 to 69,160 per hectare). Many of the hybrids which were first selected to yield well at high populations were prone to lodging.

Disease Resistance

Many diseases attack the corn plant. Fortunately, they are not severe in most years, and the majority of our present-day hybrids have some degree of resistance to the common diseases in their respective areas of adaptation. Severe attack is only from diseases new to the area. Yet, resistance to specific diseases is one of the most valuable characteristics of a hybrid for your farm.

In modern hybrids, resistance to the common diseases is not an accident. Breeders and pathologists work long and hard to find good sources of resistance, and to use these in developing hybrids which will tolerate major disease attack.

A good example of the possibilities in this area is the recent development of hybrids highly resistant to Northern leaf blight caused by the fungus *Helminthosporium turcicum* (page 276). After many years of study, a University of Illinois scientist, Dr. A. L. Hooker, found two sources of a very effective resistance to this disease.

Pathologists are constantly on the lookout for new diseases such as maize dwarf mosaic and new races of old diseases such as race T of southern corn leaf blight which had such a devastating effect on the 1970 corn crop.

Most of the diseases of corn are caused by *viruses* (infectious particles approximately one-millionth of an inch in size), *bacteria* (very small one-celled plants) and *fungi* (very small multi-celled plants). All of these organisms are capable of and often do develop new races through mutation and hybridization. Therefore the disease picture is always changing.

Plant pathologists must constantly search for new sources of resistance to old diseases and to monitor the corn crop for diseases that appear to differ from those that are known and common. Hopefully identification of something new or different can be in time to allow the corn breeder to incorporate resistance, if available, into commercial hybrids.

Fortunately in the case of maize dwarf mosaic and race T of southern corn leaf blight genetic resistance was available and they were brought under control quite quickly. The history of race T is outlined in the following paragraphs.

History of Race T
Southern Corn Leaf Blight (SCB)

The recovery from race T of SCB was almost as dramatic as was its devastating effect on the 1970 crop. While it caused a serious reduction in the 1970 corn crop the following corn crop was of near record size. Weather conditions, which were very important in the development and spread of the disease in 1970, were much less favorable in 1971. In addition the proportion of the acreage planted to susceptible corn was less in 1971 than in 1970.

Prior to the appearance of race T, southern corn leaf blight was considered to be a minor disease found primarily in the southern United States. The new race differed from the old race in several important characteristics which made it much more damaging. The old race (O) primarily attacks leaves. The new race T attacks leaves, leaf sheaths, husks, shanks, ears and stalks, (see page 277). Race T has a lower optimum temperature and therefore is not limited to the warmer southern Corn Belt as is race O. It thrived in the cooler temperatures of the central Corn Belt.

Weather conditions played a major role in the 1970 epidemic of SLB race T. Unfortunately at least 80 percent of the commercial corn crop was susceptible to it. But the wind currents, temperatures and the moisture conditions in both the southern and the northern parts of the country probably contributed more than anything to the development and spread. The disease can be traced northward from Belle Glade, Florida through Georgia, Alabama, Mississippi and into the central Corn Belt where much of the commercial corn acreage is concentrated. To travel this distance, weather conditions which encourage the development and spread of the disease had to be favorable over a wide geographic region and remain favorable for several months. That was unusual in 1970.

The new race was named "T" because the hybrids produced by using the "Texas type" of cytoplasmic male sterility were most susceptible. An over-simplified description of cytoplasm is that it is the mass of material enclosed by the cell wall which contains the nucleus. The genes which normally control inheritance are located within the nucleus. Whereas the genes determine most of the characteristics of the corn plant, the cytoplasm or certain bodies within it also have an influence. Viable pollen is one of the characteristics that may be controlled by the cytoplasm. Cytoplasm is passed on to the next generation only on the seed parent side. None is transmitted to the offspring through the genes in the pollen.

As explained later in this section, when producing hybrid seed corn the seed parent must not be allowed to pollinate itself. One of the most popular ways to prevent self-pollination has been through the use of male sterility. Prior to 1970 the source of male

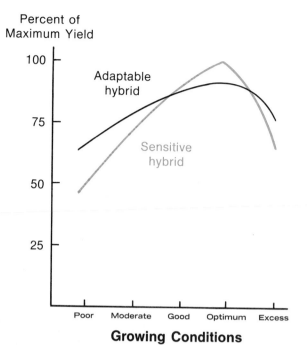

Growing Conditions

Figure 33. Some hybrids are very adaptable to changes in growing conditions, and can yield well with either less or more than optimum environments. Others are very sensitive to stress conditions of any kind. A sensitive hybrid of this type may yield more than any other when all conditions are right, but it is more risky.

sterility most widely used was located in a cytoplasm discovered by a researcher working in Texas hence the name "Texas male sterile cytoplasm".

This source of male sterility was widely accepted by plant breeders because it was easily incorporated into most inbreds, was relatively unaffected by a wide range of weather conditions and there were no known hazards associated with its use. Hence the 80 percent of the 1970 corn crop planted with susceptible seed mentioned earlier.

The new race of southern corn leaf blight was not definitely identified by Dr. A. L. Hooker until early in 1970 and that was too late to produce a new supply of seed corn for the 1970 planting season.

Weather conditions have such an important influence on the spread and development of disease that even after the new race had been identified no one foresaw the widespread and serious epidemic which was to develop. Because of the influence of weather

the seriousness of diseases often cannot be predicted more than 2 or 3 weeks in advance.

Fortunately the means for controlling race T was relatively simple and was already available to the seed corn industry. All that was needed was seed corn that did not have "T-type" cytoplasm. For every inbred with the T-type cytoplasm there is a counterpart which differs only in that it has normal cytoplasm. The normal counterpart is needed to increase and maintain the "male sterile" inbred. Since this counterpart does not produce viable pollen, a normal "male fertile" counterpart, identical except for viable pollen, is needed to provide pollen to maintain the male sterile inbred.

In spite of a very extensive 1970-71 winter seed increase in such places as Florida, Texas, Hawaii, South America plus bringing in seed from other countries, the transition from the T-type cytoplasm to resistant seed could not be completed before planting time. Thus much of the 1971 crop was vulnerable to attack. Fortunately the weather during the growing season did not favor the development and spread of race T and damage to the 1971 corn crop was minor.

Breeders began immediately in 1971 to develop alternative ways to the T-type cytoplasm to avoid having to detassel seed fields (see page 41).

Adaptability

The performance of a hybrid is not the same under all conditions. A superior hybrid should yield and stand relatively well in both favorable and unfavorable conditions. *No one hybrid* can do all jobs equally well; what really is important is that your hybrid have consistently good performance under your growing conditions, and that it isn't grossly unsatisfactory under any conditions you can reasonably expect. This is difficult to judge in hybrid performance, but very important.

A hybrid which gives maximum yield under very favorable weather and fertility conditions may be affected severely by

Figure 34. Detasselled field.

drouth. Another hybrid, perhaps somewhat lower in yield under the very best conditions, may outyield others in a generally unfavorable year. Breeders and physiologists have not yet discovered the key to consistent and inconsistent performances; extensive testing and field experience are required before a hybrid can be judged on its ability to yield consistently. In general, a hybrid which will perform well under nearly all conditions should be preferred to one which is top-yielding one year and very low the next, even if the long-term average performance of the two is about the same (figure 33).

How Hybrid Corn Is Produced

A brief discussion of how hybrid corn is produced will aid in understanding the difference between single crosses, sister line crosses, double crosses and the significance to the seed corn industry of male-sterility

in a seed parent.

The basis of all hybrids is the *inbred.* The inbred is a pure breeding line that results from 5 to 7 generations of inbreeding and selection. During the process of inbreeding (self pollination), growth characteristics are fixed in a genetically pure (homozygous) condition, and the pure line breeds true (doesn't change) in future generations. In developing the inbred as many undesirable characters as possible are discarded. The growth vigor that is lost during inbreeding is regained in the offspring only when the inbred is crossed with an unrelated inbred.

To produce a hybrid, pollen production of one of the parents must be controlled to avoid a mixture of selfed individuals and hybrids. Therefore the parent selected as the female or seed-bearing parent is detasseled, figure 34, or otherwise prevented from producing viable pollen.

41

Detasseling the female parent by hand is the classical method of controlling pollination in a crossing field. It is expensive and inconvenient. Even though the parents in a crossing field are uniform, variations in soil and topography cause non-uniform tassel emergence. Several trips are normally required through the field to get all the tassels before they shed pollen. The work is very seasonal, the work force needed is large and tends to be unreliable because detasseling must be done rain or shine, dry soil or mud. Machines have been developed which cut off most of the tassels but hand pulling is still needed for final cleanup. In addition mechanical detasseling often results in the loss of one or more leaves which, under some conditions, reduces seed yields.

The advantage of a biological or chemical control of pollen production is obvious. When a successful method through the use of cytoplasmic male sterility was discovered and developed the seed corn industry accepted it enthusiastically. More than 20 different "male sterile" cytoplasms have been identified. For numerous reasons the Texas type or "T" cytoplasm was the one most widely used until the epidemic of race T of southern corn leaf blight in 1970 discussed on pages 39 to 40. The immediate solution to the race T problem was to return to hybrids with normal cytoplasm and to hand or mechanical detasseling.

After the blight year of 1970 the search was on again to find biological or chemical methods to control pollen that could be used without constricting either the genetic or cytoplasmic base of the hybrids used. One method invented by Dr. E. L. Patterson of the University of Illinois involves a genetic control of pollen shed. Neither the genetic nor cytoplasmic base is affected. Therefore it will not tend to restrict either genetic or cytoplasmic variability in the commercial corn crop.

Chemical sprays which cause sterile pollen (gameticides) also show promise. These can also be used without affecting the genetic or cytoplasmic makeup of the hybrids produced.

Before 1960, very little Corn Belt acreage was planted to any type of hybrid other than the conventional double cross. In a period of five years, this picture changed sharply. Most of the acreage in the central Corn Belt is now planted to single crosses or single-cross type hybrids. Single cross hybrids are more uniform in plant and ear height and usually higher yielding than the double cross hybrids that first made the planting of hybrid corn profitable for commercial corn producers.

How do single crosses, sister line crosses, three-way crosses and double crosses differ? The types of hybrids differ in how the building blocks (inbreds) are used as parents. Normally unrelated inbreds are used in producing a single cross. For instance, inbred A used as the seed parent is pollinated by inbred B. The result is single cross AB.

Single cross

Seed parent (Inbred A) × Pollen parent (Inbred B) = Single cross AB

This single cross may be planted to produce commercial corn or it may be used by the seed corn producer as one of the parents in a 3-way cross or a double cross.

Three-way cross

Seed parent (Single cross AB) × Pollen parent (Inbred C) = Three-way cross ABC

Sister line crosses or special hybrids as they are often called are essentially three-way crosses. They are normally made using a single cross as the seed parent and an inbred line as the pollen parent. However the single cross used in producing this hybrid is the result of a cross of related inbreds whereas the true single cross is made with unrelated inbreds. The inbreds in this single cross differ just enough genetically to result in a little hybrid vigor and greater seed yield but do not differ enough genetically to result in noticeable non-uniformity of plant or ear height.

The single cross is very uniform in plant and ear height. The sister line or special cross may be slightly less uniform. The true three-way cross will be less uniform in plant and ear height than the single cross.

Double cross

$$\underset{\text{(Single cross AB)}}{\text{Seed parent}} \times \underset{\text{(Single cross CD)}}{\text{Pollen parent}} = \underset{\text{ABCD}}{\text{Double cross}}$$

The double cross, because it involves 4 unrelated inbreds, will normally be the least uniform of all. This non-uniformity may be of advantage under certain stress or disease situations.

Uniformity of plant type, ear height, and general appearance is very attractive, and *leads to uniformly good performance if all growing conditions are favorable for that particular genetic combination.* However, if conditions are *not* favorable, the same high degree of uniformity may be a handicap. Attack by disease or insects, drouth, poor response to high plant populations, and other unfavorable conditions can produce a more uniformly poor growth in a susceptible single cross than in almost any double-cross hybrid. Thus, the fact that single crosses are highly uniform is sometimes — but not always — an advantage.

On the average, when single crosses, double crosses and other types of hybrids are compared for yield, the best single crosses outyield the best double crosses by a noticeable margin each year.

The higher potential yield capacity and the uniformity of single crosses have been clear to corn breeders since the earliest days of hybrid corn. In fact, Dr. G. F. Shull, who first published a suggested program for utilizing the hybrid method in corn breeding, stated that the single cross between two inbred lines would be the hybrid type used by farmers. However, this method proved impractical because of the low seed yield from most parental inbred lines and the difficulty of producing seed with inbred lines. Hybrid corn did not become practical until Dr. D. F. Jones proposed and tried the double-cross technique. For many years, attempts to produce commercial lots of single-cross seed failed because the costs were high because of low yields and the seed quality was unsatisfactory.

The more recent development of commercially-feasible single-cross hybrids has resulted from two advances in breeding and seed production methods:

• First, many inbred lines now are reasonably vigorous and capable of producing moderately good seed yields or of supplying ample pollen to fertilize the silks of a seed parent. As a result, seed of several true single crosses can be sold at reasonable prices.

• Second, the "sister-line" crossing technique discussed on page 42 can be used to produce "special-cross" or "three-way" hybrids, many of which are nearly as uniform as a true two-line single cross. Seed of certain "sister-line" hybrids can be sold at prices which are competitive with those of the best double-cross types.

In selecting a hybrid for your farm, you cannot afford to put all your acreage in one hybrid. Spread your risk by selecting several which differ in genetic makeup and maturity. Some good corn growers have prospered by planting only a very few hybrids but the risk is there, and your best chance for continued high profits lies in spreading the risk by growing several hybrids each year.

At the other extreme, a few seed firms produce hybrid mixtures or blends, which sometimes are sold for special uses such as silage corn. Often, these blends are made up deliberately, and may be useful for limited acreages where there is a need for maturity spread or safeguard against a high-risk situation. However, a so-called blend may be a mixture of left-over seed, and even if priced low, may not be a bargain. *Be sure to check with your seedsman and know what you are getting before you buy a blend or mixture.*

Where to Get Help in Choosing a Hybrid

The choice of a hybrid for your farm *is an individual and specialized matter.* Ultimately, you should make your own choice, using all the information at hand. Where can you get this information? In most corn-growing areas there are several good sources.

• *Your seed dealer:* If you are a Corn Belt farmer, you probably have several neighbors who sell seed corn. These usually are "farmer-dealers," representing one of the many commercial seed firms, large and small, who produce seed for your area. In some cases, you may be near a smaller-scale seed grower, who sells his corn in the counties nearest his processing plant. Or, less commonly in the Corn Belt, but often in the southern states, you may buy your seed from a seed dealer, elevator operator, or feed mill in town. Nearly all these men, and the agents who represent them, have considerable information about the hybrids they sell. They know local conditions, they know the performance potential of their corn, and they usually can do a good job of advising you on the best choice for you among *their* hybrids. Of course, each seed dealer wants to sell his own brand of seed, and usually he has certain hybrid numbers he would rather sell in your area; a seed dealer doesn't make any money selling his competitor's hybrids. So, you must make your own choice, and thus should use other information as well, but the *reliable* local seed dealer is one of your very best sources of advice and information on hybrid performance.

• *County agents and vo-ag teachers:* Most of these men keep up-to-date on hybrid performance in their specific areas. They have ready access to official test information from the state college of agriculture and usually no axe to grind for any particular company or hybrid. Usually, these men have less specialized information than either the commercial seedsmen or the state experiment station or extension personnel, but they are less biased than the first group and better informed on your local conditions than the men from the state university.

• *State research or extension personnel:* Most of the major corn-growing states have corn performance testing programs, usually conducted by experiment station or extension service specialists from the state university. In the Corn Belt, most states conduct programs of this type, and publish the results annually as either an experiment station bulletin or as an extension circular.

When you use information of this type, be sure to note that the results are from small test plots, and that the growing conditions of the test site may be different from yours. The tests usually are reasonably accurate, but interpreting the results isn't always easy. *This means that you should use them only as a general guide to help you choose your hybrid; don't make your choice on the basis of test plot results alone.*

• *Experience in your own area:* This is probably the best method of making the final choice for your own farm. After taking advice, checking test plot results, and making sure you have up-to-date information, you still need to know how specific hybrids perform under your own conditions. There is no substitute for your own experience, or observations on your neighbors' farms, when you come to this final choice.

The important point here is to be sure that you check actual weighed or measured yields, and that you have fair comparisons. You can't tell much from one or two rows across the field, and border rows are not the same as the center of a field. Plant a block — eight or sixteen rows — of each hybrid you want to try. Harvest it with your regular equipment, and weigh the ear corn or shelled grain. Be sure to have a moisture sample before you figure yields.

To calculate the acre yield of test strips,

you need to know:
- The exact fraction of an acre that you have harvested.
- The weight of the ears.
- The percentage of moisture in the grain.

To calculate the fraction of an acre that you will harvest, begin by multiplying the length of the field by the width of the strip (in rods). (Get this by multiplying the number of rows by row width in feet and dividing by 16.5.) This gives you the number of square rods in your sample. Since there are 160 square rods in an acre, divide 160 by the square rods in your sample. This tells you the number of harvest-size areas in one acre.

Multiply the number of areas per acre by the field weight of your harvest area to get gross ear weight per acre.

Now divide the gross ear weight figure by the pounds of ear corn per bushel to determine the moisture content in the grain, using the information in reference table 3 on page 369. The resulting figure will be bushels per acre corrected to 15.5 percent moisture—No. 2 corn.

If you use the metric system, substitute the appropriate metric units for feet, the area of a hectare for an acre, and the weight of a quintal for a bushel.

Special Types of Dent Corn

Not all corn profits are made with the familiar yellow dent hybrids. In some areas, demand for a special grain type provides an opportunity for extra profit. Generally speaking, the same factors are needed for these special hybrids as for regular corn, but there are some additional aspects such as keeping the grain separated from other types until it is delivered to the market. Special types of corn often are produced only under contract arrangements which guarantee a premium price when the grain is delivered. Often, these contracts put special requirements on purity of type or quality of the grain, if a premium is to be paid.

White Corn

Most of the white corn grown in the United States is used to make cornflakes and cornmeal. Most people prefer white cornmeal to yellow, and manufacturers of several food products insist on white corn in their processing because of the color. White corn usually sells at a few cents a bushel more than yellow, and sometimes this premium may be as much as 1½ to 2 times as much as yellow corn. The higher price, and more recently, opportunities for contract growing at a fixed premium, may interest the profit-minded grain producer in growing white corn. Most of the white corn in the U.S. is grown in twelve states. Table 3. Very few white hybrids are available in maturities adapted to the central Corn Belt. Some of the hybrids suited to the main white corn growing area will perform satisfactorily and yield well in central Illinois or Indiana in favorable seasons, but are extremely sensitive to drouth or stress of any kind. Such experiences show that a farmer considering white corn as a crop should be sure that *tested* white hybrids *adapted to his area* are available.

Table 3.

Major producing states for white corn. U.S.D.A. 1974 figures except 1973 for Nebraska and Ohio.

State	Acres	Hectares
Alabama	43,000	17,400
Georgia	117,000	47,300
Illinois	54,000	21,900
Indiana	51,000	20,600
Iowa	14,000	5,700
Kansas	45,000	18,200
Kentucky	124,000	50,200
Missouri	68,000	27,500
Nebraska	16,000	6,500
Ohio	3,000	1,200
Tennessee	80,000	32,400
Texas	55,000	22,300

Types with Modified Starch Protein or Oil

The discovery by breeders that the composition of the starch and the protein in corn could be altered through genetics has resulted in the development of special types of corn to better meet the needs of the livestock feeder, the food industry and other industrial users of corn.

The average corn kernel contains about 72.8 percent carbohydrates, 9.4 percent protein, and 4.3 percent oil. Because of its high carbohydrate content it is the most widely used high energy feed for livestock in the U.S. About 91 percent of the corn used in this country and most of that exported to other countries is fed to livestock. The remaining 9 percent of the corn used in the U.S. is processed into food and industrial items. Corn syrup, starch and oil are important food items and there are many more. Starch, oil and other by-products of the milling process have many industrial uses.

• *Waxy maize:* Before World War II the U.S. obtained most of its amylopectin starch in the form of tapioca. Tapioca is processed from roots of the cassava plant which is adapted to the tropical areas of South America, Africa and Asia. Asia was the major supplier and this source was cut off during the War.

Normal corn starch is made up of about 75 percent amylopectin starch and 25 percent amylose starch. The genetic means of increasing the amount of amylopectin starch to 100 percent with the "waxy gene" had been known for many years. But the need to produce commercial waxy corn did not exist until the supply of tapioca for the U.S. was shut off. Waxy maize has become an important source of amylopectin starch.

Prior to 1971, waxy maize was produced entirely under contract, nearly all in a few counties in Iowa, eastern Illinois and western Indiana. Most of the seed was produced by The Bear Hybrid Corn Company, of Decatur, Illinois, and was distributed to contract growers by field agents of the processor. The farmer growing waxy maize under contract had little opportunity to choose which hybrid he grew; his main decision was whether or not to become a waxy maize contract producer.

In the 1971 scramble for corn with normal cytoplasm which was resistant to race T of the southern corn leaf blight, some surplus waxy seed was sold to commercial corn producers who were also livestock producers. These growers discovered that beef cattle thrived on the waxy corn. Subsequent carefully controlled feeding trials conducted at the University of Illinois proved that waxy corn gave more efficient gains than normal dent corn when fed in a ration supplemented with soybean meal. For some reason waxy was not superior to normal corn when both were fed in a ration supplemented with urea as the protein source.

The discovery of the value of waxy maize as a feed greatly increased the interest in this type of corn and now waxy hybrids are offered by many hybrid seed corn companies. The need for waxy maize by industry continues as does the practice of contracting for acreage to supply this need.

Isolation from field corn is necessary or else the corn from border rows in the waxy field may have to be discarded to meet purity requirements. Representatives of the waxy maize processor check for purity before fields are harvested, and will refuse to accept grain showing more than 5 percent of contamination with regular corn pollen.

• *Amylomaize:* The proportion of amylose in corn starch can also be genetically controlled. Commercial hybrids are available that contain as much as 70 to 80 percent amylose starch. Corn amylose starch is not currently used in as large quantities in food and industrial products as is waxy maize. More information concerning the properties and production of amylomaize may be obtained from The Bear Hybrid Corn Company.

• *High protein and High Lysine Corn:*

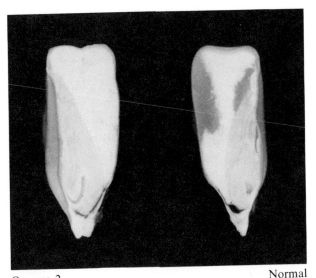
Opaque 2   Normal

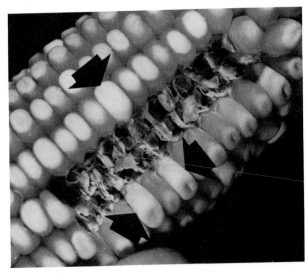
Opaque 2

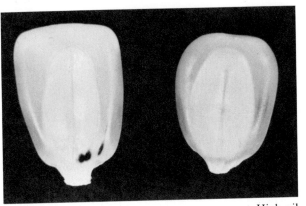

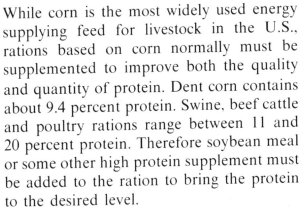
Normal   High oil

Dent   Waxy

Figure 35. Comparison of grain of normal and special types.

While corn is the most widely used energy supplying feed for livestock in the U.S., rations based on corn normally must be supplemented to improve both the quality and quantity of protein. Dent corn contains about 9.4 percent protein. Swine, beef cattle and poultry rations range between 11 and 20 percent protein. Therefore soybean meal or some other high protein supplement must be added to the ration to bring the protein to the desired level.

Genetic stocks are available that contain as much as 27 percent protein. Unfortunately corn breeders have not yet been able to materially increase the protein content of corn and maintain high yield. As the protein is increased the yield decreases.

High protein corn has often been advertised but really high-yielding, dependable, high protein hybrids were not yet available in 1975. In fact an improvement in the protein content of corn would be of little advantage for non-ruminant animals such as swine and poultry unless the amino acid content was also improved. Most of the protein in corn is located in the endosperm and is low in the amino acids lysine and tryptophane. Both of these are essential in animal nutrition. The microflora in the rumen of cattle, sheep and goats can synthesize these amino acids from protein sources which are low. Non-ruminants, including man, do not have this capability. Therefore increasing endosperm protein which is low in lysine and tryptophane would be of little value to the non-ruminants.

The discovery of the opaque 2 gene (figure 35) in 1964 by E. T. Mertz and O. E. Nelson

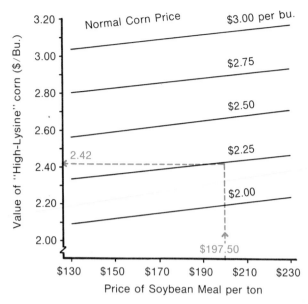

Figure 36. The value of high lysine corn as the price of normal corn and soybeans changes.

at Purdue University was a significant contribution to animal and human nutrition. This gene increases the lysine content of corn endosperm protein. Feeding trials involving opaque 2 or high lysine corn clearly demonstrate its advantage over normal dent corn in swine rations. Its superiority over normal corn in the human diet has also been demonstrated in several countries where corn is an important food.

The value of high lysine corn in poultry rations is limited by a third amino acid— methionine. The methionine content of corn is adequate for swine but not for poultry. Since the opaque 2 gene does not affect the amount of methionine, high lysine corn rations, like those with normal corn must be supplemented.

The development of successful high lysine hybrids is time consuming and somewhat difficult. In some genetic backgrounds the incorporation of the 0^2 gene results in greater susceptibility to ear rots. In others there is a tendency for higher moisture at harvest.

The yield of some high lysine hybrids has been disappointing. Corn breeders are convinced that in time these deficiencies can be overcome and current progress supports

their optimism. Some hybrids are available that essentially equal their normal counterparts in performance.

The opaque 2 gene is recessive. Therefore when high lysine corn is pollinated with pollen from normal corn the resulting kernel is low in lysine. The suggestions about protecting waxy maize from foreign pollen also apply to the production of high lysine corn.

Since lysine is one of the amino acids in all protein it will vary up or down with protein content. Corn, high lysine or normal, that has 12 percent protein will contain more lysine than that which has 8 percent protein.

The lysine content of 136 samples of high lysine corn produced in Illinois in 1973 was determined. These samples, which came from all sections of the state, ranged from a low of .29 percent lysine to a high of .54 percent. Seventy-seven percent of the variation in lysine content was due to contamination with normal corn or associated with protein content. The sample with only .29 percent lysine contained only 7.3 percent protein. The sample with the highest lysine content also had the highest protein content, 12.5 percent.

Figure 36 shows the value of a bushel of high lysine corn as the price of normal corn and soybean meal varies.

• *High Oil:* The increased interest in fat or oil high in the polyunsaturated fatty acids for human use has been reflected in the greater use of vegetable oils including corn oil. Normal corn contains about 4 to 4.5 percent oil. Hybrids with 1½ times this amount of oil, which are competitive with normal hybrids in yield, are commercially available. High yielding hybrids with twice the normal amount of oil will soon be available. As the oil content in corn is increased the probability of processors recognizing high oil corn through premiums improves. High oil corn may become a profitable specialty corn.

Feeding trials with swine suggest that feed efficiency may be improved but that percent-

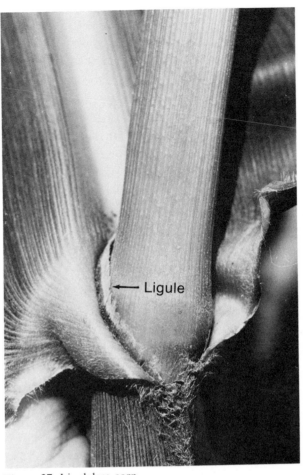

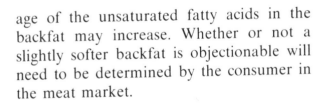

Figure 37. Liguleless corn.

age of the unsaturated fatty acids in the backfat may increase. Whether or not a slightly softer backfat is objectionable will need to be determined by the consumer in the meat market.

Liguleless Types

Light penetration into the leaf canopy decreases as the plants per unit area increases. One solution is to search for genetic combinations that will function under the low-light intensities encountered in high plant densities.

Another solution may be to change the geometry of the corn plant. This approach involves genetic control of leaf angle. The leaf angle on what we consider to be a normal corn plant is between 30° and 40° from the vertical. Some researchers reason that if this angle were smaller, plants could

be crowded closer together with no increase in shading each other — and more ears per acre could be produced.

Two of the genes that decrease leaf angle are liguleless 1 and liguleless 2. The genes are named liguleless because they prevent the formation of the ligule of the leaf. This is a short vertical membrane or collar that clasps the stalk at the base of the leaf blade or at the junction of the leaf blade and the leaf sheath. The leaf angle of plants with the liguleless 1 and 2 genes range from 6° to 11°, figure 37. Preliminary research involving hybrids with these more upright leaves is promising especially in narrow rows (20 in., 50 cm) at high populations.

Researchers are also working with narrow leaves, tassel seed, and other mutant genes in their search for plants that will produce more grain per unit area.

Multi-eared Hybrids

The number of ears per acre or hectare and the number and weight of kernels per ear determine the yield of corn. Ear weight is a good indicator of the number and weight of kernels on the ear. A half pound ear (227 grams) will have about 650 normal sized kernels. The small tip kernels and the extremely large butt kernels are not included in this figure.

The corn breeder is obviously interested in developing hybrids that will produce the maximum number and weight of ears possible. To do this requires attention to many characteristics such as resistance to lodging, disease, and to barrenness. Corn breeders are particularly interested in resistance to barrenness. The weight of each ear increases as number of ears per unit area decreases but not enough to fully compensate for a reduction in population below the optimum.

There are two approaches to producing more ears per unit area. One is to increase plant population and the other is to produce more than one ear per plant — multi-eared hybrids.

Corn breeders are interested in breeding for multi-eared hybrids. But when hybrid corn was developed the inbreds used were those obtained by inbreeding the open pollinated varieties that were available in the 1920's and 1930's — all of which had undergone generations of selection for the one-eared type to make hand picking easier.

Consequently current Corn Belt hybrids are primarily one-eared. Many will produce more than one ear per plant at populations less than optimum. But they produce their highest yields at populations high enough that most plants have only one ear.

The multi-eared types have been used more successfully as a genetic source of resistance to barrenness at high population than as finished hybrids. The potential of successful multi-eared hybrids is real and corn breeders will continue to search for one that will compete with the single-eared types.

Increasing population has been a successful approach to producing more ears per acre or hectare. Better hybrids, the increased use of fertilizer especially nitrogen, better weed and insect control, and improved cultural practices such as narrow rows have permitted corn producers to use higher planting rates. But many researchers are of the opinion that light will become the limiting factor as population increases much above current levels.

Brown Midrib Hybrids

Brown midrib corn is a new type of corn and as the name implies it has a brown colored leaf blade midrib. The cell walls of the non-grain portion of the brown midrib corn are lower in lignin than those of normal corn. Since lignin is relatively undigestible, silage made from brown midrib corn may be more digestible. Limited feeding trials indicate that this is the case and as a result feed efficiency is greater.

High Sugar or Sweet-Stalk Corn

High sugar or sweet-stalk hybrids are male sterile varieties. Since the male sterile plants when planted without a pollen source do not produce grain, the sugars that would normally be translocated from the leaves where manufactured to the grain are concencentrated in the stalk, leaves and cobs. The male sterile plants remain green and succulent until killed by frost, disease or drouth.

High sugar hybrids are lower in yield than normal grain forming plants and, though they produce good quality fodder, more feed per acre can be produced with normal hybrids.

The silage produced from high sugar hybrids is no more palatable than that made from normal corn because essentially all the sugar in both types is used by the microbes that form the organic acids in the pickling process in silage.

50

Figure 38. This puts the dwarf in dwarf corn. The distance between joints (nodes) is less than on normal corn. Thickness of stalk, number and size of leaves, and size of ear are nearly the same in both.

Dwarf Corn

Dwarf corn (figure 38) is more lodging resistant but lower in yield than normal hybrids. However, the interest in the dwarfing genes is as a source of increased lodging resistance continues. Some companies have produced early, short varieties that are competitive with taller hybrids. For special needs, such as growing under sprinkler irrigation systems or making high grain silage, dwarf or short types may be useful.

Popcorn

Most of this country's commercial popcorn is grown in a few areas of Iowa, eastern Illinois and Indiana. There are two major kinds of popcorn grain — the pearl and "hulless" types. Pearl popcorns and the larger "South American" types have rounded, flinty kernels which usually are deep yellow or orange-yellow in color. "Hulless" popcorns, also sometimes called *rice* types, have pointed, somewhat curved kernels and are nearly always white.

Since most popcorn is grown under contract, your choice of hybrid probably will be made by the contracting buyer. Most commercial popcorns are three-way or single crosses, and thus very uniform. In general, the pearl popcorns yield more than the hulless types, but added premiums for hulless may make up the difference. Stalk and root strength have often not been satisfactory in popcorn hybrids, and should be carefully checked before you undertake to grow them. Popcorn which is pollinated by nearby field corn is low in quality, so care must be taken to isolate it from other corn. Grain quality is important; conditions which might lead to high disease damage should be avoided.

4

Seedbed Preparation

Seedbeds for corn have changed as much as methods of planting, cultivating and harvesting. Until in the '20s, farmers were taught to turn under all trash and crop residues. Farmers used to work a seedbed until it was fine and firm. Now we know that to overwork the soil is not only unnecessary but often harmful. Proper choice of seedbed preparation and planting method can save time and fuel, and reduce erosion.

What Do You Need in a Seedbed?

You start with three pieces in a puzzle: soil, machinery, and seed. How do you fit them together? Some soils can be worked at almost any time; others must be handled with great care. Some machines are designed to kill weeds; some to loosen the soil; others to pack the soil.

In order to prepare an ideal seedbed aim for the following goals:

• Provide a good place for seeds to *germinate* and for seedling roots to *grow*.

• Control the weeds, both perennials like quackgrass and bindweed, and annuals that start from seed each year.

• Make a seedbed suited to the tools you have for planting and cultivating.

• Preserve or improve the tilth.

• Prepare a seedbed that will let as much water as possible enter the soil.

The Ideal Seedbed

Corn kernels need a soil that is warm, moist, well supplied with air, and only fine enough to give contact between the seed and soil. If you begin by plowing, the best seedbed that you can prepare for corn is a well-plowed field plus just enough packing *in the row.* Any extra harrowing that you do will make the field look better, make the first cultivation easier, and help to control perennial weeds. But it probably won't help the corn grow any better. A finely worked seedbed not only is unnecessary but also is more likely to seal over when it rains — increasing runoff and erosion.

Arthur Peterson of the University of Wisconsin points out that a field serves as a seedbed for no more than five percent of the growing season. The other 95 percent it is a rootbed. Since corn requires only an area of 3 to 5 inches (7.5 to 12.5 cm.) in diameter for germination and sprouting, isn't it logical to assume that fitting the area between rows is often unnecessary?

Figure 39. Freshly plowed soil in good physical condition is suitable for planting without further seedbed preparation, if the planter gives adequate firming in the row.

Many farmers have planted directly on plowed ground (figure 39). This saves labor, preserves the tilth of the plow layer, and increases water intake, as well as reducing runoff and erosion. It also often helps to control annual weeds in normal or slightly dry periods since the area between rows is too loose and open for good germination of small weed seeds and the establishment of seedlings. Yet corn germinates well because the soil is compacted in the row by the planter presswheel and because the corn kernel is larger and placed deeper than the weed seeds.

Although it may not be practicable for you to plow and plant in one operation, it will pay you to work the seedbed as little as possible. The main hazard to corn planted on the plow furrow is extreme drouth just before and after planting. (For suggestions on how to combat this, see page 71.)

A machine was developed in the early 1950's to work up a seedbed in an established meadow (figure 40). A seedbed about a foot wide was prepared for the corn row. The legume or grass continued to grow between the rows. This was a prototype of modern zero tillage. But corn planted in this way suffered during drouth because the growing sod between the rows competes with the corn for water early in the season. Besides, unless the sod between the row is killed, only part of the nitrogen in the grass or legume will be available for the corn.

Weed Control by Seedbed Preparation

Preplant tillage aimed at controlling weeds must be adapted to your special weed problems. If you have perennials like quackgrass, Canada thistle, or sow thistle, you may want

Figure. 40. This experimental machine represents one of the pioneer efforts to reduce the number of trips over a field. It prepared a seedbed in the row only and planted in one trip even on sod. Recently developed equipment uses many of its principles.

to start fitting the seedbed well in advance of planting. You can harrow several times and "wear down" the weeds before planting. This will help to hold weeds in check until the crop is up and ready for cultivation.

Many farmers who have a problem with annual weeds start fitting their ground early. Their plan is to kill several "crops" of weeds before planting corn. To do this, they harrow about once each week. But thoroughly killing *annual weeds at or just before planting time* is just as effective as killing several crops of annual weeds by harrowing three or four times at weekly intervals before planting. Greatly increased fuel costs created a strong incentive for less seedbed tillage. Pre-emergence chemical weed killers give better weed control and often cost less than harrowing several times.

Another way to reduce annual weeds is to leave the seedbed between the rows so loose that the weed seeds cannot germinate. This is very effective in years when the surface soil dries out soon after planting, but not when rains keep the surface wet.

Prepare a Seedbed Suited to Your Tools for Planting and Cultivating

Trash may be left on the surface if you use a planter that has rolling disks rather than shoes dragging through the surface soil. Trash and plant residues can also be left on the surface if the crop does not require cultivation to control weeds. This is the case if you have completely reliable herbicides pre- or post-emergence (see also page 255).

The seedbed may be left rough and uneven if the first cultivation can be done with a smoothing tool like a weeder, rotary hoe or spike-tooth harrow.

55

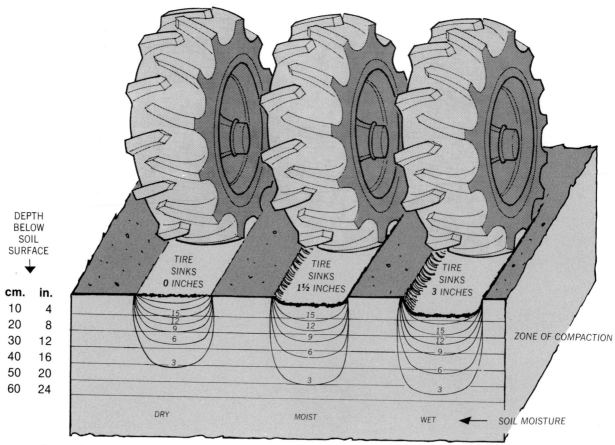

DEPTH BELOW SOIL SURFACE ↓

cm.	in.
10	4
20	8
30	12
40	16
50	20
60	24

TIRE SINKS 0 INCHES

TIRE SINKS 1½ INCHES

TIRE SINKS 3 INCHES

ZONE OF COMPACTION

DRY   MOIST   WET ← SOIL MOISTURE

See text for explanation.

Preserving and Improving Tilth

Light-textured soils, such as sands and sandy loams, can be worked at almost any time because you do not rely on good granulation for ease of working and for rainfall penetration. In silt loams and heavier soils you must have good tilth (plenty of granules) for ease of working, good drainage and aeration. The forces that hold granules together become weak when the soil is wet. Hence, you must plow, fit and cultivate these soils when they are moist but avoid working them when wet.

If you plow and harrow heavy soils at just the right moisture content, you can actually create granules or aggregates by the tillage operation. These artificial granules won't stand up under beating rains or the wheels of heavy machinery, but they are valuable while they last.

What Happens When You Overfit the Seedbed?

• Overfitting wastes time and fuel and costs money.

• It compacts the wheel track (see diagram), but perhaps more important, it packs the lower part of the plow layer and the soil directly beneath it since these lower layers are usually wetter than the surface at the time fields are fitted for planting. Thus, they are packed more even though they are farther removed from the tractor tire.

• When the surface is too fine, rain causes it to run together and seal over. This reduces the rate at which rain can enter the soil surface.

• When the rate at which water enters the surface is reduced, more runs off and erosion is increased causing floods, polluting streams, lakes and reservoirs and eventually reducing the yielding capacity of the soil.

• When the surface of an overworked seedbed dries out after a beating rain, it often forms a crust and corn seedlings "break their necks" trying to emerge.

• Because of increased runoff, the crop suffers more in drouth periods.

Tillage Terms

Tillage covers all the operations in working soil. These include plowing, chiseling, harrowing, planting and cultivating. This section covers tillage operations associated with preparing a seedbed and planting the crop. Cultivation is mentioned here only in connection with breaking a crust. Cultivation for weed control is covered in Section 8. For convenience, the operations connected with seedbed preparation are grouped into *primary tillage and secondary tillage. Primary* tillage is the first and often major step in getting the field ready to plant. *Secondary* tillage refers to the harrowing, packing and smoothing operations.

PRIMARY TILLAGE

The main objectives of primary tillage are to break sod, to turn under trash and residues, to kill weeds, and to loosen the plow layer.

Should Residues Be Left on the Surface?

Leaving residues on the surface serves these purposes:

1. Protects the surface against beating rains thus preserving structure, increasing infiltration, reducing runoff and erosion.

2. Protects against drouth by increasing water intake and reducing evaporation from the soil surface.

Moldboard plow

3. Protects against wind erosion. This attribute is decisive mainly near the western limit for corn in the Corn Belt where rainfall is often marginal for satisfactory yield.

One situation where leaving residues on the surface is unquestionably superior is on land that would otherwise be too steep to grow corn without an unacceptable amount of erosion.

Disadvantage of Residues on Surface

1. They delay soil warmup and drying in the spring, thus possibly delaying planting, germination and inhibiting early growth.

2. They interfere to some extent with cultivation and in extreme cases you must rely entirely upon effective herbicides to control weeds.

3. Some herbicides are less effective in heavy residues perhaps because weeds are shielded and thus escape a lethal dosage.

Leaving large amounts of residues on the surface will not likely increase very rapidly on non-erosive soils in the Corn Belt.

The Moldboard Plow

Moldboard plows have been extensively used in the United States since about 1775. Many tools have been invented to replace them, but they still are used by more farmers than all other primary tillage tools in areas which receive medium to high rainfall.

A moldboard plow is superior to any other tool for breaking up tough sod and for turning under green-manure crops, heavy straw, cornstalks and other trash. It buries weed seeds deeper and injures perennial weeds more than most other tools.

A moldboard plow *cuts*, *lifts*, *shears* and *turns* the furrow slice. When applied to heavy soils at the proper moisture content, these forces greatly improve the tilth of the plow layer. A long moldboard is needed on a heavy grass sod to turn the furrow slice upside down. The shorter the moldboard, the greater the shearing force.

Farmers often ask whether it pays to plow extra deep. Experiments throughout the eastern half of the United States show that 8 inches is usually deep enough. Plowing more than 8 inches deep has sometimes produced slightly higher yields and with modern tractors 8 to 10 inches is feasible. A rule of thumb for plowing depth in order to turn the furrow slice properly is no more than one-half the width of the moldboard.

Fall Versus Spring Plowing

Long-term research comparisons show little difference in corn yields from fall or spring plowing; however, when there is a difference it is usually in favor of fall plowing. Fall plowing will normally allow earlier planting than spring plowing; this almost always means higher yields.

Fall plowing is by far the easiest for managing heavy soils. If you plow when the soil is too wet or too dry, the winter weather will largely correct your mistake. The large, hard clods will break into desirable-size granules as a result of freezing, thawing, wetting and drying. In wet springs, it is sometimes impossible to prepare a seedbed without clods on spring-plowed soils unless planting is delayed so long that there is danger of reduced yields or unripe corn when fall frosts come.

In years with very dry springs, fall plowing of hayland or legume catch crops produces higher yields because it prevents fall and early spring growth from depleting the supply of stored water. In deciding when to plow a legume sod, you need to consider not only the influence on the seedbed and the water supply, but also the amount of nitrogen added by the legume (see page 160).

Soils that are especially high in silt should not be fall plowed because the granules are held together too weakly. By spring the granules are often destroyed and the plow layer may be nearly as compact as before it was plowed.

You should not fall-plow fields that are likely to erode badly under the impact of fall and spring rains. A Wisconsin agronomist suggests that 3 percent slope is the safe limit for fall plowing without contouring. By plowing on the contour you can fall-plow fields up to 6 to 7 percent slope in the northern Corn Belt. In the central and southern Corn Belt, where the soil is not frozen for so long nor covered with snow, the safe limit is somewhat less. A rough surface or one with some uncovered trash will erode less from water or wind than a smooth one. You can safely fall-plow heavy sods on slopes that would be too steep to fall-plow after small grains or row crops because the sod roots will hold soil in place.

Fall plowing can be a disadvantage on dairy farms because the fields are too rough to spread manure on after they freeze. It has the same drawback for farmers who want to spread fertilizer or limestone in the winter.

Environmental protection regulations may prohibit winter application of livestock wastes in some situations.

The Chisel Plow

Rigid-tined harrows capable of penetrating to plow depth came rapidly into use in the early 1970's in the Corn Belt as primary tillage tools in place of moldboard plows. A chisel plow loosens and shatters the plow layer *provided the soil is fairly dry* (figure 41).

Its special advantages are that it is faster than plowing, requires less draft, does not turn up a sticky, hard-to-work layer in gumbo soils, and leaves trash on the surface. This is an advantage in dry regions but not

Figure 41. The action of the chisel plow in a relatively dry soil.

always in the main Corn Belt (page 58). Chisel plows are used increasingly in the fall to increase water intake and to hasten drying in the following spring.

The disadvantages of the chisel plow are that it is ineffective when the soil is wet because it only cuts slits through the soil, it is not well suited to sod ground, and it does not bury either weed seeds or residues.

The Disk Plow

Disk plows are best suited to rather dry regions. They work well on bare ground or small grain stubble. Under proper conditions, a disk plow nearly completes seedbed preparation in one operation. It leaves most of the trash and residues on the surface. This is desirable in dry regions since it helps to control wind erosion and also increases the amount of water that enters the soil. Researchers have learned rather recently that small amounts of residue, as little as 1/8 to 1/4 ton per acre (.3 to .6 ton per hectare) on the soil surface, will greatly reduce wind erosion during the winters and until planting

Figure 42. Listers are widely used in the dry western part of the Corn Belt. The row is at the bottom of a trench, increasing the likelihood that the seed and young seedling will have adequate moisture.

time in the spring.

Disk plows are not suited for heavy sod because they fail to turn it over far enough to kill the grass.

The Lister

A lister or "middlebreaker" throws soil both ways and leaves a trench in the middle (figure 42). The tool is used most in semi-dry regions and in southern U.S. Corn is planted in the furrow or trench. With each cultivation, part of the soil is thrown into the furrow — until it is filled.

The lister has two advantages under dry-land farming conditions. First, the corn root systems are set deep and the plants can stand more drouth. Second, the furrows reduce runoff, thus helping store water for the crop while reducing erosion. In the southern states, corn is planted on the ridge or bed rather than in the trench left by the middle-breaker. A modified form of this is widely used in Nebraska (see page 92). It is excellent on soils of loess and alluvial origin which

are of medium texture but has not been found satisfactory on soils high in clay. Planting in a trench is undesirable in areas with plenty of rainfall.

The Subsurface Tiller

Subsurface tillage tools are designed to leave all trash and residues mixed in (not on) the surface soil to protect it from wind erosion and water runoff. These tools have blades or wide sweeps that run a few inches below the surface (figure 43). They cut the roots of weeds and stubble. This kills the weeds in dry regions but is often ineffective in the Corn Belt and eastern states where soils have more moisture because many weeds re-root and continue to grow in normal seasons. Furthermore, subsurface tillage leaves weeds seeds in the surface whereas plowing buries them.

Subsurface tillage tools are designed to fracture the plow layer and thus loosen the seedbed which they do in dry regions. But where rainfall is greater and the lower part

60

Figure 43. An early model of a subsurface tillage tool designed to kill weeds and loosen the soil while leaving the residues on the surface. This principle works in regions with low moisture only.

Figure 44. Large rotary tillers require a lot of power and may destroy the desirable structure in some soils.

61

Figure 45. This small model chisel penetrates 12 to 18 inches (30 to 45 cm) deep and is designed to break a plow pan and fracture the subsoil so that water and plant roots can enter it more readily. Experience in humid regions indicates that deep chiseling is not likely to be profitable (see text).

of the plow layer is more moist, surface tillers are not effective; they slide through the soil instead of shattering it.

Leaving residues on the surface increases corn yields in dry years in the Great Plains region but reduces yields in wet years. It will slightly reduce yields most years in the main part of the Corn Belt.

The Rotary Tiller

Rotary tillers are once-over tools designed to produce a finished seedbed in one operation (figure 44). They have spring steel hooks or knives of various shapes that rotate at very high speeds. The amount of trash coverage can be adjusted by raising or lowering the hood.

In field trials, rotary tillage has usually been inferior to moldboard plowing. The high-speed rotors break up many of the aggregates in loams, silt loams, and clays. As a result, the soil is more likely to crust if heavy rains fall shortly after planting. Rotary tillage is best suited to light-textured or organic soils that do not have soil tilth problems. Rotary tillage is ideally suited for home gardeners because no additional fitting is needed.

Deep Chisels, Subsoilers and Pan-Breakers

Tractors and heavy tractor-drawn machines are often blamed for compacted layers, plow soles, or pans that develop at or just below the normal planting depth. Two questions may be raised. Are deep chisels and subsoilers effective in breaking plow pans? Is there an actual plow pan?

Several manufacturers have developed tools, such as the one shown in figure 45, to break the plow pan on naturally well-drained soils. On these soils, deep chiseling removes a serious barrier to root penetration and the result is that yields improve.

In northern states where the ground usually freezes below plowing depth, this breaks up the plow sole or pan and chiseling for that purpose usually won't pay.

Some soils have a natural hardpan beginning at 12 to 18 inches that was not caused by heavy equipment — it was formed by natural soil-forming processes during thousands of years. This hardpan usually has a heavy concentration of silt and clay and therefore stays wet most of the growing season. But when it does dry, it is extremely dense and hard. Frequently the subsoil *below the hardpan is also quite compact* and poorly drained (figure 46). What success would you expect from chiseling this soil? In the first place, the hardpan is rarely dry enough yo fracture with a subsoiler. When it is wet, the chisel only cuts a narrow slit through it and has no lasting effect.

Suppose the soil is dry and you fracture the hardpan to let the water through. *Where will it go?* The layers *below* the pan *are also poorly drained!* Chiseling is not effective in this soil situation because you cannot break through to a well-drained layer.

Research results bear this out. They show that subsoiling heavy soils in humid regions will rarely increase crop yields even in the first year.

The only hope for a lasting effect is to get crop roots to grow into the chiseled zone and thus keep it open. However, there are problems in achieving this since the hardpan layer is often too acid and too low in phosphorus for good root growth. Researchers have placed limestone and fertilizer in the subsoil and temporarily increased root growth in the chiseled zone. But subsoiling combined with deep placement of lime and fertilizer has not yet proved to be profitable in any area where the subsoil stays moist. Improvement, if any, is short-lived. Nevertheless the concept has stayed alive among farmers and machinery suppliers for over 40 years.

6 inches (15 cm.)

12 inches (30 cm.)

24 inches (60 cm.)

36 inches (90 cm.)

Figure 46. Chiseling has little lasting effect in a soil such as this. The subsoil is rarely dry enough to fracture and besides, the soil beneath chisel depth is compact. Thus, water that rapidly enters the chisel opening has no way to move through the lower layers.

63

SECONDARY TILLAGE

Secondary tillage refers to all soil working between plowing (or other primary tillage) and planting. The purposes of secondary tillage are to accomplish one or more of the following: (a) pack the seedbed, (b) loosen the seedbed, (c) break clods and refine the seedbed, (d) cut trash or sod, (e) kill weeds, or (f) smooth the seedbed. The following pages list some of the most important tools, their type of action, their strong and weak points.

Persons who thoroughly understand seedbed preparation are amazed at the number of good farmers who work their fields more than is necessary between plowing and planting. Minimum tillage, discussed on pages 67 to 75, was, perhaps, a poor choice for a name because it still means some extreme method of soil preparation to many farmers. If it had been called "reduced tillage" from the start more farmers might have accepted the idea that elimination of one or two diskings is practical on their farm.

Disk (opposite page)

The desk is the most popular fitting tool in many areas.

- *Type of action:* Cuts, throws, and loosens the surface 3 to 6 inches (7.5 to 15 cm.), but *packs* the lower furrow slice. Overworking a field with a disk leaves the surface very fine and loose but the lower half of the plow layer may end up as hard as before it was plowed!

Fair for breaking large clods; cuts trash into the surface; smooths a rough surface somewhat. Poor for fields with many large flat stones.
- *Suitability for hard ground:* Excellent.
- *Suitability for plowed ground with loose trash:* Excellent.
- *Suitability for freshly plowed sod:* Excellent. Does not tear up sods or pull trash to the surface.
- *Depth of penetration:* 3 to 6 inches (7.5 to 15 cm.).
- *Special uses and advantages:* Excellent for firming the lower half of the furrow slice in freshly plowed ground; better than drag-type tools for working in a seedbed with lots of trash.
- *Special disadvantages:* Not suited to fields with large flat stones; packs the lower half of the furrow slice too much if used several times or when the soil is wet.

Spring-Tooth Harrow

The spring-tooth harrow is a widely used fitting tool in the Northeast and is extensively used in the Midwest.
- *Type of action:* Digs, lifts and loosens the surface 3 to 4 inches; breaks clods and fines the seedbed; levels a rough surface, pulls trash to the surface.
- *Suitability for hard ground:* Fair; stiff-tined spring-tooth harrows rate good.
- *Suitability for loose trash in the surface:* Poor in long trash: drags the trash to the surface and clogs up; fair for short trash.
- *Suitability for stony fields:* Very good because the stones slide around the narrow spring teeth.
- *Suitability for freshly plowed sod:* Fair; if set too deep the teeth pull up the sod pieces; you can avoid this by harrowing the same direction as the field was plowed the first time; set the teeth a little deeper on the second pass through the field.
- *Depth of penetration:* 2 to 4 inches with spring teeth; slightly deeper with rigid teeth.
- *Special uses and advantages:* Excellent for loosening the surface without compacting the lower part of the plow layer; excellent for stony fields; better than a disk for maintaining tilth of the surface, especially on soils that must be worked when slightly too wet or too dry; especially good for pulling up quackgrass roots and exposing them to die.
- *Special disadvantages:* Clogs badly in trash; tears up sods in freshly plowed fields unless operated carefully: not effective on hard ground; some tough perennial weeds like Canada thistles, sow thistles, bindweed, dock and milkweed slide around the narrow teeth and are not cut off.

Figure 47. Spring tooth harrow.

Field cultivator

Spike-tooth harrow

Field Cultivator

• *Type of action:* Digs, lifts and loosens the soil; cuts roots below the surface; leaves trash on the surface.

• *Suitability for hard ground:* Excellent.

• *Suitability for loose trash in the surface soil:* Fair, clogs less than a spring tooth but more than a disk.

• *Suitability for stony fields:* Fair; the wide duckfeet give more trouble than narrow spring teeth; rigid shanks supporting the teeth have heavy springs that recoil when they strike buried stones.

• *Suitability for freshly plowed sod:* Fair to poor, tends to tear up sod unless set very shallow; satisfactory after plowed ground has been disked.

• *Special uses and advantages:* Excellent for fallowing to control weeds because the wide teeth that overlap slightly do not allow tough weeds to slide around; can be a substitute for primary tillage tool on bare ground or following crops with little residue like field beans, soybeans, sugar beets, potatoes, and most vegetables.

• *Special disadvantages:* Clogs in long, loose trash; tends to pull sod pieces to the surface on freshly-plowed heavy sods.

Spike-tooth Harrow

The spike-tooth or peg-tooth harrow is mainly used to smooth the seedbed and break clods. It is effective only on clods that break easily. It is very good for killing small weed seedlings that start up when planting is delayed after the seedbed has been prepared.

Cultipacker

The cultipacker is especially useful to compact and level freshly plowed soil.

• *Type of action:* Pulverizes clods; firms the surface 2 to 4 inches but has little effect in the lower half of the furrow slice; leaves the surface ridged rather than smooth as the smooth roller does; presses stones into the soil surface.

• *Suitability for stony fields:* Fair, may ride on top of large stones or even medium-size flat stones; may push stones ahead of it.

• *Special uses and advantages:* Unequaled for breaking clods, and for making a finer, firmer seedbed, especially for small-seeded forage grasses and legumes.

• *Special disadvantages:* Only fair on very stony fields; may compact the seedbed too much if used when the soil is too high in moisture.

Cultipacker

MINIMUM OR REDUCED TILLAGE

Will Minimum Tillage Work for You?

Few practices were cussed and discussed more during the 1950s than minimum tillage. This is no longer a new way to plant corn; if you aren't using some kind of reduced tillage, you have already fallen behind the leading farmers.

In many ways, minimum tillage got off to a bad start. Research workers in the agricultural experiment stations began with methods that seemed impractical to most farmers. A lot of farmers looked at the toggled-up research tools and thought about the total lack of suitable machines available from farm implement dealers. But they failed to see that a new style in seedbeds was being pioneered. There was too much focus on *how* to do the job rather than *what* should be accomplished in the way of seedbed preparation.

The researchers persisted and a few farmers who had imagination and vision and were clever with equipment began to develop ways to get the job done. What was the job they were trying to do? Simply to prepare an adequate seedbed in the row and plant corn with the least possible number of trips over the field without sacrificing yield.

The pioneer research was done from 1938 to 1946 at the Ohio station, where it was shown that preparing a seedbed *only in the hill* was enough for corn on plowed ground.

Figure 48. Wheel-track planting was the first widely used minimum tillage method for corn. Success depends on a good job of plowing, a mellow soil, proper moisture in clay soils, and minimum delay in planting after plowing.

Figure 49. True plow-plant equipment built by R. B. Musgrave, Cornell University, in 1954. This method is low-cost and results in yields comparable to conventional tillage when soil tilth and moisture after planting are adequate for good stands.

R. L. Cook at Michigan State University began wheel-track planting (figure 48) in 1946. R. B. Musgrave at Cornell University in New York first attached the planter directly behind the plow in 1951; then in 1954 he mounted the planter on the plow (figure 49). During the 1950s, many ways to minimize tillage were tried by farmers and researchers.

Minimum tillage came of age in the early 1960s when major farm machinery manufacturers began marketing tools designed especially for it.

When minimum tillage began to receive attention in the early 1950's, farmers had come full circle from the days of the early settlers. Pioneer farmers dropped the seed in a hole in rough-plowed ground. When farmers worked the ground with horses they seldom overworked it. The introduction of tractors led to overfitting on many farms and resulted in some undesirable compaction. The trend now is by choice back to less tillage in seedbed preparation whereas in earlier days it was by necessity.

Compaction from tractor tires was likely at its peak in the 1950s and is now becoming less on many farms. Farmers had plenty of tractor power to work the seedbed but had not yet been alerted to the fact that overworking was both unnecessary and harmful. But with the development of ever more powerful tractors, farmers shifted to wider tools; they hook tools in tandem and thus make fewer trips over their fields; they substitute chemical weed control for one or two cultivations, and return more crop residues because of higher yielding crops. Since 1960, extra wide tires (figure 50) and later, dual tires, have moved rapidly onto farms. These steps have diminished the threat of compaction. A sharp increase in price and actual shortages of fuel have accelerated interest in reducing tillage. The greatest danger of compaction today is in driving on fields that are too wet.

The Aims of Minimum Tillage

• *To save dollars* by cutting out some of the usual trips over the field.

• *To increase the rate at which water enters the soil*, thus storing more water on sloping fields, at the same time reducing runoff and erosion.

Figure 50. Extra-wide tires sank only 3 inches in this freshly plowed ground (above) compared to 6 inches for standard tires (below). Dual tires have even greater weight-bearing surface.

Figure 51. A mellow furrow slice (A) is necessary in order to get good seed-soil contact with minimum tillage. The soil in (B) was wet and plastic; seed coverage was impossible without additional fitting.

- *To reduce soil packing.*
- *To reduce annual weeds.*
- *To conserve fuel* for other more critical uses.

Keys to Success with Reduced Tillage on Plowed Ground

- *Get a good stand.* Research results and farmer experiences have shown that corn yields as well with reduced or no secondary tillage as corn on a standard seedbed if plant populations are equal. There are three important requirements for a good stand:

1. A fine firm seedbed in the row! Germinating seed and young roots cannot get enough water from a coarse seedbed unless rainfall is above normal during the first month after planting.

2. A good job of plowing — especially if it is done just before planting. Planting is possible on field A, figure 51, but there is no chance of an acceptable stand of corn without more work on the seedbed in B.

3. One-half to one inch deeper planting is suggested for average conditions but is unnecessary for very early planting or when soil moisture is plentiful.

- *Be prepared to firm the area between rows* in dry seasons when the corn is 6 to 12 inches tall. Many people have noticed that reduced secondary tillage growth slows down at this stage in dry years. This is probably due to the fact that secondary roots, which come out *above* the first roots are penetrating loose, dry soil. Running over the field with a rotary hoe or cultivator will help.

- *Adapt the method to your soil.* Any minimum tillage system works well on *sandy soils.* There is no tilth problem from working them too wet or too dry. You can always get a fine seedbed and good soil-seed contact.

- On *loams* and *silt loams* most systems based on reduced or no secondary work quite well if the soil has good tilth and you plow and plant reasonably near the right moisture content.

On *clay loams* and *clays* the system must be carefully chosen and it must be carried out in the proper way and at just the right soil moisture. The most reliable system for clays is to fall-plow (unless the fields are too sloping and likely to erode) and then harrow only once, or harrow and plant in a single trip.

Farmers who have practiced reduced tillage for several years on clay soils claim that each year the field is easier to plow and more mellow. Research data have not been collected to confirm the claim.

Reduced secondary tillage can be recommended to all farmers, but real minimum tillage only to those who are willing to study methods carefully, to experiment a little, and to get down on their hands and knees at planting time and examine the conditions for the seed within their soil.

Different Methods for Minimum Tillage

For a summary of conservation tillage methods see page 217.

Wheel Track Planting on Freshly Plowed Ground

This is the original minimum tillage system initiated by R. L. Cook at Michigan State University in 1946. There are many ways to make the tracks. In figure 48 the rear tractor wheels make tracks for two rows. Special wheels ahead of the corn planter make the other two.

This is an excellent system where soil tilth is good and on all light-textured soils. It usually works well on clay soils following sod and even after row crops or small grains if the soil moisture is just right. Planting can be done when the soil is slightly too wet to disk or harrow because the tractor makes only one pass over the field.

A major disadvantage is that plowing must be delayed until near planting time. This limits the system to small to moderate acreages. If the field is not planted within a few days after plowing, the field must be harrowed to kill the weeds that will have started.

71

Figure 52. Killing the sod *in the row area only* is completely unsatisfactory in dry years. Note the crop failure on the right in this experiment. Normal seedbed preparation, left, resulted in a good crop in spite of drouth.

Figure 53. This farmer is preparing a strip in the row area only with rotary hoe sections. This system is excellent for fall or early spring plowed fields where weeds are still small. In this field an herbicide is being applied over the row; weeds between the row will be cultivated after the corn is up.

Plow-Plant

The ultimate minimum tillage system involving plowing was developed by R. B. Musgrave at Cornell University, New York, in 1954. The planter units (figure 49) in this setup were mounted on the plow but can be trailed behind.

It is suited to about the same conditions as well-track planting: an excellent job of plowing, some device to fill and compress the furrow slice ahead of the planter shoe, and careful placement of the row which must be on, rather than between, furrow slices unless the furrow is very mellow. It works best on sandy and silt loam soils but some farmers use it on clay after they learn when the moisture content is just right and how to adjust the device for preparing the row area.

Plow-plant means delayed plowing, a disadvantage for large acreages, especially in wet springs.

Strip Tillage, Row Preparation Only

Several versions of this idea have been tested on plowed and unplowed ground but none has been widely accepted. A till planter was introduced by International Harvester in the early 1950's (figure 40) and modified versions have been produced by other companies.

The row strip can be prepared in many ways: sweeps, rotary hoe blades, rotary tillers, shovels and revolving spring teeth.

Strip tillage in living sod has two great disadvantages: (a) because of competition from the sod between rows the corn is extremely sensitive to drouth and total failures have often resulted (figure 52); (b) extra fertilizer is needed to offset the nutrients taken up by the sod and to make up for those that would have been released from the decaying sod if it had all been plowed under.

Strip tillage looks good as a means of killing weeds on fall-plowed fields and for firming the row area on freshly plowed fields.

Several machines are available to accomplish this (figure 53).

Planting in Sod Killed with Chemicals: Zero Tillage

This was tried experimentally in several states as early as the mid-1950's. The first edition of Modern Corn Production suggested that with continued research, planting in sod might soon be a success. That prediction has come true.

The breakthrough came in the form of a successful chemical sod killer, paraquat (often combined with other chemicals), and a planter designed especially for planting in sod, figures 66 and 67, page 90. Leadership in this research centered in Kentucky and at the nearby Dixon Springs Experiment Station in southern Illinois. Zero tillage received an additional boost in the rolling to hilly area south of the Corn Belt because the equipment is well suited to planting soybeans in wheat stubble in a double cropping system. The main purposes are to reduce labor and save fuel but perhaps most important is that you can grow corn on fields that are too steep for conventional methods without unacceptable runoff and erosion. Planting can usually be done on time even in somewhat wet springs because the soil is not tilled and soil compaction is less serious than on plowed ground.

The main drawbacks are: (a) more fertilizer is needed; (b) trash on the surface lowers the temperature and this is undesirable early in the season in northern corn growing areas; (c) with present herbicide prices, the system costs more than other methods.

An unexpected problem developed in some sod planted fields. The sod was a fine home for field mice which had a remarkable knack of finding and eating the corn kernels in the slit made by the planter. If you try sod planting, you may have to poison the mice.

Zero tillage in sod is discussed in more detail on pages 89 to 91.

Figure 54. A double disk ahead of the corn planter kills weeds and prepares an adequate seedbed on fall or early spring plowed fields, thus eliminating one or two trips over the field.

Reduced Tillage on Fall-Plowed Ground

This is the least extreme system. It requires no special equipment; involves no more risk than usual methods; conserves fuel and saves money; is suited to any soil that can be fall plowed; and yields as high as conventional methods. It is questionable on fields where perennial weeds are the main problem; annuals cause no trouble since they are controlled as effectively as with several harrowings.

There are three possible procedures:

• Put sweeps or rotary devices on the cultivator bar ahead of the planter to smooth the surface and kill weeds either in the row or the entire area.

• Chemical weed control in place of tillage.

• Disk or harrow once, then plant. Machinery companies have hookups that put the planter behind a disk or field cultivator to till and plant in one trip (figure 54).

This system eliminates one, two, or three of the usual trips over fall-plowed fields.

Fall Plow, Grow Cover Crop, Plant with Zero Tillage

Many farmers would like to fall plow for corn but are deterred by the likelihood of water erosion on sloping land and wind erosion on all land. The solution may be to plow early, plant a cover crop, and then plant

74

Is this trip necessary?

directly in the dead or living sod the next spring. Though not yet thoroughly tested on farms, spring oats appear to be first choice. Spring oats grow more rapidly than winter oats, rye or ryegrass and will winter-kill in the Corn Belt latitude. Cover crops that live over winter would require an herbicide in the spring or some kind of vigorous tillage to kill the sod before planting. Furthermore, as some farmers and researchers have learned to regret, if spring plowing or spraying is delayed by wet weather, the cover crop can get too tall and difficult to handle. At the other extreme, in an unusually dry spring, a live, growing sod makes the situation worse by using up soil moisture.

Growing any grass cover crop over winter will not only reduce wind and water erosion but will also absorb nitrates which serves two purposes —
• The nitrogen is preserved for the following crop.
• Less nitrate leaches into surface and groundwater.

Whether any smoothing of plowed ground is needed in order to get a good stand of oats is a matter of judgement in each case. It seems unlikely in most fields because a thick stand is unnecessary. One bushel of oats per acre is adequate.

5

Planting for High Yields

Earlier planting is the single best opportunity for most good corn growers to further increase yields. In spite of impressive research results, very few farmers take full advantage of the opportunity for extra early planting, but if a spell of warm, dry weather occurs two or three weeks ahead of their normal planting date, most farmers let the planter set in the shed.

Why have farmers been so hesitant to accept early or extra early planting? Most likely because:
— They misinterpret published research data.
— They like to see corn come up quickly with a perfect stand.
— They are unduly concerned over hazards of early planting.
— They may recall one unfortunate experience with early planting.

The issue of early planting is so important, and some facets evidently so misunderstood that it is worth examining in detail.

First let's see why early planting usually produces higher yield.

Why Plant Early?

• The corn plant develops better and has a higher yield potential when the vegetative period of its development occurs in the cooler, moisture weather of May and June.

• Earlier planting tends to place the tasseling and silking period ahead of the greatest risk of moisture stress and drouth damage.

• Early planted fields have a deeper root system by late June or early July and thus are more likely to have subsoil water available to them when summer drouth comes. This does not help, of course, if the subsoil is dry.

• The earlier corn silks the greater the solar energy available during kernel development (see Page 363).

• Early planted corn is shorter and has lower ear height and less lodging, thus you can shoot for an extra 2,000 to 3,000 plants per acre (4,942 to 7,413 per hectare). To achieve this you should plant an extra three or four thousand (7,413 to 9,884 per hectare) seeds.

• Early planting of properly chosen hybrids leads to earlier maturity which results in easier, more efficient harvesting, less chance of damage from early frost and less danger of loss from breakage and harvesting in bad weather.

• Early maturity means less drying cost, a factor which may become even more important in the future.

• If your situation permits it, early maturity and early harvest gives you a better chance to fall plow.

What Is the Right Date to Plant?

Obviously, part of the answer depends on *where* you are growing corn. In southern Georgia, Alabama or Mississippi, early March or even late February is the right time for early planting. In the Corn Belt, the ground is sometimes frozen until late March or even early April. In an area like the central Corn Belt, soils in some years may warm up, are workable and ready to plant in early to mid-April. What should you do in those years? Look at figure 55 and select the best date to start planting. If you chose May 1, you did not correctly interpret the chart. That would have been the proper decision only if you were assured of perfect planting weather and you could plant your *entire acreage on 1 day*.

Since the yield lost by planting too early, first column, is less than for planting an equal period too late, third column, your goal should be to have *60 percent planted by the optimum calendar date.*

There is another reason why the optimum planting date is earlier than is indicated by research results. Researchers generally have the same plant population in their date of planting trials whereas you can grow 2,000 to 3,000 more plants per acre (4,942 to 7,413 per hectare) when you plant early.

Conditions differ from year to year, but any time after April 10 to 15 in the central Corn Belt is not too early to start planting if the soil is dry enough to carry the equipment for seedbed preparation and planting. When the soil can be worked and the corn planted — for example on April 15 — it is better to begin planting than to wait a few days by the calendar. When you *intentionally delay planting for a week, this is no assurance that the weather won't delay you another one, two, or three weeks!*

A good case can be made for some extra early planting. It is a reasonable goal to plant 25 percent of your corn acreage at least two weeks and 10 percent three weeks before the normal planting date for the area.

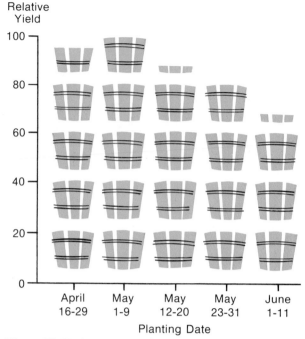

10-year Average Yield at Lansing, Michigan

Figure 55. Early planting increases yield without raising cost. Note that yield drops off more sharply from too late planting, column 3, than from too early planting, column 1. Early planting is more important in northern than in central and southern corn growing areas, not because of yield but because of frost danger.

• The average yield reduction from planting ten days too early is less than from planting ten days too late.

• Having some extra early planted corn further spreads the risk of unfavorable weather at the critical silking time.

• There is often a slight price advantage for early harvested corn in the fall.

Risks of Planting Too Early

The hazards of early planting include: a) poor stand because of a cold, wet soil; b) weed problems in case the soil is too wet for cultivation; and c) frost injury. The risk of frost injury is undoubtedly much less than most farmers believe. The earliest date of planting in the Michigan experiments reported in figure 55 was frosted in several years yet yielded almost as well as the second planting and better than the third. Top leaves at the time of frost soon become the bottom leaves which are destined to be shaded by

78

later developing leaves. Besides they usually break off as soon as the stalk begins to enlarge.

The weed problem can be largely offset by the proper choice of preemergence herbicide. The hazard of poor stand from cold, wet soil is real but is far less than 30 years ago because of modern seed treatment which protects against it. Furthermore, an inadequate stand can be corrected by replanting with only the cost of seed and the planting operation itself. In one sense extra early planting is somewhat of an insurance program because you still have the opportunity to correct a poor stand by planting approximately on time if the first planting is unsatisfactory.

In the days when farmers selected their own seed and planted it without treatment, early planting could lead to problems in germination and stand. It is still possible to plant *too early*, but a date that might have been one or two weeks too early thirty years ago may be ideal now. Modern hybrids are bred for resistance to soil-borne disease and cold; they are vigorous enough to get started even if conditions are unfavorable. This is especially true of the newer hybrids bred for northern areas. Careful harvesting, drying and processing results in high seed quality; perhaps most important is that all commercial seed is carefully treated with fungicides that give excellent protection against seedling diseases and soil-borne fungi. Soil treatment with insecticides further protects the seedling early in the spring. High-quality modern seed corn can take a week or more of unfavorable conditions and still come up to a good stand. In summary you have much to gain and little to risk by planting early.

Planting by Soil Temperature (Figure 56)

Most types of corn will not sprout at all if the soil temperature is 50°F (10°C) or below. Even at 55°F (13°C), germination is slow. By the time the soil has warmed up to 60°F (15.5°C), germination is prompt and

Figure 56. Every corn farmer should have a thermometer suitable for taking soil temperatures.

the seedlings will be above ground in 7 to 10 days after planting.

Plant according to the thermometer early in the season, but after the normal planting date has been reached, plant even if the soil is still below the desired temperature. Maybe that sounds simple and direct, but in practice, it isn't.

Unless you have followed soil temperatures you may not know that the temperature at 2 inches (5 cm) often changes 10 to 15°F (5.5 to 8°C) during a single day.

Air temperature does not affect soil temperature at 2 to 4 inches (5 to 10 cm) nearly as much as the amount of sunshine. Soil warms up rapidly on a clear day even though the air is cool.

Soil moisture, soil color, and type of cover or amount of residues on the surface affect the rate at which soils warm up. You likely can't depend upon the temperatures given by local TV or radio stations because they usually are taken under sod. Under bare ground the temperature is often 8 to 10 degrees F (4.4 to 5.5°C) higher during midday. After sundown the temperature drops more rapidly in bare soil than under sod or residues.

When to take the temperature is a problem. As a tentative guide for corn, for example, perhaps 50°F (10°C) at planting depth at 7:00 to 8:00 a.m., or 55°F (13°C) at 1:00 p.m. on a clear day is acceptable. This will assure a suitable temperature for several hours of the day for corn to germinate and grow. In a typical spring there will be short periods of slow or no growth, but they will seldom be long enough for severe damage from diseases.

How Deep to Plant?

The long-time experience of farmers in the community is often the best guide for *average* conditions. This will take care of differences between soils, geographical conditions, varying temperatures, and the probability of dry soil at planting time. For typical Corn Belt conditions, with moist soil and average planting date, a depth of two inches (5 cm) is ideal. Many farmers plant at least one inch (2.5 cm) deeper than is necessary with adequate moisture. Here are some points to consider for unusual situations:

For very early planting, plant about ½ to 1 inch (1.25 to 2.5 cm) shallower than normal since cool soil is a hazard to quick germination. Temperature will be higher at 1 to 2 inches (2.5 to 5 cm) depth than at 3 inches (7.5 cm) or deeper. Besides, there is less chance of a dry seedbed with early planting.

In a dry soil, try to get the kernels down to moisture, even if you have to go as deep as 3 to 3½ inches (7.5 to 8.8 cm) on clays, 4 to 4½ inches (10 to 11.25 cm) on silts, and 5 inches (12.5 cm) on sands.

"Calendarizing" the Corn Crop

Even with high-capacity modern equipment, most growers cannot plant their full acreage in one or two days. If the grower plants more than one hybrid, some may be earlier than others. He then faces the question of which hybrid to plant first. A planned scheduling of planting dates according to maturity has been developed in Iowa and is known as *calendarization.* The biggest advantage of calendarization is that it spreads out the time and labor of harvesting. It also reduces the risk of hot, dry weather hitting at ear-shooting time since plantings silk as much as ten days apart.

Under a calendarized system, the order of planting is the opposite of what you might expect. The earliest hybrids are planted first and the full-season hybrids last.

Planting the earliest hybrid first insures a wide spread in pollination time, since you can arrange to have the early hybrids tassel and silk 10 to 20 days before the full-season types. This difference will carry through to harvest, making it possible to begin early and keep harvest equipment operating right through until the latest-maturing corn is ready to come out of the field. Properly handled, especially if planting is begun early enough, this system will spread the work load of both planting and harvesting over a longer time, and reduce peak loads considerably. Other row crops — especially soybeans — can be fitted into the calendarization scheme. Soybean varieties can be calendarized in planting date, too, if it seems desirable.

Planting the early hybrid first is sound for a reason that is sometimes overlooked. Most of the shorter-season hybrids have been developed for northern corn growing areas where soils are cold and growing conditions unfavorable in the early part of the season. Therefore, these hybrids are suited to early planting. Also, the early varieties are often more sensitive to hot, dry weather in mid to late summer than are full-season hybrids. Thus, while early hybrids usually yield less than full-season types, some of this disadvantage can be offset by proper choice of planting dates and by higher population.

Calendarization can give the corn grower a real advantage in harvesting his crop. He can begin harvest earlier, with no need to wait until his whole acreage is dry. This means that he can harvest the bulk of his crop at nearly optimum moisture content. In many years, this will cut down harvest losses significantly.

Naturally, this is not a perfect system. Some farmers may not want to spread out planting or harvest times; others may find difficulty in getting satisfactory performance from the earliest or latest varieties available to them. The important thing is to choose the correct hybrids for your area and then time planting dates properly. With the wide range of hybrids now on the market, the efficient operator should be able to work out his calendarization plan without serious disadvantages. You might, for example, begin planting very early with the shortest season hybrid and then proceed directly to the longer season hybrids as weather permits.

Plant Populations: How High?

When hybrids took over in the Corn Belt, farmers learned that some hybrids would yield more if planted thicker than the usual 10,000 to 12,000 plants. Stands up to 16,000 plants per acre (39,536 per hectare) become more common. As fertilizer use increased sharply in the 1950's, corn breeders made special efforts to develop hybrids which could be planted thick without risk of lodging and barren stalks. Now, 16,000 plants per acre (39,536 per hectare) is a very low population, 20,000 plants per acre (49,420 per hectare) is average, and 24,000 (59,304 per hectare) is not uncommon. One point to remember is that when you plant extra early you can plant 2,000 to 3,000 more kernels per acre (4,942 to 7,413 per hectare) for three reasons: (1) seedling mortality is a little greater; (2) plants are shorter and they lodge less; (3) moisture supply is more likely to be adequate.

Hybrids react differently to increased planting rates, as table 4 shows.

The cross (Hy2 x Oh7) has a long record of giving its best yields at rather high plant populations — usually 20,000 per acre (49,420 per hectare) or more. It is a *population-tolerant* hybrid and usually will produce a good sound ear, even at populations of

Table 4.

Relative yields of shelled grain produced by single crosses at two plant populations, in two growing seasons at Urbana, Illinois. (Not coverted to metric system because relative yield makes the point.)

	1962		1963	
	16,000	24,000	16,000	24,000
Hy2 x Oh7	92%	100%	96%	100%
WF9 x C103	94%	74%	72%	52%

24,000 per acre (59,304 per hectare) or more. The cross (WF9 x Cl03) is just the opposite — it is a *population-sensitive* hybrid. At 16,000 plants per acre (39,536 per hectare), it produces a good big ear and yields well. At 20,000 plants per acre (49,420 per hectare), quite a few plants are barren. At 24,000 plants per acre (59,304 per hectare) or more, over half the plants may be barren in years with moisture stress, and many of the rest will bear only nubbins.

Drouth or unfavorable growing conditions can complicate the problems of hybrid response to population. Figure 57 illustrates this point; the yield of the sensitive hybrid fell off in a severe drouth year, while the population-tolerant hybrid yielded best at a high planting rate. This figure also shows that another set of growing conditions brought a different reaction from the same two hybrids. Here, a wet year increased stalk lodging so much in the "high-population hybrid" that it, too, yielded best at lower populations.

Most Corn Belt experiment stations and seed companies now recommend planting rates of 20,000 to 26,000 kernels per acre (49,420 to 64,246 per hectare) on fertile soils to produce final stands of 18,000 to 24,000 plants per acre (44,478 to 59,304 per hectare). Many researchers and quite a few corn growers have had great success with even

Yield

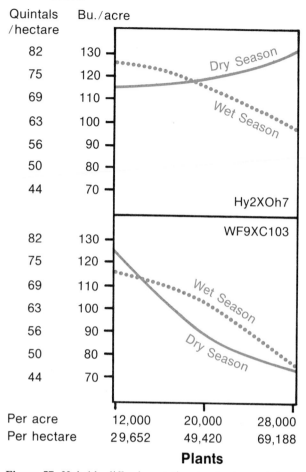

Figure 57. Hybrids differ in reaction to plant population, but don't always perform equally in different years. 1954 was a drouth year; 1955 was very wet. Hy2 x 07 declined at high population in 1955 because of excessive lodging in a wet year.

higher populations when conditions were favorable. However, reports from farmers on very high plant populations are not always reliable because they are often based on estimates rather than on actual counts. Even if based on counts at harvest, they may be too high because tillers (suckers) are hard to tell from the main stalks and so usually get included in the count. (The best time to make stalk counts is when the plants are 4 to 5 feet (1⅓ to 1⅔ meters) tall.)

Seed corn companies know the population tolerances of their hybrids and recommend accordingly.

Very high populations delay silking more than they do pollen shed especially when under moisture stress and thus may lead to poorly pollinated ears. The modern trend in corn breeding is definitely toward hybrids which will tolerate high populations without lodging, having poorly filled tips or going barren. Thus, they give a degree of insurance against mistakes in population choice, and are likely to yield as much as seasonal growing conditions permit.

Optimum plant populations over a period of years have been about 12,000 per acre (29,652 per hectare) in southern United States and on the drier western fringe of the Corn Belt without irrigation. With irrigation, 20,000 to 24,000 plants (49,420 to 59,304 per hectare) have usually yielded best.

The optimum plant population for silage is at least 10 percent more than for grain. Higher yield of green weight can be obtained by even higher populations, but this produces little advantage in dry weight. What's more, the extra weight is gained by sacrificing grain in the silage.

Populations in the range of 100,000 to 200,000 per acre (247,100 to 494,200 per hectare) have been suggested for green-chop feeding and for a green manure crop. For more information on this, see page 150.

Your seedsman's recommendations are important to your choice of planting rate. If he tells you that a hybrid won't do best at high populations, you would be well-advised to plant it at the recommended rate or choose another hybrid. The day is past when seed corn salesmen recommend thin planting to get large, attractive ears even though they know the yield will be lower than with more plants per acre. Some states plant their official variety trials at more than one plant population, and this also is a good source of information for your choice.

Research workers have known for many years and leading farmers now generally accept the fact that yields of well-fertilized corn do not fall off very sharply when plant population is above the optimum, *even in dry years.*

How Much Overplanting
Is Necessary?

With near-ideal soil conditions and moderate planting rates (18,000-23,000 kernels per acre, 44,478 to 56,833 per hectare) the mortality from lack of germination, insects and cultivation damage will usually be 10 to 15 percent. In the range of 24,000 to 28,000 kernels per acre (59,304 to 69,188 per hectare), the mortality increases, perhaps to 15 or 20 percent under favorable soil conditions.

For very early planting when the soil temperature is lower and the soil may be too wet the stand loss is even greater.

Under average conditions, it is wise to overplant by 15 to 20 percent.

Hill Drop or Drill?

Many farmers can still remember pulling a check wire at each end of the field to make a planting pattern with straight rows in both directions. *Check-row* planting was nearly universal in the Corn Belt for many years, and had the real advantage that it could be cultivated both ways.

Tests usually showed that checked corn outyielded drilled corn by several bushels per acre. But there was a joker in these results. Closer study revealed that better weed control accounted for the advantage of check-row corn. In fact, drilled corn gives the most uniform distribution of plants in the field, and should, therefore, make the most efficient use of available sunlight, moisture early in the season, and fertility (see page 58). Plants in hills shade each other more than drilled plants.

Why isn't all corn drilled? It has some disadvantages. Drilled corn tends to sucker (tiller) more freely, and it nearly always lodges more. Lodging is often especially bad if many tillers have formed. Tillers don't have much effect on yield but they are weak and often break over before harvest. This adds to harvesting problems without returning a dividend in yield. An old rule of thumb is that five stalks will lodge in drilled corn

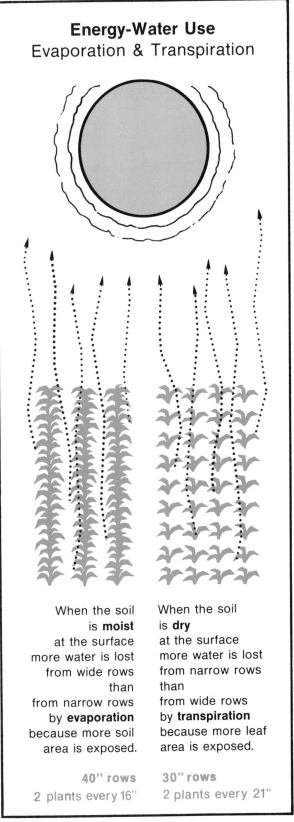

Energy-Water Use
Evaporation & Transpiration

When the soil is **moist** at the surface more water is lost from wide rows than from narrow rows by **evaporation** because more soil area is exposed.

When the soil is **dry** at the surface more water is lost from narrow rows than from wide rows by **transpiration** because more leaf area is exposed.

40" rows
2 plants every 16"

30" rows
2 plants every 21"

Figure 58. The effect of row width on water lost by evaporation from the soil vs. transpiration from corn leaves.

for every three that lodge in hill-dropped corn.

With the development of better standing hybrids, there has been a shift in the midwestern states to drilling corn. This takes advantage of the slight yield increase gained by spacing plants individually. "Power checking" with 2 kernels dropped together is fairly common.

Narrow Rows vs. Conventional Width

The increased yield from narrow rows is quite consistent but seldom striking. The average from a large number of experiments in Corn Belt states shows about 5 percent higher yields for 30-inch (75 cm) rows compared to 40-inch (1 meter) rows. In a few cases, the increase for narrow rows is 10 to 15 percent. Largest increases are likely to be with high populations where you are fertilizing and managing for top yield and in years when there is plenty of water.

Narrow rows make more efficient use of available light and also shade the surface soil more completely during the early part of the season while the soil is moist, figure 58.

When the *surface soil is moist,* differences in row width, plant distribution within the rows and plant population do not affect the total disappearance of water very much. They simply change the proportion of water that is *evaporated* from the soil surface compared to that which is *transpired* from the leaves. Narrow rows, plants individually spaced within the rows, and high populations shade more of the soil and thus reduce evaporative loss. But since this results in more leaf area exposed to radiation from the sun, transpiration loss is greater. The more uniformly you can place the plants, the better — as long as the surface soil is moist. This maximizes photosynthesis and the proportion of water that is used in growth processes rather than evaporated from the soil.

But when the *soil surface is dry,* the whole situation changes. Evaporative loss is small because there is little moisture on the surface to be evaporated. Uniform plant distribution over the area and high population no longer effectively reduce evaporative loss from the soil surface. Even distribution and high population become a disadvantage because transpiration is now the main pathway by which water is taken from the soil. And the more leaf area exposed to radiant energy from the sun, the greater the water loss.

Research results in humid areas and irrigated drylands definitely favor narrow rows, even spacing, and high populations; this means that increased efficiency in the use of sunlight for photosynthesis, and improved water use when the soil surface is moist, more than offset any disadvantage when the soil is dry — especially in the early part of the season and after each rain.

Before going to 30-inch (75 cm) or less you had better consider the hybrids that you are growing, suitability of your machinery for these row widths, the extra time needed to plant, cultivate and harvest and the extra herbicide for band application over the row. Narrower rows may well replace conventional width rows as farmers shift to 20 to 30-inch (50 to 75 cm) rows of soybeans (field beans, sugar beets or vegetables in some areas) where there is a clear-cut advantage for narrow rows. To simplify planting and cultivating, farmers will want to have soybeans and corn in the same row widths. If you eventually get herbicides that give near perfect weed control in soybeans every year and shift all the way to solid planting, the cost of narrow-row equipment would have to be borne by the corn crop.

The yield increases reported from narrow-row experiments show clearly that it is economically sound to tool up for narrow rows when you need to replace old equipment. The economic advantage may not be spectacular but it is consistent. The higher the price of corn and soybeans, of course, the greater the profit increase from narrow rows.

Wide-row corn (60-inch to 80-inch rows,

Figure 59. Wide-row corn was tested in many states in the 1940s and 1950s, mainly as a way to modify the usual corn-small grain-hay rotation, to eliminate the relatively low-value small grain crop, and to reduce erosion on sloping fields. Yield losses (see text), the need for special equipment, weed strips over the old corn rows, and some uncertainty in stands caused farmers to lose interest in very wide rows.

1.5 to 2 meters) had a brief period of popularity when studies where underway to use corn as a "nurse crop" for interseeded legumes and grasses (figure 59). In the central and western Corn Belt, this practice proved unsatisfactory, and is is now rarely seen. Stands thick enough to produce top corn yields couldn't be planted in wide rows without overcrowding the plants in the row. As compared to 40-inch (1 m.) rows, yields were usually about 9 percent lower in 60-inch (1.5 m.) and 20 percent lower in 80-inch (2 m.) rows.

New Concepts
in Corn Planter Seed Delivery Systems

For nearly 50 years most corn planters operated on the principle of a revolving planter plate with cells matched to the size of the kernels, figure 60. This worked well when the seed was well graded and the field speed was properly controlled. But farmers asked for more accurate seed delivery at ever higher speeds. Some of the innovations in kernel pickup and discharge mechanisms are

Figure 60. A planter plate, the standard method for controlled seed delivery for more than fifty years.

85

Figure 61. The International Harvester Cyclo planter picks up the kernels by applying about 10 pounds of pressure per square inch (0.7 kilos per square centimeter) to the inside of a perforated drum. The air pressure holds the kernel against the orifice until the drum rotates to the point where the kernel is to be discharged.

Figure 63. The Deere and Company pickup is by fingers on a disk rotating through the seed. The fingers turn outward to allow the kernel to get into position and then rotate toward the plate to grasp the kernel. Extra kernels are kicked off before the plate reaches the discharge opening.

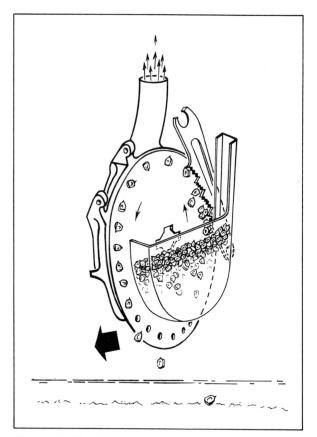

Figure 62. The Glenco-Nodet Vacu-Meter picks up and holds kernels by vacuum applied to holes in a rotating plate. The kernel is discharged at the desired point by blocking the vacuum.

Figure 64. White Plant-Aire vacuum pickup.

86

shown in figures 61, 62, 63, 64. Allis-Chalmers also has a planter designed to use air in kernel pickup and delivery.

Calibrating Your Corn Planter

Agricultural engineers at the University of Illinois (H. P. Bateman and Wendell Bowers) developed the following guides for planter calibration. After you have set your population goal and checked the planter for worn or broken parts, they suggest these steps:

• *Step 1. Read the owner's manual.*

The owner's manual tells you how to adjust your corn planter to obtain the correct population. It is also an exellent guide for determining planter speed for a given planting rate.

Do not exceed the maximum planting speed recommended in the manual. If you do, the seed plate on plate-style planters will turn too fast for accurate planting and uniform kernel spacing.

In laboratory tests, a corn planter with conventional plates (figure 60) adjusted to drop 18,800 kernels per acre (46,459 per hectare) at 3 miles per hour dropped 17,400 kernels (42,995 per hectare) at 5 miles per hour. At 7 miles per hour, the rate was only 15,000 kernels per acre (37,065 per hectare).

By using seed plates with more cells than the standard 16-cell plate, you can drive faster at the same planting rate. Your manual should indicate whether plates with more than 16 cells can be obtained for your planter.

Recently developed planters previously described are more accurate at high speeds.

• *How to determine field speed:*

Carefully mark off a distance of 176 feet (53 meters) in the field.

As you plant, use a watch with a sweep second hand to check the number of seconds required to drive between the markers.

This chart lists the time in seconds for speeds up to 8 miles per hour:

Times to Drive 176 Feet, 53 meters	Speed	
	miles per hr.	Km per hr.
120 seconds	1	1.6
60 seconds	2	3.2
40 seconds	3	4.8
30 seconds	4	6.4
24 seconds	5	8.0
20 seconds	6	9.6
17 seconds	7	11.3
15 seconds	8	12.9

• *Step 2: Match seed to seed plate (for plate-type planters).*

Plan to have an average of 100 percent cell fill so that on the average, one kernel is dropped for each cell.

To be certain that the cell fill is accurate, match the seed corn and the seed plate. These can be matched either on a seed-corn test stand or by a calibration run on the open ground in a lane or barnlot where all the kernels can be counted. Whichever method you use, check rate at field speed and desired planting rate.

In selecting the correct seed plate, begin with the seed plate recommended on your bag of seed corn. Be sure to use your own seed plates and seed corn in calibrating the planter. Even small variations between seed plates of the same size and seed corn of the same grade can result in serious planting errors. Remove any rust, seed treatment, or rust preventative from cells before making the test.

• *Step 3: Adjust planter for desired planting rate.*

Table 5.

Row Spacing			Spacing of Kernels for Drilled Planting Rates of									
		Per acre ⟶	16,000		18,000		20,000		24,000		28,000	
		Per hectare ⟶	39,536		44,478		49,420		59,304		69,188	
in.	cm.		in.	cm.	in.	cm.	in.	cm.	in.	cm.	in.	cm.
20	51		19.6	49.8	17.4	44.2	15.6	39.6	13.0	33.0	11.2	28.4
30	76		13.1	33.3	11.6	29.5	10.4	26.4	8.7	22.1	7.5	19.1
36	91		10.9	27.7	9.7	24.6	8.7	22.1	7.3	18.5	6.2	15.7
38	97		10.3	26.2	9.2	23.4	8.2	20.8	6.9	17.5	5.9	15.0
40	102		9.8	24.9	8.7	22.1	7.8	19.8	6.5	16.5	5.6	14.2
42	107		9.3	23.6	8.3	21.1	7.5	19.1	6.2	15.7	5.3	13.5

Table 6.

Row Spacing		Distance To Drive		Kernels to Count for Planting Rates of					
				Per acre ⟶ 16,000	18,000	20,000	22,000	24,000	28,000
				Per hectare ⟶ 39,536	44,478	49,420	54,362	59,304	69,188
in.	cm.	ft.	m.						
20	51	130'8"	39.8						
30	76	87'1"	26.7						
36	91	72'7"	22.2						
38	97	68'9"	20.9	80	90	100	110	120	140
40	102	65'4"	19.9						
42	107	62'3"	19.0						

Using the owner's manual and table 5, you can set your planter.

• *Step 4: Calibrate in a barnlot or roadway before planting.*

Planting speed may cause a wide variation in planting rates. For this reason, final calibration must be made at planting speed on a roadway or barnlot where all of the kernels can be counted over a short distance. Leave the planter in a raised position and use a wire or string to engage the seed-plate drive. Table 6 shows how far to drive for various row spacings. Each row is 1/200 of an acre (1/500 of a hectare). To obtain the planting rate per acre, count the kernels from one row and multiply by 200 (by 500 for rate per hectare).

To get an accurate measure of the planting rate, make all of the calibration runs at planting speed. The planting rate in these calibration runs will probably be slightly higher than the field rate, even when the seed is perfectly matched to the seed plate. This is due primarily to the reduced slippage of the drive wheels on the smooth surface.

In making the calibration run, allow a few hundred extra kernels per acre to compensate for the difference between the calibration rate and the field rate.

• *Step 5: Make a field check.*

When you have calibrated your planter on a roadway or barnlot, you can be fairly confident that it will give you approximately the desired planting rate. As a final check, however, dig out several kernels along the row and make an estimate of the average kernel spacing. By checking this spacing with the desired rate, you can determine the

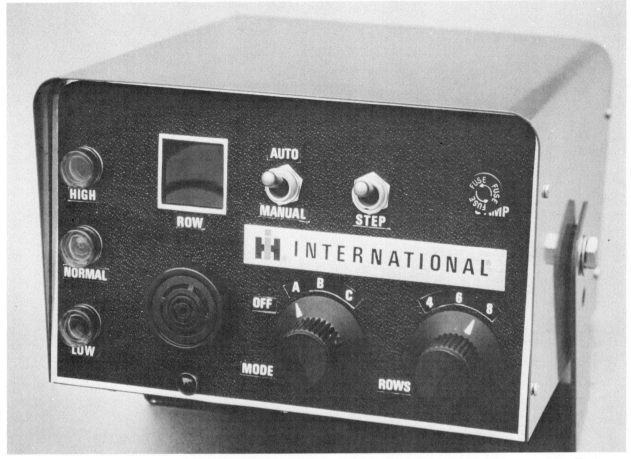

Figure 65. A "monitor" permits you to ascertain without stopping that seed is being delivered in every row. Each row can be dialed for checking. Some corn planters have a monitor as standard equipment. Several machinery manufacturers supply it as an extra item.

accuracy of your calibration and make whatever adjustments are necessary on your planter.

Many seed companies indicate on the tag the number of kernels per bushel. After you have planted a few acres you can calculate very accurately the kernels being delivered per acre.

• *Step 6: Count emerged plants and final harvest population.*

You will be able to plant corn more accurately if you keep a record for two or three years of the kernels planted, the plants that emerged, and the ears produced at harvest. Making these checks will help you determine whether the planter is being set correctly, as well as indicating the amount of loss during the season.

No-till, Zero-Till Planting

Planting with no tillage except a furrow opener for the seed is possible and is practical to some extent following corn, soybeans, sorghum, small grains and hay. The greatest initial use of this system was in grass sods. Many farmers have continued the following years with no-till on the corn stubble. Some researchers report lower yields than in the first year after sod.

The goal is usually to thoroughly kill the sod, figure 66, so it will not compete with the crop for moisture. To date Paraquat has been the basic herbicide but it is usually combined with one or more other chemicals depending upon the kind of sod and expected weed species. County extension agents, state agronomists and chemical suppliers

Figure 66. Spraying to kill the sod prior to planting with zero tillage. Usually a mixture of herbicides is needed with Paraquat being the main component.

Figure 67. Several models of planters suited to sod planting are available.

Figure 68. An excellent stand of corn in a chemically-killed stand of rye.

should be checked for the latest information on effective and approved herbicides.

Pennsylvania researchers have had good recent experience with crown vetch which is seriously set back but not killed with an herbicide. The crown vetch is a perennial so does not have to be reseeded because it recovers from the herbicide treatment. The goal is to have the vetch, being a legume, supply part of the nitrogen needed by corn.

Several farm machinery manufacturers have developed special drills for seeding in a growing or killed sod or stubble, figure 67. Excellent stands of corn are possible, figure 68.

By far the most important reason for using the no-till or zero-till system is to grow corn (or other row crops) on land that with conventional tillage would be too steep and thus cause an unacceptable amount of runoff and erosion. Loss is nil when the ground cover is as shown in figures 66 and 67. Soil loss is very low even on no-till following corn but soluble phosphorus in runoff is greater.

An important incidental benefit of no-till in sod is that because runoff is greatly reduced, the available water supply is greater than it would be with conventional seedbed preparation on steep slopes.

The system uses much less tractor fuel because of elimination of several tillage operations. But in the larger energy picture, part of the apparent saving is offset by the energy required to manufacture and apply the chemical sod killer.

No-till or zero-till planting has mixed effects from an environmental point of view. Sediment pollution is, of course, greatly reduced. But the runoff of pesticides and of soluble phosphorus compounds and of organic matter may be increased.

Planting with the no-till system on sod can usually be done on time because there is less risk of compaction and clods than on plowed ground.

There is no indication yet that the system

Figure 69. The raised area for ridge planting, as shown here, is made with a 14-inch (35 cm) furrow slice turned on top of a 28-inch (70 cm) ridge top. (The same ridges may be used for several years.) Furrows between the ridges hold water, allowing more of it to soak in.

will replace conventional seedbed preparation or chiseling on nearly level, dark colored, fine textured soils. It should be well suited to sandy soils where wind erosion is sometimes serious.

As mentioned on page 73, field mice are sometimes a serious problem in sod planted fields.

Ridge Planting

This system was developed at Iowa State University in the early 1950's. Corn is planted two or more years on the same ridges (figure 69). The advantages are: fewer trips over the field, reduced water runoff and erosion, less drowning of corn in flat areas. Ridges are made by throwing up a furrow slice every 40 inches (1 meter). After the first year, the field is disked rather than plowed.

Nebraska researchers have developed a combined ridge and till-planting system. The steps are:

1. Shredding stalks and leaving them on the surface.

2. Planting in the old ridge with a till planter that prepares the seedbed and applies a pre-emergence weed killer.

3. Cultivating when the corn is 6 to 10 inches (15 to 25 cm) tall using disk hillers in front, sweeps behind.

4. Ridging: this clears the area between the rows of residues and prepares the field for irrigation.

Aerial Planting

Farmers began experimenting with airplane planting of corn in the late 1960's. If acceptable yields could be obtained, the advantages would be rapid planting, no delay due to wet weather, and no need to own expensive planting equipment because the crop would be custom planted. But several problems have turned up:

• Uneven distribution of plants — too thick in some places, too thin in others.

• Uneven plant size due to differences in time of germination likely due to variation in seed coverage. Late emerging plants are "runts" and are badly affected by shading from larger plants.

• Corn can't be cultivated for weed control thus the herbicide must work nearly perfectly.

• Yields have not equalled those in row planting in any carefully measured trials.

Orienting the Kernels

Two types of oriented kernel placement have been studied:

1. *Planting kernels tip down.* Ohio researchers reported 3 days earlier emergence, 10 percent more plants and greater early growth than when planted tip up. But by the time the plants were 24 inches (2/3 meter) tall there was little difference between the two seed placements. Note that the early differences reported were between tip up and tip down rather than random arrangement which would result from normal planting.

2. *Placing kernels broadside to the row direction.* The idea was to have more leaves extending into the area *between* rows where they would make better use of light rather than within the rows where they would be competing with and shading adjacent plants. This concept was not productive because plants did not maintain an oriented leaf arrangement throughout their vegetative growth.

Applying Water through the Planter

In the late 1960's the Acra planter was modified to apply a small amount of water in the row at planting time. Most of the comparisons with and without water were in field strip trials rather than in replicated experiments. University of Nebraska researchers reported results from one year. All plots were planted late — June 1 — and planting was followed by a dry period. They obtained yield increases but were not sure about the cause since stands were about equal and watered corn had a growth advantage for only a short time.

Farmer reports have been mixed, but with more claiming yield increases than not. Their observations included the following:

• Advantage was greatest in the western and southwestern part of the Midwest where moisture is more often short at planting time.

• About 40 to 50 gallons per acre (374 to 468 liters per hectare) is the proper amount. Applying more caused problems with mudding up the planter shoe in some soils and seed displacement in another unless planter speed was reduced. The amount should be governed by the kind of soil and its moisture content. The experience of neighbors and advice from local dealers should be helpful.

6

Fertilizing for Top Profit

Fertilizing decisions have recently become more complex because of higher prices, some shortages, world food problems, environmental concerns, and more variety of kinds and of methods for application. Fertilizer will play an increasing role in feeding the world.

Choosing the right fertilizers and deciding when, where and how to use them is not easy, but it has an extremely important influence on profit at the end of the year. This section gives information which should enable you to make fertilizer decisions correctly and with confidence. The steps are described under these headings:

1. **UNDERSTANDING FERTILIZERS AND HOW THEY BEHAVE IN THE SOIL**
   pages 95 to 145.
2. **KNOWING SOILS AND HOW TO USE THEM**
   pages 145 to 151.
3. **USING SOIL TESTS AND FERTILIZER RECORDS**
   pages 151 to 157.
4. **ESTIMATING THE NUTRIENTS YOUR SOIL CAN SUPPLY**
   pages 157 to 162.
5. **APPLYING FERTILIZER WHERE AND WHEN IT COUNTS**
   pages 162 to 178.

6. **EVALUATING FERTILIZER COSTS AND RETURNS**
   pages 178 to 180.
7. **LIMING ACID SOILS**
   pages 180 to 183.
8. **CHECKING THE CROP THROUGH THE SEASON**
   pages 183 to 184.
9. **USE CAUTION IN TRYING UNPROVEN MATERIALS**
   pages 184 to 185.
10. **COMBINING SUPPORTING PRACTICES WITH HEAVY FERTILIZATION**
    page 185.
11. **MUNICIPAL WASTES; SLUDGE AND EFFLUENT**
    pages 185 to 187.

1. UNDERSTANDING FERTILIZERS AND HOW THEY BEHAVE IN THE SOIL

A wide variety of fertilizers to choose from is an advantage *if* you understand the materials and how they behave in the soil.

Though fertilizers come in many forms, brands, analyses, packages and colors, there is really nothing mysterious about them. They are well-known chemical compounds. Main purposes in applying fertilizers are to supplement plant nutrients already in the

95

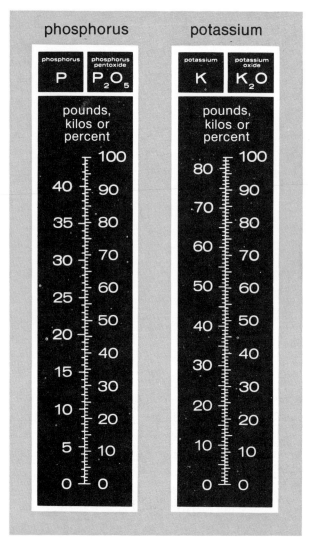

phosphorus | **potassium**

phosphorus	phosphorus pentoxide		potassium	potassium oxide
P	P_2O_5		K	K_2O

pounds, kilos or percent | pounds, kilos or percent

Figure 70. Scales developed by Iowa State University to convert P_2O_5 to P, and K_2O to K. The scales are based on these conversion factors:

% or pounds of P multiplied by 2.29 equals P_2O_5
% or pounds of P_2O_5 multiplied by 0.44 equals P
% or pounds of K multiplied by 1.2 equals K_2O
% or pounds of K_2O multiplied by 0.83 equals K

soil for efficient, profitable production and to maintain soil productivity. Fertilizers can be evaluated on the basis of their specific plant nutrients and the availability of these nutrients to the crop.

Labels, Guarantees

You don't have to guess about what is in fertilizer. Fertilizers come in bags, pressure tanks, non-pressure tanks, and in bulk trucks, but they have one thing in common: the nutrient content is always guaranteed to the purchaser on the bag, tag, or invoice.

The big three — nitrogen, phosphorus and potassium — are listed in the same order on fertilizer labels throughout the United States. Several manufacturers show percentages of both oxides (P_2O_5 and K_2O) and elements (P and K) for phosphorus and potassium. The charts in figure 70 can be used to convert from one to the other.

Some states require labeling and guaranteeing of secondary and micro-nutrients as well as nitrogen, phosphorus and potassium.

There is good reason to be suspicious of the salesman who claims nutrients which are not shown on the label. You have no assurance that the nutrients are in the fertilizer.

Grade, Analysis, Ratio

Grade and *analysis* are the same thing. They show the percent of plant nutrients. In figure 71 the analysis is 10-20-10 in terms of phosphorus and potassium oxides; it is 10-8.7-8.3 in terms of the elements. A movement began several years ago to convert to the elemental base with an initial target date of 1975. When the change occurs persons buying, selling or recommending fertilizers will have to become familiar with analyses in both the oxide and elemental form. There has been a transition period during which many bulletins, circulars and soil test report forms from many agricultural colleges used both the oxide (P_2O_5 and K_2O) and elemental (P and K) means to show fertilizer analyses and amounts of these plant nutrients. Some fertilizer companies have been using a double label system. When the change will finally be made is uncertain.

Ratio refers to the relative proportions of the nutrients. In figure 71 the ratio (oxide basis) is 1:2:1.

Premium Grades

In the late 1950s or early 1960s most companies began to offer "premium grades" at higher prices than regular grades which had the same guaranteed analyses of N-P-K. Premium grades usually contain a special

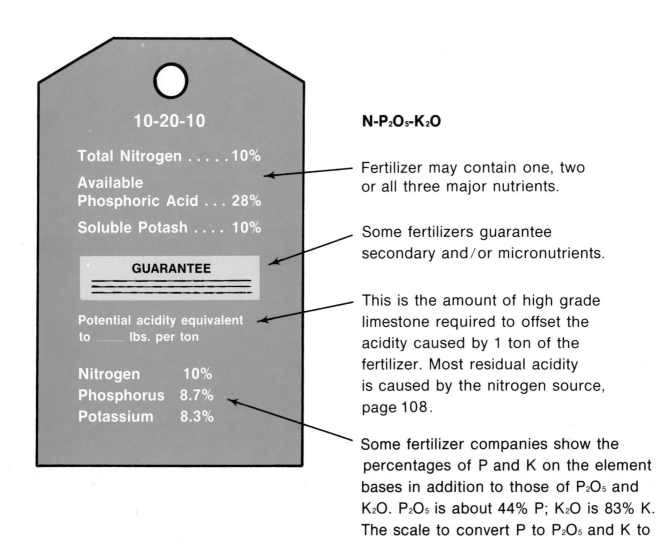

10-20-10

Total Nitrogen 10%

Available
Phosphoric Acid . . . 28%

Soluble Potash 10%

GUARANTEE

Potential acidity equivalent
to _____ lbs. per ton

Nitrogen   10%
Phosphorus 8.7%
Potassium   8.3%

$N-P_2O_5-K_2O$

Fertilizer may contain one, two
or all three major nutrients.

Some fertilizers guarantee
secondary and/or micronutrients.

This is the amount of high grade
limestone required to offset the
acidity caused by 1 ton of the
fertilizer. Most residual acidity
is caused by the nitrogen source,
page 108.

Some fertilizer companies show the
percentages of P and K on the element
bases in addition to those of P_2O_5 and
K_2O. P_2O_5 is about 44% P; K_2O is 83% K.
The scale to convert P to P_2O_5 and K to
K_2O is shown in figure 70.

Figure 71. A typical fertilizer label.

blend of micro-nutrients and secondary nutrients, but they may also be screened to a more uniform size or contain nitrogen in more than one chemical form. In deciding whether premium grades are worth the extra cost to you, here are some points to think about:

What is the evidence that micro or secondary nutrients are needed under your conditions? Your county extension agent has, or can get up-to-date information from the state agricultural college. If you don't need these nutrients, they represent unnecessary expense. If you do need them, they may be as important as N, P or K.

Are the micronutrients guaranteed or only claimed in a general way? Unless they are guaranteed, there is no proof that they are present in an available form or in an amount large enough to be of value.

Where there is a real micronutrient deficiency, is a complex mixture added to a fertilizer the best way to supply it? Sometimes complex mixtures contain only small amounts of several nutrients. The cost to correct a single nutrient deficiency is much greater using a complex mixture than with a compound that supplies only the needed nutrient.

Where a deficiency has not been proven

Figure 72. Anhydrous ammonia for direct application has had a great impact on corn fertilization since methods for applying it were developed in the 1940s. It is the most concentrated source of nitrogen (82% N) and lowest in cost to produce. Equipment for safe storage, handling and application of ammonia is generally available to U.S. farmers.

the micronutrients in premium fertilizers may be looked upon (a) as insurance against slight but unknown deficiencies, and (b) as maintenance amounts to delay the time when deficiencies may occur. You can place your own value on these two points. If you need more information on specific micronutrients, see page 140 for areas of known deficiencies and conditions under which deficiencies are most likely.

Single Nutrient Carriers and Mixed Fertilizers

Fertilizers that contain only one nutrient are commonly called fertilizer materials. Those that contain two or three nutrients are called mixed fertilizers. Both liquid and dry fertilizers may carry one, two, or three of the major nutrients — nitrogen, phosphorus and potassium — plus secondary and micronutrients.

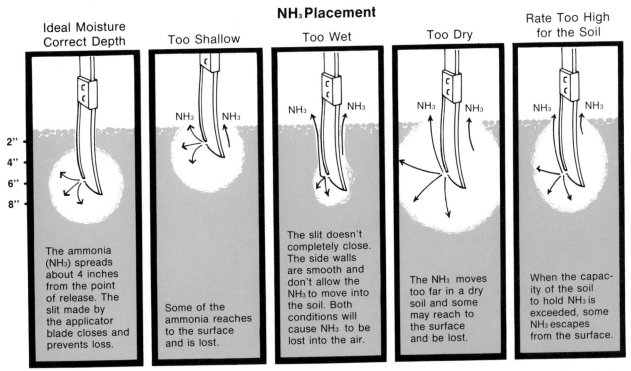

NH₃ Placement

| Ideal Moisture Correct Depth | Too Shallow | Too Wet | Too Dry | Rate Too High for the Soil |

The ammonia (NH₃) spreads about 4 inches from the point of release. The slit made by the applicator blade closes and prevents loss.

Some of the ammonia reaches to the surface and is lost.

The slit doesn't completely close. The side walls are smooth and don't allow the NH₃ to move into the soil. Both conditions will cause NH₃ to be lost into the air.

The NH₃ moves too far in a dry soil and some may reach to the surface and be lost.

When the capacity of the soil to hold NH₃ is exceeded, some NH₃ escapes from the surface.

Figure 73. Distribution of anhydrous ammonia (white areas) when released in different kinds of soil, at various depths, and under several soil moisture conditions. In a soil that is too wet, ammonia is lost in still another way, not shown in the diagram: some of the ammonia is absorbed in the water; it moves to the surface and is lost as water evaporates.

Physical Form: Gas, Solid, Liquid, Slurry

• *Gas.* Anhydrous ammonia has been the most important source of fertilizer nitrogen for corn since the mid 1950's (figure 72). It is the only fertilizer that can be called a gas, but even it is compressed into a liquid while in storage. (See the chart page 108 for information on the characteristics of anhydrous ammonia.)

Liquid ammonia under high pressure in the tank expands instantly to a gas as it moves out the holes in the applicator knives, quickly dropping the temperature at the point of release as the gas expands (figure 73).

Under proper soil conditions, the gas and liquid ammonia immediately react with water to form aqua ammonia, and the ammonia (NH₃) converts to ammonium (NH₄⁺). The ammonium ions quickly attach to the clay and organic matter. After this they behave in the same way as ammonium ions from

any other nitrogen fertilizer. Therefore, it is generally assumed that fields can be plowed about one week after ammonia is knifed in without significant loss, even though the ammonia band is exposed to air in plowing.

Part of the NH₄⁺ ions are temporarily trapped between clay sheets (figure 94) on soils that have a high capacity to fix NH₄⁺ and K⁺ but this loss is not considered extensive or permanent. Therefore, it is usually ignored in planning the nitrogen program.

The *capacity* of soil to hold ammonia depends mainly on these factors:

1. The *exchange capacity* of the soil (see page 144, figure 100). The more clay and organic matter, the greater the capacity to hold ammonium ions on the negative charges at the exchange sites.

2. The *moisture content* at the time of application (figure 73). The optimum moisture for holding ammonia is when the

ground is just right to plow. When the soil is too dry, the NH_3 gas moves too far (before reacting with water) and may escape from the surface. When silty and clayey soils are too wet, the applicator knife has a troweling effect on the walls of the slit and NH_3 does not move out into the soil where it can contact enough negative charges to retain it (after it has reacted with water to become NH_4^+ ions). It is possible that NH_3 will be held in a fairly wet soil provided the slit is covered on the surface because of the great affinity of the ammonia gas for water.

3. The *pH* of the soil. Acid soils hold more than neutral or alkaline soils.

4. The *spacing* of the applicator knives. When the applicator knives are 20 inches (½ m.) apart, the safe rate is twice as high as with 40-inch (1 m.) spacings because the NH_3 contacts twice as much soil.

5. *Depth* of application, since this influences the total amount of soil above the point of release.

The losses from properly applied ammonia are believed to be very low, probably in the range of 0 to 5 percent.

The safe rate of application at 6 to 9 inches (15 to 22.5 cm) under ideal conditions in slightly acid silt loams and silty clay loams is about 200 pounds of N per acre (224 kg per ha) in 40-inch (1 meter) spacings and double that in 20-inch (½ meter) spacings. These rates are based on common experience rather than detailed research results.

In sandy soils with one percent organic matter the limit when placed 9-inch (22.5 cm) deep in 40-inch (1 meter) spacing is perhaps 100 pounds per acre (112 kg per ha) and 150 pounds (168 kg per ha) with 1½ to 2 percent organic matter.

Farmers often ask whether ammonia kills desirable soil organisms. The answer is yes, but the damage is insignificant because the effect of high concentration near the point of release is only temporary and it affects only about one-fifth of the plow layer and none of the subsoil. The pH at the point

of discharge soon goes very high but, when the temperature is favorable for the growth of nitrifying organisms, the pH will probably decline to the original pH or lower within two or three weeks.

Since anhydrous ammonia at common application temperatures is under a pressure of nearly 200 pounds per square inch (14.3 kg per square centimeter) and the gas is both annoying at low concentration and dangerous at high concentration, it must be handled with care. The ammonia industry has developed instructions and conducted many training programs in safe handling. Proper handling reduces transfer losses from bulk tanks to applicator tanks to 2 to 3 percent. Anti-pollution regulations limit the loss in some areas.

• *Dry solids.* Until the early 1950's dry solid fertilizers made up most of the fertilizer applied in the United States and they still have a very important place. Figure 74 is a close look at three general types of mixed fertilizers. Powdered fertilizers have been replaced by pellets and/or coarse crystals to eliminate dustiness, reduce caking, and provide for free flow in handling and spreading.

Two questions are often asked about pelleted fertilizers:

How important is it to have the pellets completely water soluble? The answer depends on soil conditions which are discussed on pages 129 – 133.

Must the N, P and K all be in the same pellet (A and B, figure 74) or is it acceptable to have separate granules mixed together (CI and CII)? It is generally believed that nitrogen exerts its beneficial effect on the uptake of phosphorus when the nutrients are banded together and the nutrients N, P, and K do not have to be in the same pellet.

Some of the most significant trends in the use of dry fertilizers are:

— Movement in bulk. This eliminates the cost of bags, facilitates machine handling all the way from storage to the fertilizer hopper, and meets the demand for bulk spreading.

A. Completely
Water Soluble
Dry Pellets

Uniform composition throughout because the nutrients are
chemically combined in solution and then precipitated out
by evaporating water from the
mix.

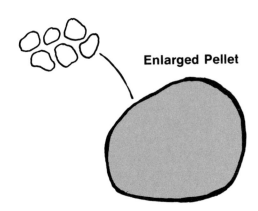

Enlarged Pellet

B. Typical Ammoniated
Super or Triple-Super
Pelleted Fertilizer

Concentric shells with nutrients partly chemically combined and partly as a mixture
of finely divided powder glued
together in the drying process.

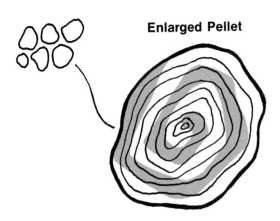

Enlarged Pellet

C. Dry Mix
or Bulk Blend

These are physical mixtures of
dry crystals or pellets in which
each pellet has only 1 or 2
nutrients.

I.

II. (with Diammonium
Phosphate)

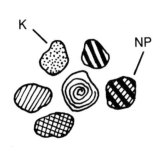

Figure 74. A look at the inside of dry mixed fertilizers.

Figure 75. Wide booms and high ground speed permit very rapid application of liquid fertilizers that do not contain free ammonia (which would volatilize into the air). Large flotation tires on either liquid or dry spreaders reduce compaction and permit application on fields that would be too wet for normal tires.

— Bulk blending of dry ingredients to reduce cost.

— Higher analyses which reduce the cost to store, transport and apply.

— Larger fertilizer hoppers on planters to reduce the number of stops for filling and to facilitate bulk handling.

— Augers for transferring the fertilizer from the truck or trailer into the planter hoppers.

From the standpoint of effectively supplying plant nutrients to crops, dry fertilizers are generally equal to gas, liquid or slurry.

• *Liquid fertilizers.* These include mixed fertilizers, nitrogen solutions and phosphoric acid. Only liquid mixed fertilizers are discussed here. The other two are described later in this section under specific fertilizers.

Liquid mixed fertilizers have been gaining in popularity generally and especially for application through the corn planter because they can be pumped and therefore don't have to be moved by hand. The cost per pound of nutrients is usually slightly higher than for dry fertilizers. But improvements are constantly being made in formulating techniques and it is possible that in some areas liquids are already priced as low as dry fertilizers. Liquid fertilizers are well suited to rapid application, figure 75.

The fertilizer research branch of the Tennessee Valley Authority has pioneered the formulation of liquid fertilizers and improvements have been forthcoming almost yearly.

A common way to make liquid fertilizers is to first neutralize phosphoric acid with ammonia in water and then dissolve muriate of potash in the solution. If extra nitrogen is desired, it can be added in several ways.

Since the chemical compounds in liquid mixed fertilizers are essentially the same as those in many dry fertilizers, liquid and dry fertilizers will usually give about the same yield increases. A point of difference between all liquids and *some but not all* dry fertilizers

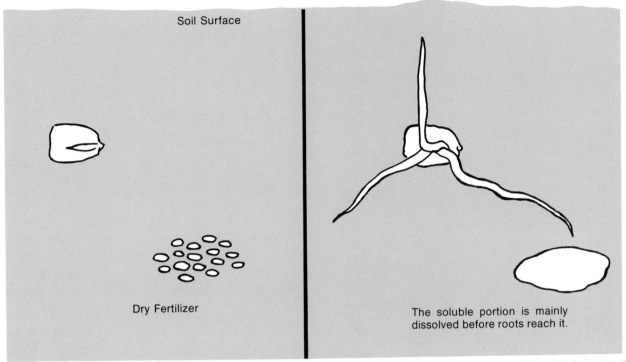

Soil Surface

Dry Fertilizer

The soluble portion is mainly dissolved before roots reach it.

Figure 76. In a moist soil the soluble part of dry fertilizer dissolves before the young roots reach it. The grayish material that can be found weeks later is the insoluble residue left after the plant nutrients have moved out of the pellet.

is in the percentage of water-soluble phosphorus. For a discussion of whether this is important under your conditions, see page 133.

Improved ways to make liquid fertilizers have greatly increased the range of available analyses. *Sequestering* agents which inhibit the formation of crystals when the concentration of nutrients is too high or the solution cools too much reduce "salting out".

These questions are often asked about liquid mixed fertilizers: Are they more quickly available than dry fertilizer? Are they better for a dry soil since they supply water and are already in solution? Are they more or less likely to cause fertilizer "burn"?

The fact that liquid fertilizer is already in solution does not make a significant difference in availability. In a moist soil the soluble part of dry fertilizer begins at once to attract water and dissolve. Within a day much of it is in solution. Since four to six days elapse before the corn kernel germi-

nates and sends its roots into the fertilizer band, there is plenty of time for dry fertilizer to dissolve and meet the needs of the young seedling (figure 76). Besides, there is no advantage in having it all immediately in solution because the corn plant takes up only a small amount each day.

What happens in a very dry soil? If there is no moisture, dry fertilizer obviously can't dissolve. But most dry fertilizers are salts that are somewhat hygroscopic (they attract water) and so they will dissolve in moderately dry soils. On the other hand, moisture evaporates from liquid fertilizer in very dry soils and the nutrients crystallize out (except for those that have already moved to the exchange sites on clay and organic matter). Furthermore, when soil is so dry that solid fertilizers don't dissolve and liquid fertilizers crystallize out of solution, there is not enough moisture for corn kernels to germinate or for the nutrients to be taken up by the roots of established plants.

In summary: it is likely that soon after they are applied in a moist soil, both liquid and soluble dry fertilizers are in solution, whereas in an extremely dry soil, both are in dry pellets or crystals.

The amount of water that is supplied with liquid fertilizers is insignificant, about one pint in six to ten feet (½ liter in 2 to 3 meters) of row. Since liquid fertilizer is purposely not placed close to the seed, it does not supply moisture to aid in germination.

Liquid and dry fertilizers are equally capable of causing injury when placed too close to the seed, but neither will injure germination when properly placed.

• *Slurry fertilizers.* Slurry fertilizers are a combination of liquid and dry forms. Part of the plant food is in solution, some is in solid particles held in suspension. In many cases, they also contain free ammonia gas.

One way to make them is to mix finely ground rock phosphate, nitric acid, and potassium chloride (muriate of potash). The nitric acid serves two purposes. First, it supplies nitrogen. Second, the acid reacts with the phosphate rock to make the phosphorus more available.

A second method is to use a nitrogen solution, phosphoric acid and potassium chloride. A third method involves dry triple superphosphate, an ammonia solution, and potassium chloride.

Slurry fertilizer differs from liquid fertilizer in that it contains solid particles that normally settle out. Settling is prevented in slurries, first, by adding a special type clay that keeps the crystals small, and second, by constant stirring within the tank truck. Nozzle clogging is avoided by using large openings in the "slingers" that throw rather than spray the fertilizer.

If they contain free ammonia, slurries must be placed under the soil surface or quickly covered when they are broadcast.

Slurry fertilizers contain plant nutrients in the same chemical compounds as many dry, liquid and gas fertilizers and therefore are

Table 7
The sixteen elements essential for plant growth.

Group A. Elements Used in Relatively Large Amounts	
from air and water Carbon (C) Hydrogen (H) Oxygen (O)	You do not need to consider these in your fertilizer program. Plants obtain them from air and water.
from soil solids Nitrogen (N) Phosphorus (P) Potassium (K)	These are the "big 3" in your fertilizer needs. They are often called MAJOR or PRIMARY nutrients.
Calcium (Ca) Magnesium (Mg) Sulfur (S)	These are sometimes lacking. They are often called SECONDARY nutrients.

Group B. Elements Used in Relatively Small Amounts	
from soil solids Boron (B) Chlorine (Cl) Copper (Cu) Iron (Fe) Manganese (Mn) Molybdenum (Mo) Zinc (Zn)	MICRONUTRIENTS. Also called TRACE or MINOR elements. You need to consider adding them only for special crop and soil situations.

equally effective in increasing corn yields.

Slurry fertilizers have not increased in popularity as many predicted in the mid-1960's.

• *Suspension fertilizers.* These differ from slurry fertilizers in that the nutrients are mainly in solution and are prevented from crystalizing when the temperature drops by sequestering agents which keep the crystals from grouping in large aggregates. They are mainly experimental but recent technological developments may lead to increased commercial use.

The Elements Essential for Plant Growth

Nearly all crops need the same elements though not in the same proportions. The sixteen elements known to be needed are listed in table 7.

Micronutrients, often called minor or trace

elements, are just as necessary as major nutrients for corn. "Minor elements" is a confusing term because it suggests minor importance, when in fact, a severe micronutrient deficiency can be just as serious as the shortage of a major nutrient. Micro means small and therefore indicates that these elements are needed only in small amounts.

"Natural" Fertilizers in Contrast to "Chemical" Fertilizers

Some people have attacked the use of chemical fertilizers for many years. They claim that such fertilizers are harmful to soils, crops, animals and humans. They suggest that using "natural" products such as rock phosphate, greensand, animal manures, plant composts, volcanic deposits and similar materials will produce higher yields, reduce insects and plant diseases, and lead to better health.

But research shows that plant nutrients enter the plant root in the same chemical form whether the nutrient came from fertilizer, manure, or plant residues. Therefore, the source of the nutrient has no effect on the health or composition of the crop or on the animal or human that eats it. In this respect fertilizers are different than certain pesticides and food additives which may be found in foods (though limits are set by Food and Drug Administration) in chemical compounds that do not occur in nature.

Agronomists recognize the importance of organic matter to profitable farming (its importance is stressed in many sections of this book). But the way to produce more organic matter is to use more fertilizer, not less! When optimum amounts of fertilizer are applied, yields are high and the amount of residues returned to the soil is high. This increases the number of earthworms, bacteria, and fungi, which all depend on organic matter for food. *In other words, fertilizers used in high profit farming increase rather than destroy the biological population in soil.*

For the foreseeable future world food supply will depend increasingly upon commercial fertilizer.

Composting leaves, lawn clippings, and other residues is to be encouraged for small plots in urban areas. Farmers regularly return most of their crop residues in the most desirable manner by leaving them in the fields where grown.

Returning urban wastes to agricultural land is mainly a means of disposing of wastes rather than of meeting the fertility and organic matter needs of agriculture.

Notwithstanding many testimonials to the contrary, no one has proved any advantage in flavor or nutritional value for foods grown without fertilizer.

Producing for the "Organic" or "Natural" Food Market

There is a small but increasing market for "organically" grown food. Though no unbiased scientific research has shown any difference in chemical composition or in flavor from food grown without the use of chemical fertilizers, some persons claim advantages and are willing to pay a premium for such food. A limited number of farmers find it profitable to satisfy this special natural diet market. If they have large amounts of animal manure available at low cost and can sell their crop at a price enough above the commercial market, they may find it profitable to grow "organic" or "natural" food.

To qualify for this special market, you must not use any commercial fertilizer (rock phosphate as a source of phosphorus and greensand for potassium are acceptable) or chemical pesticides. Whatever their reasons, real or imagined, purchasers of food that is labeled "organically grown" have a right to expect it to be grown according to these standards.

For home gardens, compost made from lawn clippings and leaves may be adequate but for farm scale production legumes (alfalfa, clover, vetch, lespedeza) and/or animal manures would be needed. Whether sewage sludge meets the requirements for so-called "organic" foods is a matter for the buyer

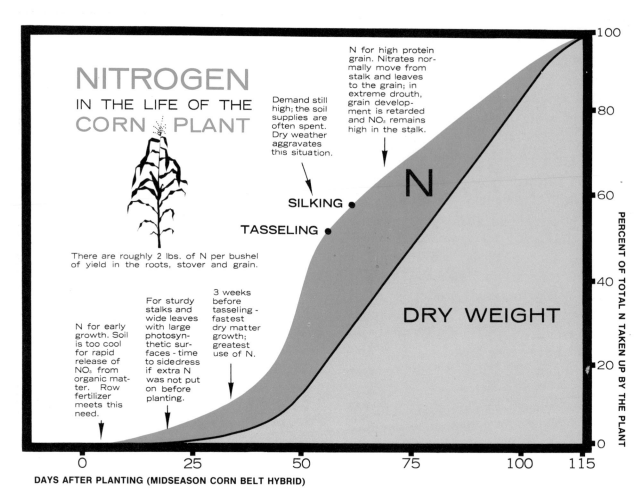

NITROGEN
IN THE LIFE OF THE
CORN PLANT

There are roughly 2 lbs. of N per bushel of yield in the roots, stover and grain.

N for early growth. Soil is too cool for rapid release of NO₃ from organic matter. Row fertilizer meets this need.

For sturdy stalks and wide leaves with large photosynthetic surfaces - time to sidedress if extra N was not put on before planting.

3 weeks before tasseling - fastest dry matter growth; greatest use of N.

Demand still high; the soil supplies are often spent. Dry weather aggravates this situation.

N for high protein grain. Nitrates normally move from stalk and leaves to the grain; in extreme drouth, grain development is retarded and NO₃ remains high in the stalk.

SILKING

TASSELING

N

DRY WEIGHT

PERCENT OF TOTAL N TAKEN UP BY THE PLANT

DAYS AFTER PLANTING (MIDSEASON CORN BELT HYBRID)

Figure 77.

to decide. Sludge certainly contains several heavy metals and some organic compounds that are either not present in natural systems or are found much less abundantly.

Nitrogen

There are 33,000 tons of nitrogen in the air over every acre, but corn can't get at it. The corn plant can take oxygen, hydrogen, and carbon from the air but not an ounce of nitrogen. Nitrogen for corn comes from many sources, but won't stay where you put it. Sometimes it leaches out of the root zone. It often volatilizes back into the atmosphere. In fact this is what completes the nitrogen cycle and maintains the 80 percent nitrogen content of air. There is no soil test comparable in relability to those for P and K to predict available N over a wide range of soils and crops. It is used by corn through the entire season (figure 77). Nitrogen fertilization is the most challenging part of corn fertilization.

Though corn can effectively use ammonia (NH_4^+) nitrogen, nearly all nitrogen is absorbed by corn in the form of nitrate (NO_3^-). This may be mainly because conditions that favor corn growth also favor the conversion of nitrogen compounds to nitrate. But nitrogen can't be stored in the soil in nitrate form for long periods because of leaching and denitrification. Very little N is applied as nitrate in fertilizer.

Most of the nitrogen used by corn is converted to the nitrate form during the growing season by some means within the soil itself.

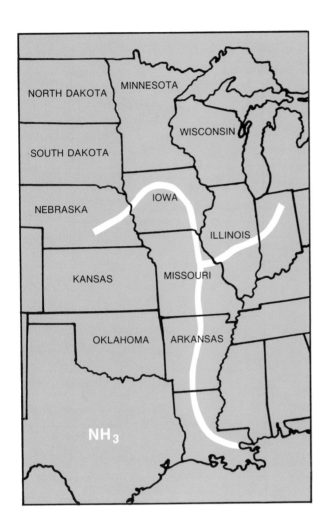

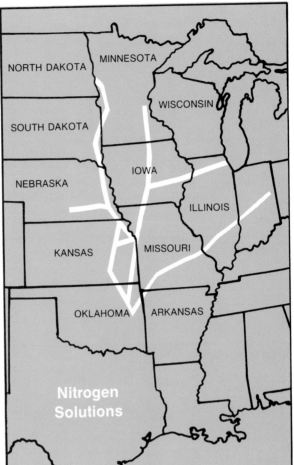

Figure 78. NH₃ and liquid fertilizer transmission lines.

Fertilizer	% N	Chemical Formula	Physical Condition	Limestone to offset acidity per 100 lbs. N *		Method of applying
				Pierre	Andrews	
Anhydrous ammonia	82	NH_3	Compressed gas, 204 lbs. per square inch at 104°F (14.6 kg per square cm)	180	360	Injecting 6'' (15 cm) or deeper in moist but not saturated soil. In 40 or 20 inch spacing (1 to ½ meter)
Aqua ammonia	21	NH_4OH in water	Liquid with slight NH_3 pressure	180	360	Injecting at least 1 inch (2.5 cm) below soil surface; deeper is preferred.
Ammonium nitrate	33.5	NH_4NO_3	Dry prills or pellets	180		Broadcast, sidedressed. Can be left on soil surface.
Ammonium sulfate	20.5	$(NH_4)_2SO_4$	Dry pellets or granules	535	715	Same as ammonium nitrate. Also used in bulk blends.
Urea	45-46	$CO(NH_2)_2$	Dry prills	180	355	Wide range. Broadcast, sidedress, add to solutions. Liquid spray on some crops but not corn.
Nitrogen solutions (only 2 important ones listed here. Get information on others from dealer)	32 (less if diluted with water)	Urea in ammonium nitrate solution	Liquid, no ammonia pressure	180		Sprayed or dribbled on soil surface, or sidedressed.
	41 (less if diluted to lower NH_3 pressure)	NH_3 in ammonium nitrate solution	Liquid with some free ammonia	180		Injected 1 to 2 inches (2.5 to 5 cm) deep preplant or sidedressed.
Sodium nitrate	16	$NaNO_3$	Dry granules	180 Basic	0	Broadcast or sidedressed. Can be left on the surface.
Calcium nitrate	15.5	$Ca(NO_3)_2$	Dry granules	135 Basic	40 Acidic	Broadcast or sidedressed. Can be left on the surface.
Calcium cyanamide	21	$CaCN_2$	Black dry prills	285 Basic	120 Basic	Broadcast or sidedressed.
Ureaform	38 or less	$CO(NH_2)_2$ combined with formaldehyde	Dry granules	180	355	
Ammonium phosphate	11% N 21% P (48% P_2O_5)	$NH_4H_2PO_4$	Dry granules	500	675	Broadcast, drilled as row fertilizer.
Ammonium phosphate and Ammonium sulfate	16% N 8.7% P (20% P_2O_5)	$NH_4H_2PO_4$ $(NH_4)_2SO_4$	Dry granules	515	695	Broadcast, drilled as row fertilizer.
Diammonium phosphate	18 to 21% N 20 to 23% P (46 to 53% P_2O_5)	$(NH_4)_2HPO_4$	Dry granules	About the same as ammonium phosphate		Broadcast, drilled **not in contact with seed,** widely used in bulk blends.
Potassium nitrate	About 13.5% N 38.0% K (46% K_2O)	KNO_3	Dry granules			
Nitric phosphate						

N-P-K dry, liquid, and slurry fertilizers. Because of the wide range in analysis and chemical formulations, information should be obtained from the dealer or manufacturer.

* For Metric equivalent multiply figures by .45.

NITROGEN FERTILIZERS

Reactions in the soil	Special advantages	Disadvantages
1. NH_3 reacts with water. NH_3 changes to NH_4 and is held on exchange sites on clay and humus. 2. Some NH_3 reacts with organic matter.	Low price. High analysis thus less labor to transport. Non-leachable.	Requires high pressure storage and applicators. Danger from exposure to gas if lines or storage burst.
NH_4 ions attach to exchange sites on clay and organic matter.	Low price. No high pressure storage or applicator needed. Non-leachable.	Low analysis. Must be covered to avoid ammonia escaping into air above soil.
NH_4 attaches to exchange sites. NO_3 remains in soil solution. until taken up or denitrified. NO_3 not held on clay.	Low price for dry source. NO_3 is immediately available. Second only to urea in % N among dry fertilizers.	NO_3 (½ of the N it contains) is leachable, and also subject to denitrification in warm, wet soil. Hardens upon exposure to air.
NH_4 attaches to clay and organic matter.	Excellent condition. Acidifying effect desirable on alkaline soils.	Low analysis. Medium price. Highest acidifying effect of N sources, this adds about 2c per pound of N when used on acid soils.
NH_2 changes within few days to NH_3, then NH_4 and then behaves as above for other ammonium sources.	Highest % N of dry fertilizers. High solubility. Non-leachable after it is converted to NH_4.	Leachable by rain shortly after application. Some risk of loss of NH_3 to atmosphere.
See urea and ammonium nitrate above	No pressure equipment needed. Can be applied on the surface.	Slightly higher price. Possible small loss when surface applied.
See anhydrous ammonia and ammonium nitrate above.	Low pressure equipment. Non-leachable until changed to NO_3.	Slight vapor pressure of NH_3. Must be covered 1 to 2 inches (2.5 to 5 cm.) to prevent loss.
NO_3 remains in solution and moves with water, not held on clay and humus. Na (sodium) is basic and therefore raises pH (reduces acidity).	Immediately available, non-acid forming.	Very high price, low analysis of N.
Same as sodium nitrate with calcium in place of sodium.	Same at sodium nitrate.	
Complex.	Can be used as a herbicide and as a defoliant (powdered form).	High price, intermediate reaction products are toxic, low analysis.
This is a slow release N source due to combination with formaldehyde. Reactions same as urea but slower.	Nitrogen is released over several weeks rather than all being available immediately for nitrification.	High price for field crops. Variable rate of N release. Depends somewhat on moisture and temperature.
NH_4 behaves as usual, attaches to exchange sites.	Phosphorus is completely water soluble. Desirable N to P ratio for row fertilizer. Especially suited to soils where K is not needed.	High residual acidity.
See ammonium sulfate, also ammonium phosphate.	See ammonium sulfate, also ammonium phosphate.	
In near neutral soils ammonia (NH_3) is released, otherwise same as ammonium phosphate.	High analysis, low price, completely water soluble source of P. In bulk blends it avoids possible separation of N and P.	Some risk of injury to germination if ammonia concentration becomes too high.
	Preferred over muriate (KC1) for crops on which chloride ion is objectionable (tobacco).	

109

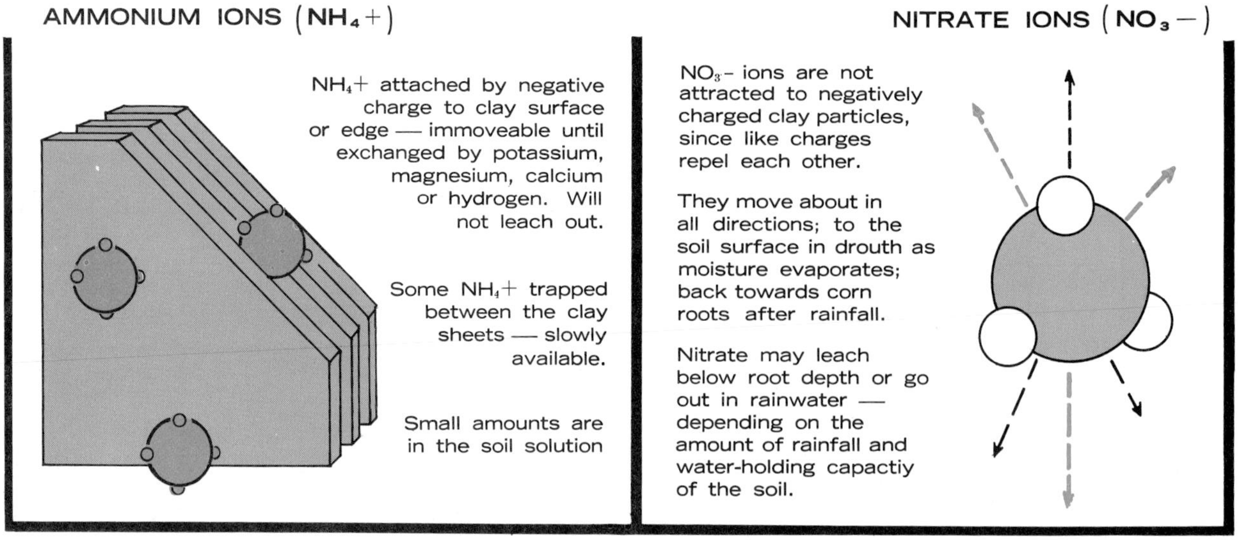

NH₄+ attached by negative charge to clay surface or edge — immoveable until exchanged by potassium, magnesium, calcium or hydrogen. Will not leach out.

Some NH₄+ trapped between the clay sheets — slowly available.

Small amounts are in the soil solution

NO_3^- ions are not attracted to negatively charged clay particles, since like charges repel each other.

They move about in all directions; to the soil surface in drouth as moisture evaporates; back towards corn roots after rainfall.

Nitrate may leach below root depth or go out in rainwater — depending on the amount of rainfall and water-holding capactiy of the soil.

Figure 79. Diagrammatic sketch of a clay particle in the soil solution. It is somewhat like a deck of cards. The surface is covered with negative electrical charges which attract and hold positively charged ammonium ions NH_4^+ (left) but not negatively charged nitrate ions NO_3^- (right). See also figure 100.

Chemical Reactions
of Some Nitrogen Fertilizers in the Soil

The chart of nitrogen fertilizers on pages 108 and 109 gives a brief statement about chemical reactions of nitrogen fertilizers. Here is more detail on three types illustrating what happens with nearly all nitrogen fertilizers:

• *Anhydrous ammonia* — NH_3.

At the fertilizer plant, this is the lowest cost source of nitrogen. Part of the price advantage is offset as a result of the need for high pressure handling, transport, and storage. Ammonia is well suited to movement through pipes, and pipelines were constructed in the 1960's from the Gulf coast production centers into the main using area, the Corn Belt, figure 78.

Most of the NH_3 (ammonia) reacts almost instantly with hydrogen ions in the soil solution and picks up one hydrogen ion to become NH_4^+ (ammonium). Henceforth it behaves as an ammonium ion and is temporarily attached to the negative charges on clay and organic matter (figure 79).

Some of the NH_3 undergoes a direct chemical reaction with soil organic matter and then behaves as part of the soil humus.

If there are openings to the soil surface from the point of release, some escapes directly into the air (figure 73, page 99). The white cloud you see behind the applicator is not NH_3 itself but moisture vapor that forms as ammonia lowers the temperature. Ammonia cannot be applied to a soil near the freezing point because it will ball up at the orifices, leave a wide slit, and gas will escape.

If the rate of application is more than the soil can hold around and above the point of release, some moves slowly to the soil surface and escapes into the air as a gas over a period of several days.

Safety and environmental regulations have affected anhydrous ammonia more than other forms of nitrogen fertilizer.

• *Ammonium nitrate* — NH_4NO_3

The ammonium half of the nitrogen behaves like ammonium ions, NH_4^+. Some remains in the soil solution but most NH_4^+ ions attach themselves to the negative charges on the clay and organic matter (figure 79). Some are trapped between clay sheets. Some NH_4^+ teams up with negatively charged ions to make ammonium chloride — NH_4Cl; sulfate — $(NH_4)_2SO_4$, etc.

110

The nitrate (NO_3^-) half of the nitrogen may be:

a. Taken up by plant roots.

b. Moved up and down by soil water.

c. Used by soil organisms (page 116).

d. Denitrified, especially if the soil is warm and wet (figure 86, page 120). After denitrification, it may be lost into the air as a gas.

• *Urea* — $CO(NH_2)_2$

Urea is very soluble and for a short time after application (1 or 2 days in warm moist soil, but up to several weeks in a cold soil) it moves freely up and down with soil moisture almost in the same way as nitrates. A small amount is attached to clay and organic matter and does not move.

Sooner or later the urea is converted to ammonia (NH_3) — either chemically or by the enzyme urease. Henceforth, it behaves like NH_3 from anhydrous ammonia, which means that it soon picks up a hydrogen (H^+) and becomes ammonium (NH_4^+).

If the conversion of solid urea or urea in liquid fertilizers takes place on the soil surface on crop residues or leaves, some of the NH_3 is lost as a gas into the air. The ammonia reacts with water to produce an alkaline condition which promotes loss of N. The amount lost is highest:

— In neutral or alkaline soils.

— When the temperature is warm. Loss is less likely in late fall, winter and early spring when soils are cool.

— In soils with low exchange capacity (low in clay and organic matter) because there are fewer negative charge sites to hold ammonium.

— When application rates are high (100 to 200 pounds per acre, 112 to 224 kilograms per hectare of nitrogen).

Most yield comparisons indicate that urea is usually as efficient as other nitrogen fertilizers. This indicates that under field conditions, urea is often worked into the soil by tillage or washed in by rain. In either case, the loss becomes negligible. Several research studies show that nitrogen losses from surface-applied urea can be quite serious if all unfavorable conditions prevail on low-exchange, sandy soils.

Many predict that urea will be the fastest growing nitrogen fertilizer during the 1970's. It is the highest analysis dry nitrogen fertilizer which is an advantage for shipping and applying. In contrast to anhydrous ammonia it requires no special equipment for storage, handling or applying which is especially important in less developed countries. The price disadvantage which it suffered during the 1950's to early 1970's has largely disappeared.

Though urea contains only 46 percent nitrogen compared to 82 in anhydrous ammonia, the extra weight of steel to withstand ammonia pressure results in the gross weight being nearly the same for equal amounts of nitrogen hauled to the field.

If urea is applied up to normal corn planting time, the risk of loss from surface application on bare soil is small. Working it into the surface is desirable early in the season and necessary when the soil is warm. Urea will not likely fit well with sod planting because of the possibility of excessive loss if the urea hydrolyzes on the residue before being washed off by rain. Watch for new research results on this subject.

Nitrogen Solutions, Aqua Ammonia

There are two general types of nitrogen solutions for direct application: (1) those that contain some free ammonia — ammonia in an ammonium nitrate solution; (2) those that do not contain free ammonia — urea in an ammonium nitrate solution.

The chemical reactions of the ingredients in the soil are the same as for the fertilizers just discussed under anhydrous ammonia, ammonium nitrate, and urea.

Solutions with free ammonia should be placed beneath the soil surface 1 to 3 inches (2.5 to 7.5 cm) to prevent the loss of NH_3.

Aqua ammonia is anhydrous plus water.

All of the ammonia can theoretically be lost from the water solution unless it is held in the soil by negative charges on clay and humus. Therefore, aqua should be applied in much the same way as anhydrous, though it does not need to be applied quite so deep, nor will it escape as readily from dry soil.

Slow Release Nitrogen Fertilizers

Agronomists and fertilizer chemists have searched vigorously for more than 25 years for means to control the release of fertilizer nitrogen in order to meter it more in tune with crop needs. This would reduce leaching and denitrification, permit application ahead of the crop without loss, and spread out the response to avoid a big surge of growth (mainly in lawns) followed by a shortage. Attempts have included plastic coated particles, urea-formaldehyde combinations, potassium azide, sulfur coated urea, and a nitrification inhibitor — pyridine.

• *Coated fertilizer pellets.* Each pellet has a protective coating which dissolves slowly and thus prolongs the period during which the nitrogen remains in its original form. This approach has promise but no commercial product is generally available.

• *Ureaform.* Urea is reacted with varying proportions of formaldehyde to make chemical compounds with any desired degree of water solubility. The more formaldehyde, the slower the release. The commercial products on the market are formulated so that the nitrogen becomes available over a single season. But the rate of nitrogen release depends on soil conditions, and is very slow when the soil is cold and dry. Thus far, the extra cost of nitrogen in ureaform fertilizers has made them impractical for use on corn.

• *N-Serve.* This is the product of a single company. A pyridine compound inhibits growth of the soil organisms that trigger the first step in converting ammonium to nitrate. The nitrogen, therefore, remains in the NH_4^+ form longer and is not subject to leaching. Because the product is somewhat volatile,

it is band applied in order to maintain adequate concentration to inhibit nitrification. The product has been available since the mid 1960's and has been widely tested both on dry fertilizers and in anhydrous ammonia. Limited trials on corn in the Corn Belt have not shown a yield advantage on typical fine-textured soils.

For many years, it was believed that most crops except rice could not efficiently use nitrogen in the ammonium form except in the early stage of growth. That has now been disproven. Be alert for possible new results in connection with early spring application of nitrogen on sandy and gravelly soils. Extra K is needed when ammonuim is the main form of nitrogen taken up by corn.

One of the main reasons for considering slow release nitrogen fertilizers is to reduce the amount of nitrate that reaches surface and groundwater. This is discussed on page

Effects of Nitrogen Fertilizer on pH and Lime Need

The effects of adding nitrogen fertilizers to the soil are quite complex because their immediate and long-term effects are different. The indications of these effects are listed in table 8.

When nitrogen is added in neutral salts (1, 2, 3, 5, 6, 11, 12, and 13, table 8) there is no immediate effect on the pH of the soil.

Diammonium phosphate, number 4, raises the pH because one of the two ammonium ions splits off and forms ammonium hydroxide which produces an *alkaline reaction.*

The fertilizers with free ammonia, NH_3, (7, 8, 9), also produce ammonium hydroxide immediately and thus raise the pH at the point of application.

By the end of the first growing season the effects of nitrogen fertilizers have changed and in most cases reversed the early effect. Sodium, calcium and potassium nitrates result in a rise in pH because these are basic ions.

Table 8
The effects on pH or acidity from adding nitrogen fertilizers.

	Immediate or Short-term Effect	Long-term Effect
1 Ammonium nitrate	None	Moderately acidic
2 Ammonium sulfate	None	Strongly acidic
3 Monoammonium phosphate	None due to N	Strongly acidic
4 Diammonium phosphate	Basic because 1 molecule of NH$_4$ is released	Moderately acidic
5 Ammoniated superphosphate	None due to N but acidic around phosphate granules	Moderately acidic
6 Nitrogen solutions with no free ammonia (ammonium nitrate — urea)	None	Moderately acidic
7 Nitrogen solutions with free ammonia (ammonia in ammonium nitrate)	Basic	Moderately acidic
8 Anhydrous ammonia	Strongly basic	Moderately acidic
9 Aqua ammonia	Strongly basic	Moderately acidic
10 Urea	Very slightly basic	Moderately acidic
11 Nitrate of soda	Very little	Basic
12 Calcium nitrate	Very little	Basic
13 Potassium nitrate	Very little	Basic

All other nitrogen fertilizers lower the pH (produce an acid effect) for two reasons:

• When they are nitrified in the soil by soil organisms they add hydrogen (the acidic element) in this way —

$$NH_4^+ \longrightarrow NO_3^- + 4H^+$$
Ammonium   **Nitrate**   **Hydrogen**

• Some of the nitrate that is not absorbed by the crop leaches out of the soil and carries a base element (calcium, magnesium, potassium) with it.

All fertilizers, including nitrogen, that increase crop yields lower the pH because of the increased amounts of the base elements removed from the soil in larger yields.

The overall effect of nitrogen fertilizers on soil pH cannot be accurately predicted. Agronomists generally felt for several years that the figures under the column headed Pierre, page 108, were too low. But Pierre's figures may be about right after all.

If you grow corn, small grains, and legumes in rotation the acidity due to nitrogen fertilizer on corn won't affect your liming program very much because the amount of nitrogen applied once in three years will be small. If, on the other hand, you grow corn on a major part of your acreage and fertilize heavily with nitrogen, your land may require an extra ton of limestone in two to six years depending on which nitrogen fertilizer you apply. *Regular soil testing is the only sure method of deciding when to apply lime and how much the soil needs.*

For application on acid soils, fertilizers that produce significant residual acidity are a disadvantage; on alkaline soils they are an advantage. The credit or debit is likely to be about 1 or 2 cents on each pound of nitrogen.

Physical Movement:
Leaching and Upward Movement

Figure 79 shows how nitrogen moves around through the soil in two main chemical forms. The ammonium form *stays in place temporarily* because it is held on the

Figure 80. This fertilizer was applied about 1½ inches (3.8 cm) deep along the corn row. The fertilizer dissolved in the moist soil and then moved to the soil surface along with water during a dry period. As the moisture evaporated from the soil surface, some of the fertilizer nutrients were left in a band over the row.

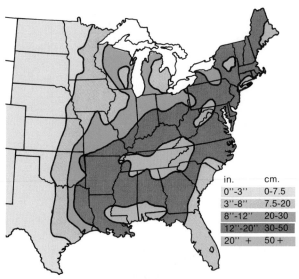

in.	cm.
0″-3″	0-7.5
3″-8″	7.5-20
8″-12″	20-30
12″-20″	30-50
20″ +	50 +

Figure 81. Estimated amount of water that moves into the soil from about Nov. 1st to May 1st. Figures are based on rainfall minus: (a) estimated evaporation from the soil, (b) transpiration from plants, and (c) 4 inches (10 cm) of water stored in the soil. Many soils on which corn is grown will hold 8 to 10 inches (20 to 25 cm) of water within the root zone and therefore the amount left to leach nitrates should be reduced accordingly.

negative charges of clay and humus. But as soon as soil organisms convert it to nitrate it becomes as mobile as nitrate fertilizer.

Movement in a dry soil: the distance that nitrates move in the soil is governed by how far the water moves: one inch (2.5 cm) of rainfall that enters the soil wets a silt loam about 4 to 6 inches (10 to 15 cm), a clay loam slightly less, a loamy sand about 12 inches (30 cm). Part of the nitrates move down as far as the water penetrates. A 4-inch (10 cm) rain, therefore, moves part of the nitrates about 1½ to 2 feet (½ to ⅔ meter) in slits and clays.

But another 4-inch (10 cm) rain two weeks later does not take nitrates from that point and move them down another 1½ to 2 feet (½ to ⅔ meter) for two reasons:

• As moisture evaporates from the soil surface, water moves up again and this brings nitrates and other salts back toward the surface, sometimes all the way to the top (figure 80).

• After two weeks of dry weather, the first foot of soil may be dry enough to hold another 2 inches (5 cm) of rainfall. Before

the second rain can move nitrates further down, it has to replace the moisture that evaporated during the dry period, leaving only 2 inches (5 cm) of the 4-inch (10 cm) rain to carry nitrates still deeper into the subsoil.

The net rainfall left for penetrating downward in the soil is rainfall minus evaporation. Figure 81 shows the estimated net rainfall in different regions during the fall, winter, and early spring period when the soil is normally unfrozen.

Movement in an already wet soil:

When the soil is already wet at the time of a rain, the rainfall does not move along a uniform wetting front, but rather flows through the largest pores in the soil. As a result, a considerable portion of the water penetrates more deeply than indicated in the preceeding paragraphs and carries nitrates down with it.

Summary:

Nitrates can move downward 4 to 5 feet (1½ to 1⅔ meters) and still be available to corn since roots penetrate 5 to 6 feet (1⅔ to 2 meters) in well-drained soils.

Agronomists now feel that, except on sandy soils, leaching from normal rainfall is not a major pathway of nitrogen loss from the fall of one year until the end of the growing season in the following year in the northern half of the United States. However, it is important in southern states because rainfall is greater and the soil is not frozen during the winter.

Fall application was strongly promoted by the fertilizer industry during the 1950's and 1960's in order to reduce the peak of demand in the spring. This would lower the need for transport, storage, and application equipment thus lowering the cost of fertilizer. But the practice never became very popular in the Corn Belt, accounting for less than 10 percent of the total nitrogen. The concern for possible excessive nitrates in streams, lakes and groundwater is reason enough for farmers and the fertilizer industry to soft pedal fall application. Though research has not been conducted to show how much more fall applied nitrogen leaches out of the root zone, the fact that agronomists generally suggested 15 to 20 percent more nitrogen in the fall than in the spring makes fall application suspect from the environmental point of view.

Farmers' experiences with shortages and fast rising prices as in the fall of 1973 and spring of 1974 will almost certainly result in new interest in fall application.

On the other hand, a sharp increase in the price of nitrogen generally will encourage more efficient use which comes from spring application or sidedressing.

Non-farmers and pollution control agencies who object to fall application on environmental grounds may be forced to balance this concern against their interests in food supply and price.

The forces acting for and against fall application need to be watched carefully from year to year.

Fertilizers with the ammonium form of

Fall and Early Winter

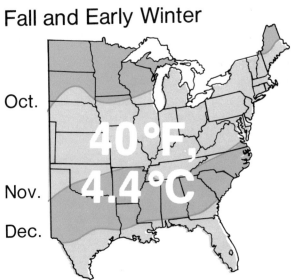

Figure 82. Approximate date when daily minimum air temperatures reach 40°F (4.4°C) in the fall. Nitrogen applied in the ammonium form at about these dates will usually stay in non-leachable form because soil temperatures will soon be near 40°F (4.4°C). At that temperature nitrifying soil organisms are almost inactive and thus ammonium is not converted to nitrate.

nitrogen are preferred for fall application. They give added protection against leaching from extra heavy rains in the fall and winter, provided they are put on late enough — when the soil is cool and the fertilizers stay in the ammonium form rather than converting to nitrate.

50°F (10° C) is often used as the practical soil temperature at which nitrogen in the ammonium form can be safely applied in the fall without appreciable conversion to nitrate form and leaching. Actually, the nitrifying organisms continue to function down to 32°F (0°C) but at a slower rate. Hence, 50°F is acceptable for fall application in the Corn Belt because the temperature at the 4-inch (10 cm) depth normally declines about 2 to 3 degrees F (1 + 2°C) each week and thus will soon be low enough to curtail nitrification, figure 82.

Tieup and Release by Biological Changes

A curious fact is that turning under alfalfa supplies nitrogen, whereas turning under corn stalks or straw actually robs the young corn plant.

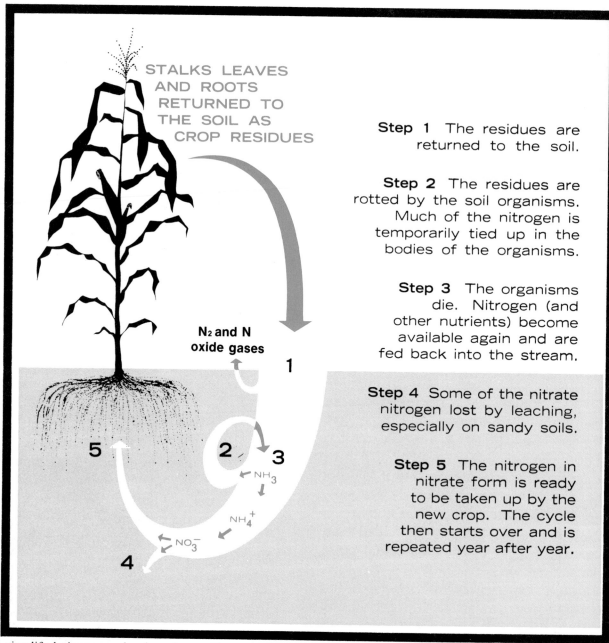

STALKS LEAVES AND ROOTS RETURNED TO THE SOIL AS CROP RESIDUES

N_2 and N oxide gases

NH_3

NH_4^+

NO_3^-

Step 1 The residues are returned to the soil.

Step 2 The residues are rotted by the soil organisms. Much of the nitrogen is temporarily tied up in the bodies of the organisms.

Step 3 The organisms die. Nitrogen (and other nutrients) become available again and are fed back into the stream.

Step 4 Some of the nitrate nitrogen lost by leaching, especially on sandy soils.

Step 5 The nitrogen in nitrate form is ready to be taken up by the new crop. The cycle then starts over and is repeated year after year.

A simplified nitrogen cycle when plant residues are added to the soil.

This is due to the activity of soil organisms which rot the alfalfa and corn stalks. Before the residues are added, the soil organisms reach a balance with their food supply. When fresh plant residues are added, the whole picture changes (figures 83, 84). The organisms feed on this new food supply and multiply rapidly to produce new generations of organisms. They are everywhere in the soil.

To build their bodies, which have about one part of nitrogen to each 8 to 12 parts of carbon, they obtain the proper balance by grabbing up available nitrogen in nitrate form (figure 84). Corn roots cannot effectively compete with billions of microbes within the root zone of a single corn plant.

Attention here is focused on the biological activities that affect nitrogen, but it should be pointed out that phosphorus (figure 91), sulfur, and some micronutrients follow somewhat the same pathway in going from

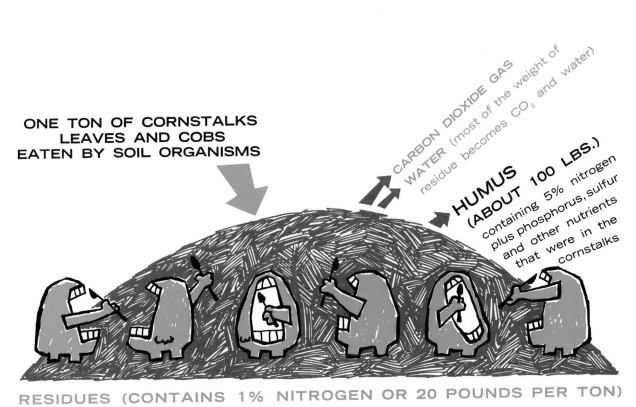

ONE TON OF CORNSTALKS LEAVES AND COBS EATEN BY SOIL ORGANISMS

CARBON DIOXIDE GAS WATER (most of the weight of residue becomes CO_2 and water)

HUMUS (ABOUT 100 LBS.) containing 5% nitrogen plus phosphorus, sulfur and other nutrients that were in the cornstalks

RESIDUES (CONTAINS 1% NITROGEN OR 20 POUNDS PER TON)

Figure 83. Soil organisms eat plant residues and convert them to humus, carbon dioxide, gas and water. A ton of cornstalks produces only about 100 pounds (45 kilos) of humus because of the low nitrogen content of the corn residues. (20 pounds per ton in the bottom line is 8.2 kilos per metric ton.)

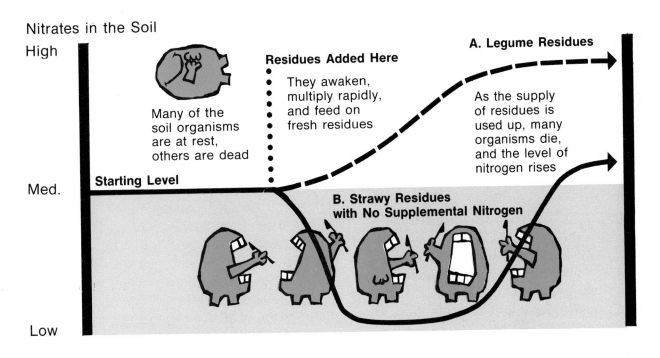

Nitrates in the Soil

High

A. Legume Residues

Residues Added Here
They awaken, multiply rapidly, and feed on fresh residues

Many of the soil organisms are at rest, others are dead

As the supply of residues is used up, many organisms die, and the level of nitrogen rises

Starting Level

Med.

B. Strawy Residues with No Supplemental Nitrogen

Low

Figure 84. The effect on available nitrate nitrogen for crops when two kinds of residues are worked into the soil. When strawy residues are added (B), the soil organisms multiply rapidly and reduce the nitrate nitrogen nearly to zero. After a few weeks, nitrates begin to appear and reach a new high level. Legume residues (A upper line) increase the nitrate nitrogen soon after they are added.

117

fresh residues through the bodies of soil organisms into forms that are available for the next corn crop.

About 1.7 percent nitrogen is a key reference point for residues. When the nitrogen is above 1.7 there is no delay in nitrate availability for corn after the residue is mixed into a warm soil. When the nitrogen content of the residue is 1.2 percent or less, available nitrates become scarce until rotting is complete.

Even when large amounts of stalks or straw are mixed into the soil, corn plants always manage to obtain some nitrogen because some roots will feed in local soil zones where there are no fresh residues that encourage micro-organisms to multiply and tie up available nitrates.

No single figure is accurate for the percent of nitrogen in all corn residues. When you increase the nitrogen supply for a growing crop, you raise the nitrogen content of stalks and leaves. Mature corn stalks on well-fertilized fields probably contain at least 1.0 percent, though the standard figure for average stalks is 0.75 percent. At any rate, corn stalks, straw, and mature grasses are all low enough in nitrogen to tie up available nitrates for several weeks.

What can be done to overcome the nitrogen deficit from high carbon residues?

• *Plow or otherwise incorporate the residues early.* This gives residues more time to rot before corn is planted. Soil organisms will tie up nitrates and keep them from leaching or being lost by denitrification. The job of decaying residues won't be finished by the time soil temperature goes below 32°F (0°C). Their activity will continue in the spring when the soil temperature goes above the freezing point and will increase sharply in the weeks before corn planting time. On fields where erosion is a problem, early spring plowing is preferred to fall plowing.

• *Apply extra nitrogen.* Extra nitrogen speeds up residue decomposition. Even more important, it *supplies available nitrogen to*

Table 9.

Suggested *relative* amounts of nitrogen to apply taking into account the amounts of N removed and the amounts needed to balance the carbon to nitrogen ratio in the residue. For example, if the optimum N following corn is judged to be 100 pounds per acre (112 kg per ha), then following oats or wheat without a legume seeding it is 80% or 80 pounds (90 kg/ha); when the optimum is estimated at 150 pounds (168 kg/ha) after corn, it would be 120 pounds (134 kg/ha) following oats.

When the preceding crop is:	The relative amount of N to apply for corn is:
Corn or sorghum	100%
Oats or wheat, no legume seeding	80%
Soybeans, field beans	70%
Sugar beets	70%
Oats or wheat, legume seeding (good growth, plowed after October 1)	50%
Alfalfa, stand 2 years or older	40%

corn during the period when the organisms are tying up nitrates. Twenty pounds of nitrogen (8.2 kilograms per metric ton) added to one ton of corn residues will raise the nitrogen to at least 2.0 percent and perhaps 2.25 on fields that had a high nitrogen supply in the previous year. Here is a rule-of-thumb: for each bushel of yield, it takes one pound of nitrogen to balance the carbon in stalks, leaves and roots (1.8 kgs per quintal). In other words, a 150-bushel yield needs 150 pounds of actual N (94.1 quintals need 168 kilos). This is not necessarily the optimum total amount of nitrogen to apply, but it is the amount needed to prevent a temporary deficit of available nitrate (figure 84).

Table 9 is a guide to the *relative* amounts of nitrogen fertilizer that are profitable for corn following different crops. For a more detailed analysis of the amount to apply at different price levels, see page 181.

Many farmers and fertilizer men are concerned when they see unrotted corn stalks

NITRIFICATION

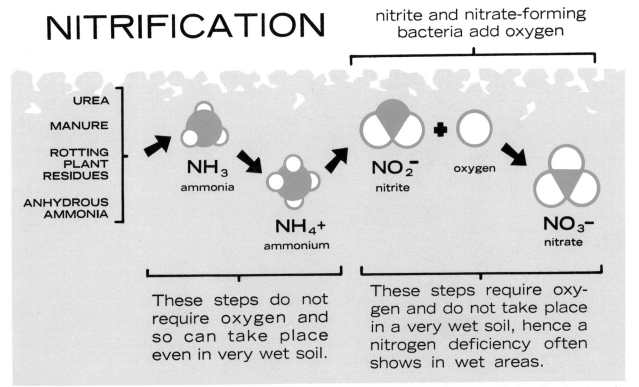

Figure 85. Ammonium ions (NH_4^+) for the nitrification process comes from several sources. Nitrification involves the addition of oxygen to ammonium, thus changing it in a series of steps from NH_4^+ to NO_3^- .

turned up a year after they were plowed under. This is nothing to worry about if the corn had enough nitrogen for top yield. Your goal should always be to assure adequate nitrogen for the current crop. You can do this without mixing fertilizer nitrogen intimately with the stalks. For example, when anhydrous ammonia is knifed in between the rows, the corn can get all the nitrogen it needs, but the corn stalks between the applicator slits may not be rotted during the first year. *It is not undesirable, but it is unnecessary, to mix the nitrogen in close contact with stalks to assure rapid decay.*

Dry weather is a prime cause of unrotted stalks. Without adequate rainfall, nitrates — even though in good supply — move too slowly into the zones where stalks are rotting. Microbes use up nitrates that are nearby, and then slow down until a new supply of nitrates is brought to them by rain. This process is too slow in dry seasons to get the job finished before the field is plowed again.

The Role of Nitrification (Figure 85)

It has been shown that corn can effectively use most of its nitrogen in the ammonium (NH_4^+) form. But in fact most nitrogen enters corn roots as nitrate (NO_3^-). This is because ammonium is rapidly converted to nitrate when soil conditions (temperature, air supply, pH) are favorable for corn growth. Natural soil conditions that inhibit nitrification of ammonium (cold, wetness, strong acidity), are unfavorable for corn. Theoretically a nitrification inhibitor such as N-Serve (page 112) could be used to prevent nitrification of both added fertilizer and NH_4^+ that is released from the decay of plant residues, animal manures and sludge. This would serve several purposes:

— The nitrogen would be preserved against leaching thus helping to meet the needs of the crop and at the same time it would contribute less to unwanted nitrates in surface and groundwater.

— The nitrogen could not be lost to the

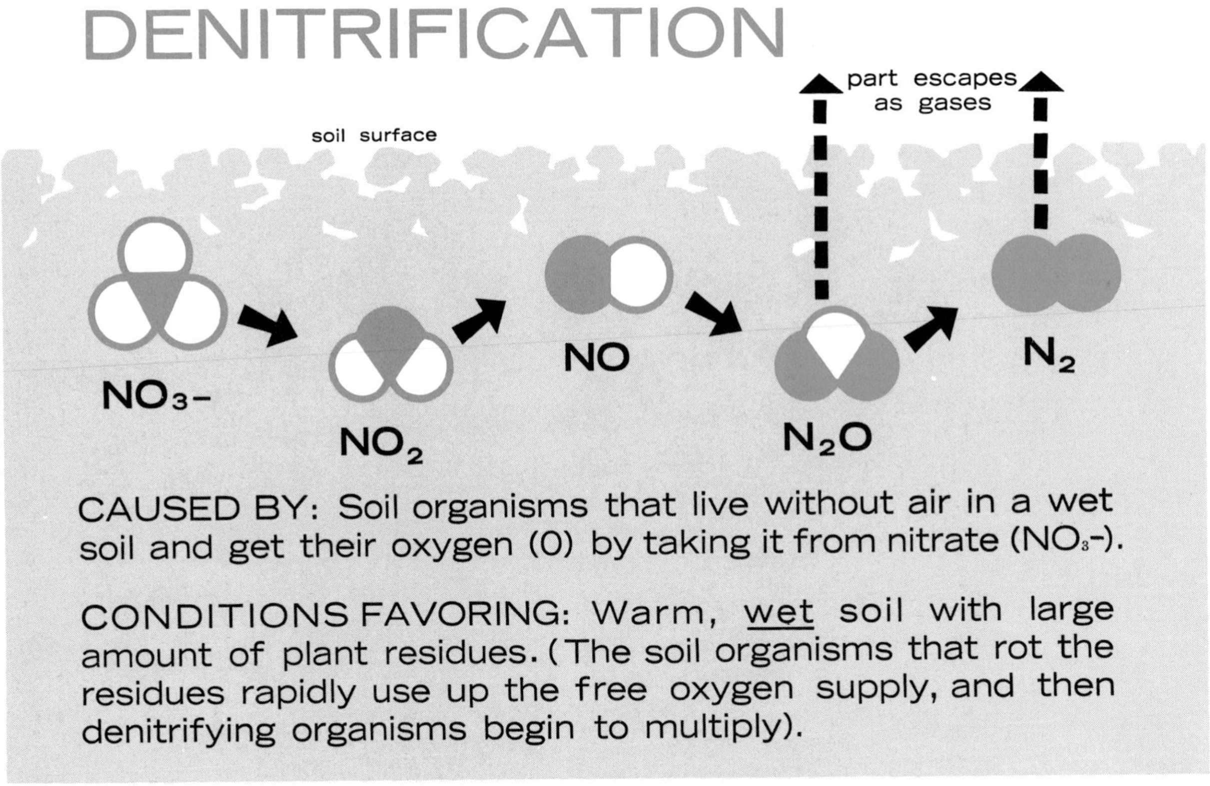

DENITRIFICATION

CAUSED BY: Soil organisms that live without air in a wet soil and get their oxygen (O) by taking it from nitrate (NO_3-).

CONDITIONS FAVORING: Warm, <u>wet</u> soil with large amount of plant residues. (The soil organisms that rot the residues rapidly use up the free oxygen supply, and then denitrifying organisms begin to multiply).

Figure 86. The denitrification process. Note that each step from left to right has one less oxygen ion relative to nitrogen. The last two are gases and partly escape into the air.

air following denitrification, figure 86.

But there might be important undesirable side effects on other soil processes from large amounts of pyridines or other inhibitors. The cost would be prohibitive at the present time.

Denitrification: Why It Is Important, What It Is, Why It Happens

Denitrification is one way, and under some conditions the *main way* your soil loses nitrogen (figure 86). When water stands in a field after summer rains, corn plants show nitrogen deficiency because nitrogen uptake is inhibited and nitrogen is being lost by denitrification.

Denitrification is the opposite of nitrification: oxygen is removed rather than added. Note in figure 86 that there are three parts of oxygen to one of nitrogen at the start (left), and no oxygen at the end when the gas N_2 is formed.

N_2O and N_2 are gases which can escape from the soil surface into the air; this is how denitrification causes nitrogen losses. Denitrifying organisms attack nitrates from fertilizer but they also attack nitrate ions that come from the decay of residues, from manure, or from ammonium fertilizers which have been previously nitrified to the nitrate form. In short, nitrate from all sources is fair game for denitrifying organisms in a warm, wet soil.

The amount of nitrogen lost by denitrification is difficult to measure in the field, so there is little data on the subject. *Agronomists believe, however, that it is the main way nitrogen is lost from poorly-drained soils and is a significant factor (from chemical rather than biological reactions) even on better-drained soils.* Estimates range from 15 to 30 percent in typical Corn Belt soils.

What Can You Do about Denitrification?

• Improve drainage so your soil does not stay waterlogged during the late spring and summer when the soil is warm enough for

A

denitrifying organisms to grow rapidly.

• If your soil is flat and has a compact subsoil not suited to tile drains, with the result that it is sometimes very wet during May and early June, it is safer to sidedress the main nitrogen supply rather than put it on ahead of planting. You can thus reduce the risk of denitrification losses and still apply the nitrogen before corn needs it most.

• Keep in mind that large amounts of nitrogen are lost when soil is flooded or waterlogged for several days in May, June or July. When this happens, consider applying extra nitrogen fertilizer even though you had applied enough before planting.

• Apply ammonium forms rather than nitrate forms for early application on soils with conditions that favor denitrification.

How to Get More Nitrogen from the Supply That Is Already in Your Soil

• Plow and completely kill sod crops (A) to increase aeration. Increased aeration has the same effect on rate of decay as blowing on hot coals to make a fire burn faster. No-till systems have the opposite effect and researchers have found that nitrogen fertilizer must be increased 20 to 30 percent.

• Kill weeds that compete with corn for nitrogen, other nutrients and water (D).

• Build a good supply of quick rotting residues (B) from legumes, or from corn stalks grown with plenty of nitrogen and other nutrients.

• Add nitrogen fertilizer (C). This releases nitrogen that is already in the soil especially in wide carbon:nitrogen residues such as corn stalks, straw, and soybean residues.

• Drain the soil (E). Good drainage of wet areas will safeguard you from denitrification, give better aeration to speed the release of N from organic matter.

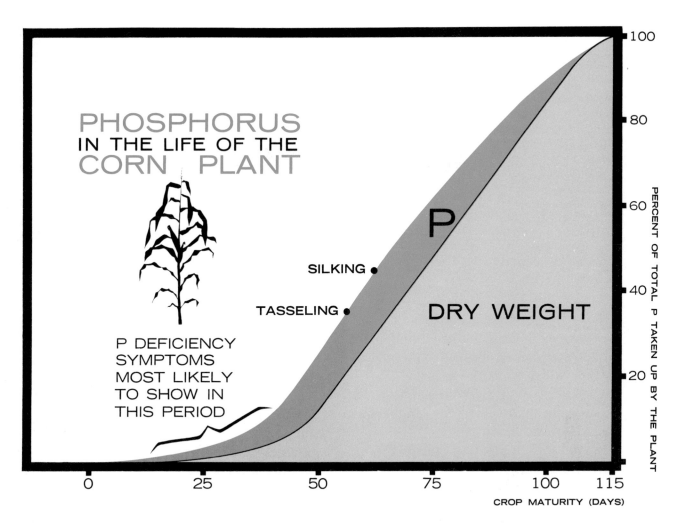

Figure 87. Though phosphorus is taken up throughout the life of the corn plant, the most critical period is early in the season. At that time, the percentage of phosphorus in the plant is very high but the capacity of the root system to obtain phosphorus is low. The reddish-purple deficiency symptoms rarely show after corn is 24 to 30 inches (60 to 75 cm) tall.

Phosphorus

The amount of phosphorus in the soil and in the corn plant is low compared with nitrogen and potassium, but nevertheless phosphorus is an equally important element in the nutrition of corn. Phosphorus doesn't leach out of the soil. The crop in the first year seldom get more than 15 tp 20 percent of the phosphorus applied in fertilizer. On any given day, less than one pound per acre is in solution in the chemical compound that corn can absorb. Phosphorus is found in the soil both as the organic form like nitrogen and as the non-organic form like potassium.

Phosphorus Uptake (Figure 87)

The bulk of the corn plant's continual need of phosphorus is taken up by the roots in the chemical compounds H_2PO_4 and HPO_4. Small amounts are absorbed in the organic form, that is, in forms left after the death of living organisms. Phosphorus moves into plant roots in the same chemical form whether it comes from fertilizer applied in the current year, from decaying residues, or from basic soil supplies.

If phosphorus deficiency is going to show at any time, it will nearly always appear before the plants are 24 inches tall (2/3 meter) for these three reasons:

- For normal growth, the young plants need a higher percentage of P in their tissues than they will later in the season.
- The capacity of the young root system to absorb phosphorus has not caught up to the needs of the plant.
- In cool soils at planting time and immediately thereafter, phosphorus is either less available (due to inadequate release from organic forms) or the roots cannot take it up as well as later.

What can you do to assure enough phosphorus during this critical early period?

- Apply fertilizer through the planter in a band near the row.
- Select a fertilizer with at least 50 percent of the phosphorus in water-soluble form (see page 125.
- Choose a fertilizer that has about one part of nitrogen to 3 or 4 parts of P_2O_5 (1.3 to 1.8 parts of phosphorus). Nitrogen in the fertilizer band increases the uptake of phosphorus — either because the phosphorus stays in more available chemical compounds or because root growth is increased in the band thus producing more roots to absorb it. Urea is undesirable in the band because upon hydrolysis it produces NH_3 which is unfavorable to root growth and phosphorus uptake.

The early-season, starter effect of phosphorus near the row becomes less from north to south and as the general soil test level is raised. Phosphorus in a band near the row is suggested especially for early planting for the northern Corn Belt even though the soil test is medium or above (except on certain high pH soils where row phosphorus increases zinc deficiency). In the latitude of central Indiana and Illinois, row phosphorus promotes more rapid early growth in most years — even on high-phosphorus soils — but this quick start seldom increases yield. If this is the case on your farm, you have to decide whether you can justify row fertilizer on the basis of more uniform early growth, a better chance to cultivate in time to kill weeds, insurance in cool, wet seasons, and a slight maturity advantage. Applying row fertilizer will slow down planting.

A shortage of phosphorus fertilizer and/or a large increase in price would favor a small amount in the row rather than a larger amount broadcast.

Phosphorus Fertilizers

Nearly all phosphorus for fertilizer comes originally from phosphate rock. The phosphorus in rock as it comes from the mine is mainly in the form of calcium fluorapatite ($3 Ca_3 (PO)_2 \cdot CaF_2$) and hydroxyapatite ($3 Ca_3 (PO_4)_2 \cdot Ca (OH)_2$). Most phosphate rock produced in the United States has a total

This Chart Shows in Simplified Form How Phosphorus Fertilizers Are Made, Their Nutrient Contents, Water Solubility, and Principal Uses

Product	% of P That Is Water Soluble	Principal Uses

1 Ordinary Superphosphate —$Ca(H_2PO_4)_2$ (monocalcium phosphate)
 	
Phosphate rock + Sulfuric = Superphosphate
(size of coarse sand) Acid 16 to 22% P_2O_5
(7 to 9.6% P)
 	
In the process:
  a) The phosphorus is made more available
  b) Fluorine gas is driven off
  c) Gypsum is formed in an amount equal
    to the superphosphate
	78	1. Direct application, dry
		2. In mixed fertilizers
		(See ammoniated superphosphates)

2 Triple or Treble Superphosphate — $Ca(H_2PO_4)_2$ (monocalcium phosphate)
 	
Phosphate rock + Phosphoric = Triplesuperphosphate
          Acid 45 to 47% P_2O_5
     (Some sulfuric (19.6 to 20.5% P)
     acid also used) (May be higher if super-
             phosphoric acid is used
             in place of ordinary
             phosphoric acid)
 	
In the process:
  a) The phosphorus is made more available
  b) Fluorine gas is driven off
	84	1. Direct application, dry
		2. Mixed fertilizers
		(See ammoniated superphosphates)
		3. Bulk blends
		4. Slurry fertilizers

3 Nitrophosphates —Several chemical formulas
 	
Phosphate rock + Nitric + Some phosphoric or
         acid   sulfuric acid to raise
               the water solubility of
               the products + some ammon-
               ium or potassium sulfate
	Varies from low to a high of about 70	1. Direct application, dry
		2. Mixed fertilizers
		3. Slurry fertilizers

4 Ammonium Phosphate (mono)—$NH_4H_2PO_4$
 	
Phosphoric + Anhydrous = Ammonium phosphate
acid   ammonia   11% N—48% P_2O_5—0% K
                11% N—21% P)
                   or
             16% N—20% P_2O_5—0% K
             (16% N—8.7% P)
 	
    Some sulfuric = Ammonium phosphate-sulfate
    acid may be   16% N—20% P_2O_5—0% K
    added to produce (16% N—8.7% P)
 	
Both mono-ammonium and diammonium phosphate have high residual acidity
	100	1. Direct application, dry
		2. Mixed fertilizers
		3. Bulk blends

5 Diammonium Phosphate $(NH_4)_2HPO_4$ Same process as ammonium phosphate 18% N—46% P_2O_5 but with continued addition of (18% N—20% P) ammonia while the pH of mix is kept at 5.8 to 6.0. This allows or a second NH_4 to be added in place 18% N—53% P_2O_5 of one H+. (18% N—23.1% P)	100	1. Direct application, dry 2. Bulk blends 3. In irrigation water

6 Ammonium Polyphosphate
 	
Ammonia + superphosphoric acid = Ammonium polyphosphate
                         10% N—34% P_2O_5—0% K
                         (10% N—15% P)
	100	Liquid fertilizer base

or 15% N—61% P_2O_5—0% K 11% N—37% P_2O_5—0% K (15% N—26.6% P) (11% N—16.3% P)	100	Liquid fertilizer base

Calcium Metaphosphate—$Ca(PO_3)_2$—and Potassium Metaphosphate—KPO_3—nave been made but neither is generally commercially available.

Phosphoric acid, ammoniated super and triplesuperphosphate are discussed on following ages.

P_2O_5 of 30 to 36 percent (13.1 to 16% P) of which about 1/10 is "available" by the citrate test that is used on fertilizers.

"Available" P_2O_5 is defined as the amount of P_2O_5 that is soluble in water, plus the amount that is soluble in a standard laboratory solution of ammonium citrate. This definition has been established by the organization of fertilizer control officials. It is a useful standard but it does not adequately express the real availability of phosphorus fertilizers that are low in water solubility when used in certain situations (see page 133).

From 1940 to 1960 large tonnages of finely ground rock (100 to 200 mesh) were sold in Illinois and Missouri, and smaller amounts in other states, to build up the basic phosphorus supply on moderately-acid soils but the amount has declined sharply. The favorable price of rock phosphate in Illinois and Missouri, plus the fact that the Agricultural Stabilization and Conservation Service paid about half the cost for use on soil-improving crops, kept rock phosphate competitive in cost for cropping systems that included alfalfa or clover where the pH was 6.5 or lower.

About 90 percent of the phosphorus in rock and colloidal phosphate is in apatite form and cannot be absorbed by plant roots until the compounds are acted on by an acid or heat to break the apatite bond. In the soil, untreated rock phosphate is slowly changed by soil acids to a form that supplies available phosphorus. But nearly all the phosphorus fertilizer used in the United States is treated with acid or heated in an electric furnace to immediately increase the availability.

Phosphoric Acid (H_3PO_4)

Ordinary phosphoric acid (54% P_2O_5, 23% P) can be made by treating phosphate rock with sulfuric acid, removing the gypsum that forms, and concentrating the liquid acid by evaporation of the water. This is called wet process or green acid. Phosphoric acid can also be made by the electric furnace method which results in a product with less impurities. This is called white or furnace acid.

It is used in several ways: for direct application as liquid phosphoric acid; to treat phosphate rock for making triple superphosphate; in combination with ammonia to make ammonium phosphates; in the manufacture of liquid mixed fertilizers: and for concentration to superphosphoric acid (up to 83% P_2O_5, 31.4% P from wet process acid; up to 70% P_2O_5, 30.5% from electric furnace acid).

Superphosphoric Acid, Polyphosphates

Superphosphoric acid is the general name used to describe more concentrated acid than ordinary phosphoric acid. Up to about 68 percent P_2O_5 (29.6% P) the phosphorus is still in the usual orthophosphate form:

$$H_3PO_4 \qquad \overset{\displaystyle OH}{\underset{\displaystyle O}{HO-\overset{|}{\underset{\|}{P}}-OH}} \qquad \overset{\displaystyle OH}{\underset{\displaystyle O}{HO-\overset{|}{\underset{\|}{P}}-OH}}$$

Phosphoric acid   **Two separate molecules**

But from 68 percent up to the maximum of 83 percent a significant change occurs. There is less water relative to the amount of phosphorus in the basic molecule. In effect a molecule of water is removed and two or more of the remaining units hook together:

$$HO-\overset{\overset{\displaystyle OH}{|}}{\underset{\underset{\displaystyle O}{\|}}{P}}-O-\overset{\overset{\displaystyle OH}{|}}{\underset{\underset{\displaystyle O}{\|}}{P}}-OH$$

1 Molecule polyphosphate

$H_4P_2O_7$

H_2O removed as steam

Several of the units may join together to produce *polyphosphates*, "poly" meaning several. They are also called *condensed* phosphates.

Polyphosphates have recently become very important in fertilizers and extravagent claims are sometimes made for them. The main advantages claimed are that the phosphorus is more available, somewhat more mobile, and that polyphosphates help to release micronutrients from the soil.

The idea of greater availability is based on the fact that polyphosphates do not directly enter into the soil reactions (figure 90) that orthophosphate does. Polyphosphates must first take on one or more molecules of water (hydrolyze) that they previously gave up and thus convert back to their starting point, orthophosphate. The theory is that plant roots will obtain a continuous fresh supply of orthophosphate before it can react with the soil and become less available.

Field trials have seldom shown any consistent difference between polyphosphates and orthophosphate in ability to supply phosphorus. Perhaps this should be expected because:

- polyphosphate fertilizers usually contain about one-half of the phosphorus in the ortho form, but the proportion may change in the future.
- only 5 to 20 percent of the P used by a crop is obtained from the fertilizer applied that year.
- the theoretical advantage of less reaction with the soil may be offset by the fact that polyphosphate is not available to the plant until it converts back to orthophosphate (hydrolyzes — takes on the water it had lost). At that time it can react with the soil the same as if it were applied as orthophosphate originally.

Research on the effect of polyphosphates on micronutrient availability has thus far shown that:

1. Where there was a severe deficiency, polyphosphates did not free enough micronutrients from the native soil supply to correct the deficiency.
2. Without added zinc, polyphosphate accentuated the deficiency on corn more than did orthophosphate. When zinc was added to both phosphate forms, the yield increase was the same.

Recent TVA research indicates that polyphosphates do not move any more, if as much, as orthophosphates.

In summary, the advantages of polyphosphates are:

- They permit the formulation of higher analysis liquid or suspension fertilizers without salting out.
- They sequester certain metal ions and thus keep some micronutrients (iron, zinc, manganese) in more available form.
- They save labor and cost in transporting because they permit higher analysis mixes.

Superphosphoric acid is especially helpful to liquid fertilizer manufacturers because of its sequestering properties which prevent sludge from settling out in the bottom of the tank and clogging nozzles. This permits the use of wet process acid and thus reduces the cost of liquid fertilizer because wet process acid costs less than furnace acid. Higher-analyses and wider range of liquid fertilizers can be formulated. Superphosphate and triple-superphosphate with higher than usual P contents are possible through the use of superphosphoric acid.

Ammoniated Superphosphate and Triplesuperphosphate

Many dry mixed fertilizers use nitrogen solutions with ammonia as the source of nitrogen. Nitrogen solutions supply low-cost nitrogen, neutralize free acid, and improve condition of the final product. The ammonia and calcium in the solutions react with phosphates to form ammonium phosphate and mono-calcium phosphate.

Adding increasing amounts of ammonia to ordinary and triplesuperphosphate affects the water solubility of the phosphorus. This is shown in figure 88. The decrease in water solubility when large amounts of ammonia are added is due to the formation of tricalcium phosphate rather than moncalcium phosphate.

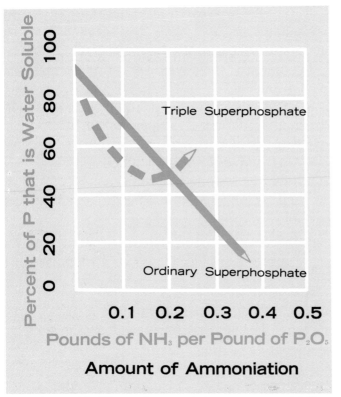

Figure 88. Effect of ammoniation on water solubility. Increasing the amount of ammonia that is reacted with ordinary superphosphate lowers the water solubility due to formation of tricalcium phosphate, which has low solubility, rather than monocalcium phosphate, which has high water solubility. When triple-superphosphate is ammoniated, water solubility decreases at first and then increases as ammoniation is continued to a higher level.

Basic Slag

This is a by-product of open hearth steel manufacturing which is used both for liming and as a P source. It has 8 to 10% P_2O_5 (3.5 to 4.4% P) of which 60 to 90% is available by citrate test.

Physical Movement

In the short run phosphorus stays where you put it; it moves the least of any major nutrient. In the first few hours or days after application, some of the soluble phosphorus moves perhaps as much as an inch from the granule (figure 90). From then on, it moves hardly at all.

For example, experiments show little increase in phosphorus below 18 inches (½ meter) after 50 years of adding P to the plow layer.

This "fixation" of phosphorus when it reacts with soil is important for several reasons:

• "Fixed" phosphorus is much less available than newly applied phosphorus. As a result, the most profitable amount of P to apply is much more than is removed in harvested crops until your soil test level has been built to a satisfactory level.

• Feeding roots must continuously grow into new zones of available phosphorus because the P will not move very far or very quickly to the roots in the soil solution as nitrogen does. This is probably part of the reason why phosphorus that is in the fertilizer band is not used much by corn after it is shoulder high. By that time most of the newly developing roots are probably out of the fertilizer band. Barber at Purdue University found that the greatest number of roots in the surface 6 inches (15 cm) was reached at 80 days and they declined rapidly therafter.

• You cannot readily build up the subsoil phosphorus supply because P applied to the plow layer will not move far into the subsoil in a farmer's lifetime.

• Phosphorus won't leach out and therefore the total P in the plow layer can easily be raised to a high level. Michigan researchers Ellis and Erickson found that one loamy sand could hold 433 pounds of P(991 lb. P_2O_5) per acre (485 and 1100 kilos per hectare). A clay held 645 pounds P(1477 lb. P_2O_5) per acre (722 and 1654 kilos per hectare). Furthermore, the retention capacity after being saturated, could regenerate in about 90 days.

What Happens to Phosphorus in the Soil?

Applying phosphorus in fertilizer or manure is like putting money in the bank (figure 89), with 80 to 85 percent going into a long-term savings account and 15 to 20

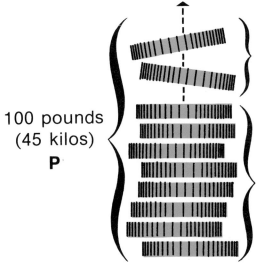

20 pounds (plus "interest" on savings account **P)**
(9 kilos)

About 80 pounds (36 kilos) of the phosphorus that is applied in fertilizer at one time remains in the soil like a **"savings account"** in the bank. You can draw annual **"interest"** on it but you can never withdraw all of the **"principal".**

You can raise the **"amount of interest"** by building a larger account.

You can increase the **"rate of interest"** by (1) keeping the pH between 5.5 and 7.0, (2) adding more fresh plant residues or manure or (3) draining wet soils to improve aeration and rooting depth.

100 pounds
(45 kilos)
P

Figure 89. Adding phosphorus to soil is like putting money in the bank — splitting it so that about 80 percent goes into a long-term savings account and 20 percent into a checking account for use this year. Each year your corn crop can use about 20 percent of the newly applied P and can get some of the P that becomes available each year from the soil reserve as shown in figure 91.

percent into a checking account from which your crops can draw available phosphorus. The rest of the P is in an unusual savings account. You can draw "interest" on it but you can never close out the account and withdraw all you put in for reasons discussed in the following paragraphs. By proper soil management you can, however, increase both the amount and rate of "interest."

When fertilizers with immediately available phosphorus are put in the soil they react within a few hours or days and henceforth are different chemical compounds than they were in the fertilizer (figure 90). As the phosphorus compounds dissolve, each produces a little acid world of its own.

This new acidity dissolves other soil compounds and these combine with the phosphorus to form new compounds that are less soluble. The P is, therefore, less available than it was in the fertilizer. These compounds gradually become less available, until finally they are part of the large reservoir of slowly available soil phosphorus, figure 91.

Each phosphorus carrying fertilizer has its own set of reactions and end products. The net effect for all is, however, somewhat reduced availability.

The water-soluble and citrate-soluble compounds in phosphorus fertilizers are converted to other forms before the seed can germinate and the young roots feed on the water-soluble phosphorus.

As was pointed out earlier polyphosphates are not subjected to these reactions until after they have been in the soil long enough to hydrolyze back to orthophosphate. Remember, however, that so called polyphosphates are about half poly and half ortho at the start.

Soil acidity and alkalinity affect the availability of phosphorus. In moderate to strongly-acid soils, the main compounds that are formed by chemical reactions involve iron, aluminum and manganese. In soils near or above pH 7.0, most of the phosphorus is tied up in compounds with calcium. As time passes, the phosphorus in these new compounds is held more and more tightly..

THE ACTION OF SUPER-PHOSPHATE IN THE SOIL

AT TIME OF APPLICATION

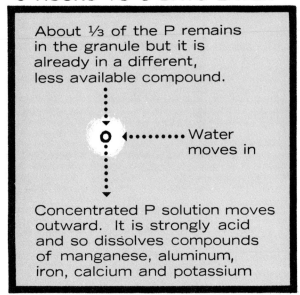

6 HOURS TO 3 DAYS LATER

About ⅓ of the P remains in the granule but it is already in a different, less available compound.

············· Water moves in

Concentrated P solution moves outward. It is strongly acid and so dissolves compounds of manganese, aluminum, iron, calcium and potassium

3 TO 7 DAYS LATER

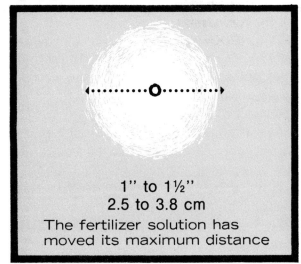

1" to 1½"
2.5 to 3.8 cm
The fertilizer solution has moved its maximum distance

Figure 90. When a granule of superphosphate is placed in the soil, it dissloves in 6 hours to 3 days. The solution that moves outward is very strongly acid. This acid dissolves many compounds and then reacts with them to form new compounds in which the phosphorus is no longer water-soluble. About one-third of the P remains at the granule site but it also has changed chemically and is not water-soluble. These reactions somewhat reduce the availability of the phosphorus compared with that of the fertilizer at the time of application. All phosphorus fertilizers udergo reactions when first applied to the soil. The nature of the reactions is governed by the kind of fertilizer and the soil type.

Phosphorus in the soil is most available in the slight to moderately acid range. The reactions described in the previous paragraph for soil close to superphosphate granules also describe the fate of all phosphorus in the soil that is not tied up in organic matter or organic compounds.

The relationship of pH to the availability of phosphorus is shown in table 10.

Soil pH also affects the amount of phosphorus that becomes available from soil organic matter (see the following discussion).

Biological Changes: Soil Organisms Influence Available Phosphorus

Since phosphorus, like nitrogen, is part of the living tissue of plants and soil organisms, it behaves in many ways like nitrogen discussed earlier. Some of the general changes in phosphorus when added in fertilizer and plant residues related to the activity of soil organisms are shown in figure 91.

Because phosphorus is part of all living tissues, it is successively tied up and released as the crop grows, matures, dies, and is returned to the soil where it is tied up in the body of microbes that decay the residues and later released upon their death. Most of the phosphorus eventually ends up in the storage reservoir.

In the prairie soils of the Midwest, 40 to 50 percent of the total soil phosphorus is in organic compounds but the proportion is lower in soils in other regions that contain less organic matter. A considerable amount of phosphorus is released from organic compounds during the growing season. But, unless taken up by plant roots, like fertilizer phosphorus, it too may form compounds with iron, aluminum, calcium, and manganese. Only 15 to 20 percent of the phosphorus released from organic matter is used by the crop in the year it is released. The rest returns to the reservoir of soil phosphorus and the cycling process begins all over again.

Residues like corn stalks and grain straw which are low in P, *temporarily* reduce the

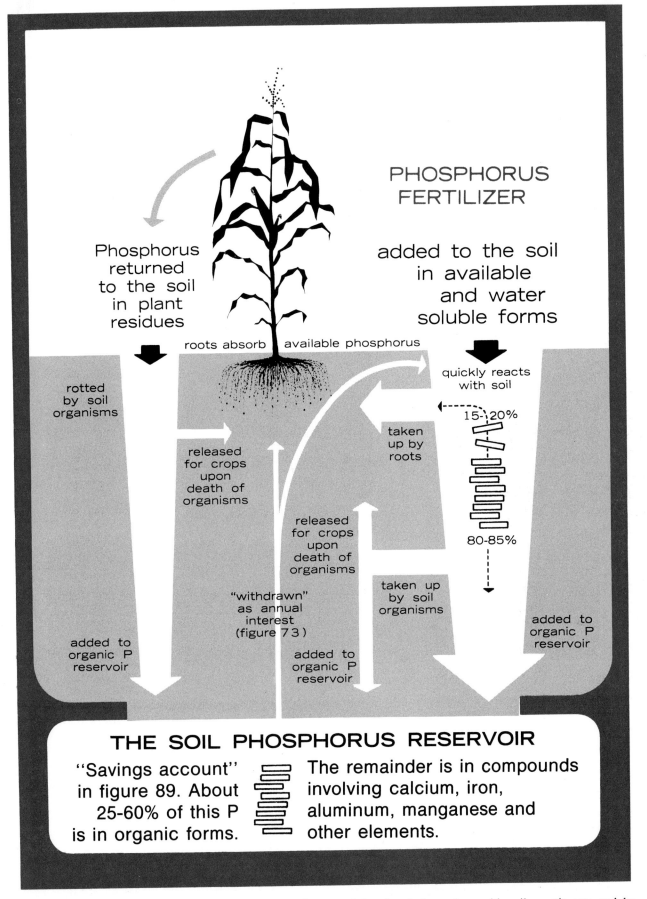

Figure 91. The important steps in the phosphorus cycle: caused by chemical reactions with soil constituents and by soil organisms which decay plant residues. Note that the wide arrows all point toward the Soil Phosphorus Reservoir; most phosphorus added in fertilizers and residues becomes part of this slowly available reserve in the soil.

Table 10

	pH	Availability of Phosphorus	
	9.0	High	
Strongly alkaline			
	8.0	Low	Much of the phosphorus is in tricalcium phosphate which is very low in availability. Tricalcium phosphate is like rock phosphate except that it has no flourine.
Slightly alkaline			
Neutral	7.0	High	Phosphorus compounds in this range are more available than in more acid or more alkaline soils.
Slightly acid	6.0		
Moderately acid	5.0	Low	In this range, much of the phosphorus is combined with iron, aluminum, and manganese into products of low availability.
Strongly acid	4.0		

amount of available phosphorus similar to the way they reduce nitrates. Legumes and manure, which decay more rapidly than straw and corn stalks, release phosphorus shortly after they are added to the soil. This explains why researchers have often noted less response to phosphorus fertilizer when they plow under a legume crop. Legume residues contain more P, they rot more rapidly, and they have a narrower carbon-to-phosphorus ratio.

Soil Factors That Influence the Amount of Phosphorus Available to the Crop:

• The pH of both the surface and subsoil. A pH of 5.5 to 7.0 has the highest available P from organic and inorganic chemical forms (figure 89).

• The amount of organic matter since it may contain one-half or more of the total phosphorus that is in the soil.

• The depth of the crop roots. Phosphorus is distributed throughout the soil and hence deep, extensive root systems contact more available P.

• The structure of the subsoil. Roots are forced to feed mainly on the outside of dense soil blocks in subsoil. The larger and more compact the blocks are, the less total area roots have to feed on.

Testing for Available Phosphorus

From the previous discussion of phosphorus reactions in the soil, it is obvious that the soil tests must be interpreted for each specific soil and crop. Since laboratories use different procedures in extracting the phosphorus, you must rely on each laboratory for information to interpret their tests and decide on fertilizer treatments. (For a full discussion of the use and meaning of soil tests, see pages 145-151.)

You may have wondered why the soil test seems to move up so slowly when phosphorus fertilizer has been added for several years. It is because about 4 pounds of phosphorus or 8 to 10 pounds of P_2O_5 is needed to raise the soil test 1 unit (4.5 kilos per hectare).

The phosphorus soil test changes much less through the season than the potassium test.

How Important
Is Water-Solubility in Fertilizer?

In some situations high water-solubility is absolutely necessary, in others it doesn't mean a thing. Here are the facts with which to determine its importance to you:

• For *band application* near the row on *soils that test low* in phosphorus, at least 50 percent of the phosphorus should be water soluble on acid soils.

• On *soils that are above pH 7.0, 80 percent* water-solubility is preferred for band application.

• For *broadcast applications* on *acid to neutral* soils, the degree of *water-solubility* is of no importance for processed phosphorus sources (this includes all except rock and colloidal phosphates).

• On *alkaline soils at least 50 percent* water-solubility is preferred even for broadcast applications.

Here are some additional guides:

As the soil test level for phosphorus is raised, water-solubility of fertilizer becomes less important because the crop gets more P from reserves in the soil and thus depends less on the fertilizer that is being applied.

The larger the amount of phosphorus fertilizer you apply, the less important is the percent that is water soluble.

Large pellets or granules are all right for fertilizers with high water-solubility, but small granules that become more widely dispersed are preferred for fertilizers with lower water-solubility.

One of the most efficient ways to make fertilizers that contain both nitrogen and phosphorus is to ammoniate ordinary or triplesuperphosphate, but this affects the water-solubility of the phosphorus (figure 88).

Best Placement
of Phosphorus Fertilizer for Corn

The main supply of phosphorus for the corn crop should be built up throughout the plow layer (except possibly on alkaline soils).

If a large amount is to be applied on a soil that tests very low in P, broadcasting and plowing under is first choice. Some of the phosphorus will be 6 to 9 inches (15 to 22.5 cm) deep and thus will be available in case midsummer drouth reduces root growth and P uptake near the surface. However, the results from broadcasting and disking phosphorus fertilizer into the surface are usually satisfactory.

For quick early growth, some phosphorus should be near the row and even with or slightly below the seed.

Sidedressing with phosphorus has been discouraged by agronomists in the past, but research in Iowa shows that sidedressing meets phosphorus needs late in the season, provided a row application had been made early in the season. The most suitable fertilizer combination for sidedressing is anhydrous ammonia and liquid phosphoric acid applied from separate tanks in separate bands. Ready-mixed solutions of the two are not feasible since you can't carry large enough amounts of nitrogen for most situations; only one part of N will react with 4 parts of P_2O_5 (1.7 parts P). If you increase the amount of NH_3, it won't react with the phosphoric acid and therefore must be handled as a nitrogen-pressure solution.

Effect of Phosphorus on Zinc Availability

Beginning in the late 1950s, several states noted that phosphorus applications reduced yields on certain soils. The trouble was traced to a shortage of zinc induced by high phosphorus. This effect has been noted in California, Indiana, Kansas, Minnesota, Nebraska, and South Dakota.

When the zinc supply is barely adequate, a phosphorus fertilizer program should be planned carefully with the advice of local extension agents or fertilizer dealers to avoid causing a zinc deficiency.

Michigan State University has reported yield depressions in theThumb region from heavy phosphorus applications that could not be corrected by zinc treatments.

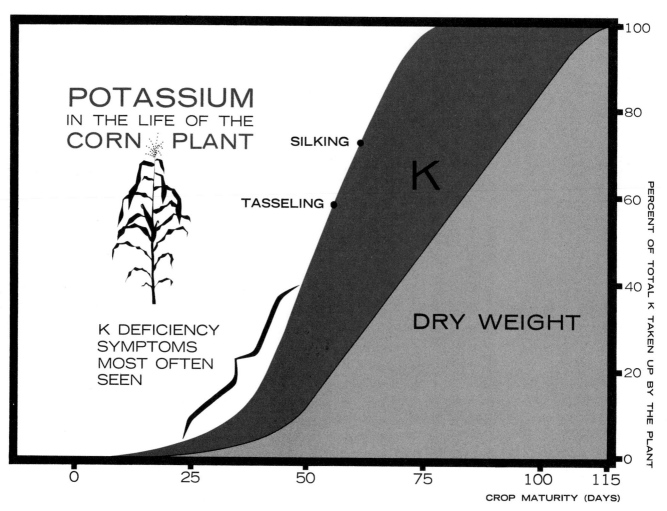

Figure 92. Early in the life of the corn plant potassium is taken up rapidly. Deficiency symptoms are most often seen from the time plants are 10 inches (25 cm) tall until shortly before tasseling. Only one-third of the potassium in above-ground parts is in the grain, hence two-thirds is returned to the soil unless the crop is cut for silage.

Effect on Manganese

Phosphorus fertilizer increases the supply of available manganese. This is important for soybeans, oats, and field beans but probably not for corn, since manganese deficiencies have not been found on corn in the field.

Potassium

Corn requires large amounts of potassium. It is essential for vigorous growth, yet never becomes a part of proteins and other organic compounds. All farm soils except sands have enormous amounts of potassium within the rooting depth of corn, but only 1 to 2 percent is available (figure 93). Soil reactions of potassium and the kinds of potassium fertilizers are far less complex and varied than for nitrogen and phosphorus. Potassium does not leach like nitrogen nor become tied up in unavailable or slowly available forms to the degree that phosphorus does. It is not much involved in biological activities in the soil. Potassium deficiencies are easy to recognize (page 262) and correcting them is inexpensive since K is the lowest cost of the major nutrients.

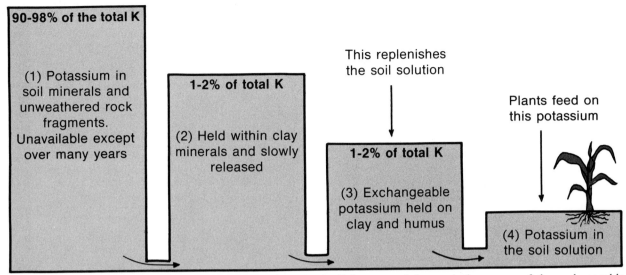

Figure 93. Corn roots absorb K⁺ from the soil solution (4). As K is removed from solution, some of the exchangeable K (3) moves to take its place. When potassium fertilizer is added to the solution, most of it moves onto the clay sheets in exchangeable position and remains available. The movement of K from within the clay minerals (2) is quite slow. When large amounts of K fertilizer are added to soils that are very low in exchangeable K, *some* of the potassium may move to position 2 and be "fixed" in very slowly available form. The K in unweathered rock fragments (1) is unavailable in the lifetime of a farmer.

Potassium Uptake by Corn

Potassium enters the corn plant as the K^+ ion. The young seedling does not need much potassium, but the rate of uptake climbs rapidly to a peak in the three weeks prior to tasseling (figure 92). Therefore, if a deficiency symptom is going to show, you will usually see it between the time the plant is a foot tall to just before tassels emerge.

In the two weeks before maturity, the total potassium in the corn plant decreases. This is probably due to the fact that K remains in solution within the plant and is washed out of the leaves by rain as soon as the leaves die.

Only about one-third of the K in aboveground parts is in the grain, 33 pounds of K_2O (27.4 pounds K) in 100 bushels (15 kilos K_2O, 12.4 kilos K). The same crop when harvested for silage contains about 3½ times as much but part of this is returned in manure.

Unlike legumes (alfalfa and clover) *corn does not* absorb more K than it needs for best yield.

Potassium Fertilizers

Potassium fertilizers are relatively simple salts which are water soluble. All have a high "salt index" which means that they produce a concentrated salt solution, and therefore must be kept 1½ to 2 inches (4 to 5 cm) away from germinating seeds unless the rate is very low.

Potassium Chloride (KC1), Muriate of Potash

The simple salt of potassium (K) and chlorine (C1) supplies 90 percent of the fertilizer K in the United States. It is white to red, granular to powdery, and usually contains 60 to 62 percent K_2O (49.8 to 51.5% K), though a small amount of 50 percent K_2O product is sold.

135

Muriate of potash can be applied directly, or mixed into dry pelleted, bulk-blend or liquid fertilizers since it is highly soluble.

The chlorine that is part of muriate forms very soluble salts with calcium, magnesium, and sodium; it rapidly leaches out so there is no large accumulation in the soil.

Muriate (KCl) is entirely satisfactory for corn though sources without chlorine are preferred for some other crops, including tobacco and potatoes. There is evidence that the chlorine in muriate reduces stalk rot of corn.

Potassium Sulfate (K_2SO_4)

This is a white salt with 48 to 50 percent K_2O (39.8 to 41.5% K) and not more than 2.5 percent chlorine.

It costs more than muriate and has no advantage for use on corn unless sulfur is known to be deficient. In that case, it may still be cheaper to use potassium chloride and buy the sulfur in some other form.

Sulfate of Potash-Magnesia ($K_2SO_4 \cdot$ $MgSO_4$ Plus Water and $MgCl_2$)

This fertilizer contains 22 to 23 percent (K_2O (18.3 to 19.2%K), 18 to 19 percent MgO (about 11% Mg) and sulfur. It is used on special crops and soils where all three nutrients — potassium, magnesium and sulfur — are needed. It supplies about 6 percent of the K used in the United States.

Potassium Nitrate (KNO_3)

This contains 13.8 percent nitrogen and up to 46.6 percent K_2O (38.7%K). It is used mainly for crops where chloride is objectionable but it has no agronomic advantage over muriate as a source of K for corn. It is well suited for use in liquid fertilizers.

Potassium Metaphosphate (KPO_3)

This extremely high analysis source of phosphorus and potassium has been produced only in a pilot plant for trial purposes. It contains 55 percent P_2O_5 and 35 percent K_2O (24% P and 29 % K).

A. Wet Soil

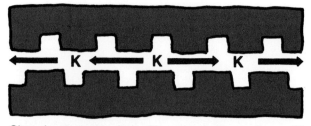

Clay sheets expanded with water between them. K^+ moves in and out freely. Though held by negative charges it can move out to replace K that is absorbed by corn roots.

B. Dry Soil

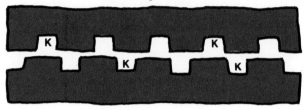

Clay sheets temporarily collapsed from lack of water between them. K is temporarily trapped and unavailable. It becomes available when soil moisture is replenished. The cycle from wet to dry can occur several times within a growing season.

C. Clay Sheets Pulled Together by K^+ and NH_4^+

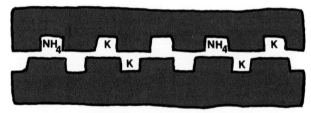

Clay sheets semi-permanently collapsed because of large amounts of K^+ and NH^+ (ammonium) ions pulling the clay from both sides. The nutrients become available over a period of a few years but are definitely less available during the first year. This is position 3, figure 93.

Figure 94. Simplified diagrams of clay sheets to show how potassium behaves in wet (A) versus dry soils (B), and how potassium and ammonium can, in soils with certain types of clay (common throughout the Corn Belt), trap themselves and each other in less available positions (C).

Soil Reactions with Potassium

Potassium can be pictured in four distinct forms in the soil (figure 93). Available K is in positions 3 and 4. It is examined in greater detail in figure 94. The greatest amount of K in the surface soil is available in a moist (but not saturated) soil. As the soil dries, some K becomes temporarily tied up between clay sheets but the K *on the outside* of the clay sheets and in solution remains available.

The mechanism shown in diagram C, by which K^+ and NH_4^+ can trap themselves and each other, is more common in soils in the northern half of the United States because these soils contain the kinds of clay minerals that allow this to happen — illite, vermiculite and montmorillonite.

Potassium is not involved in the complex biological changes in soil as described for nitrogen and phosphorus. It remains in solution in living plants and moves freely into the exchange reactions as soon as plant residues or manure are added to the soil.

Potassium Application in Relation to Crop Removal

The general soil test level for potassium can and should be raised to a high level because potassium leaches very little except on sands; it is not taken up by corn in excess amounts; and is not tied up in an unavailable form to any great extent by chemical reactions.

After the desirable level is reached, the most profitable rate at which to apply potassium will be the equivalent of slightly less than the amount removed in harvested crops. This is because some K is continuously made available from the vast slowly available forms (positions 1 and 2, figure 93). The amount of K in various crops is shown in reference table 1 , page 368.

Since one-fourth of the K is in the grain and three-fourths in the remainder of the plant, you remove three times as much when you harvest the crop for silage rather than as grain. But part of the extra K in silage is returned somewhere on the farm in manure. In order to maintain comparable long-term K balances on the whole farm, you should apply about 25 percent more K on silage corn fields. This will offset leaching losses from properly handled manure. If corn

Figure 95. Potash (KCl) greatly increased yield and reduced lodging in this experiment on soil that was low in available potassium. It is not possible in this case to separate the effects of the potassium (K) and chlorine (Cl) on lodging. Thirty pounds happened to be used in this comparison but should not be assumed to be adequate for other situations.

follows silage corn rather than grain corn and does not receive manure, you should plan to double your K fertilizer application to offset the extra K removed in silage. (You need not apply three times as much since the soil supplies some.)

The loss of potassium by soil erosion has little effect on the need for extra K in fertilizer because the inherent K content of the surface soil that erodes is no higher than in the soil that is left after erosion.

When and Where to Apply K

As pointed out in the preceding section, potassium can economically be built to a high soil test level through broadcast applications. However, on soils that are very low in available K, it is best to raise K in steps because it is believed that very large amounts

137

applied at any one time cause some to move into position 2, figure 93, and thus become relatively unavailable.

Unlike phosphorus, potassium is taken up about equally well from row or broadcast placement. When row fertilizer is applied, it is wise to include potassium along with nitrogen and phosphorus, even at medium to high soil test levels. Potassium has a high "salt index," which means that it can cause germination injury if too much is placed close to the seed; therefore it should be placed to the side and below the seed.

In a corn-soybeans cropping system, all of the K can be applied ahead of the corn. About two-thirds will be returned to the soil in the stalks, leaves and cobs for the soybeans to use.

Potassium-Nitrogen Balance

Research shows that low potassium with high nitrogen increases helminthosporium leaf blight, stalk rot, and lodging in corn, figure 95. Potassium appears to have a direct effect in reducing these troubles. Other research indicates that the chlorine in muriate of potash (KC1) also reduces stalk rot and lodging.

Potassium-Magnesium Balance

Large applications of K increase magnesium deficiencies in some crops (reported on oats in northern Michigan and on forage crops causing "grass tetany" disease). Corn is not especially sensitive to magnesium deficiency and no case has been reported where potassium reduced the yield by inducing a shortage of magnesium.

Soil Tests for Potassium

Soil tests measure the amount of K in the soil solution and in exchange positions on clay and humus (3 and 4 in figure 93).

To get the most meaningful soil test:
1. Sample carefully.
2. Never sample frozen soils! The tests are often completely misleading because they are too high. In a study in which samples

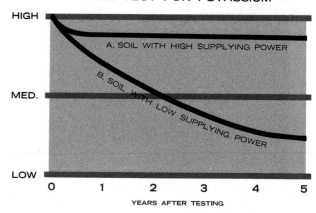

Figure 96. Different soils with the same test may supply nearly equal K for corn in the first year after the test. But sandy soils and some others with a low K-supplying power decline quickly in the following years. These soils need potassium applications more frequently.

were taken each month for four years in southern Illinois, tests in December before freezing and in March after thawing were 150 to 200, whereas tests on samples from frozen soil in February were over 300!

3. Never use heat to dry samples before sending them to the soil test laboratory. High temperatures cause the tests to be too high.

4. Determine the influence of your kind of soil on the interpretation of test results:

• Soil tests which measure exchangeable K at the beginning of the growing season are a *good guide* to available K *during the current growing season* on a wide range of soils from sandy loams to clay loams. The exchangeable K is actually held less tightly in sandy soils but this advantage is probably offset by a much larger amount of K in the rooting zone of silt loams and clays.

• Equal tests on different kinds of soil are a *poor guide* to the available *K over a 4 to 5-year period*. Soils with a high K-supplying power change little in available potassium in 5 years (when sampled in the same month each year). But sands and other soils with a low-supplying power change drastically, figure 96. These soils have been identified by soil classification experts and many states now suggest extra K for a 4 to 5-year period even though the test is high.

138

Figure 97. Research has shown that subsoil potassium is less important for corn than for alfalfa. One reason for this is that corn roots are feeding mainly in the plow layer and in zones only slightly below it during the period of most rapid uptake of K.

• Tests on moist samples (not air-dried in the laboratory before extracting) are a better guide to available K on some surface soils and on most subsoils, but this decision is made by the testing laboratories and there is nothing the farmer needs to do about it.

• The amount of exchangeable K in the deep subsoil is of less importance for corn than for alfalfa because the feeding roots of corn *during the period of most rapid uptake are concentrated in and just below the plow layer* (figure 97).

• Soil-test K changes during the growing season (figure 98). This may be due both to removal of available K by the crop and

SOIL TEST FOR POTASSIUM

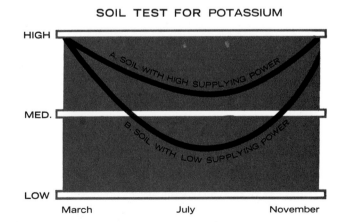

Figure 98. Tests on soil with a low natural-supplying power for K drop sharply in midseason, whereas those with a high-supplying power change less. Soil tests must be interpreted both for the type of soil and the month in which samples are taken.

139

to unknown changes in the soil. In areas where the seasonal change is large, agronomists recommend an adjustment in the interpretation of K tests for samples taken in early spring and late fall.

• If you have soils that are somewhat poorly drained, and high in organic matter and in clay, you need to aim for somewhat higher soil test levels than on other soils.

Secondary and Micronutrients for Corn

Micronutrients (also called trace or minor elements) are more challenging and more difficult to study than the major nutrients. The margin between too little, just right, and too much is extremely narrow. Most deficiencies are in the hidden hunger range and yield responses on corn, if any, are small and therefore difficult to measure.

Secondary and micronutrients differ from N, P, K in that they are deficient in specific regions and on specific soils rather than being generally required in fertilizers on nearly all soils for corn. But many small areas have been found where one or more of these nutrients will greatly increase corn yields.

Research agronomists and the fertilizer industry are giving special attention to secondary and micronutrients as one possible key to yield increases on farms where N, P, K have been applied liberally and yields are already very high.

Among the secondary nutrients, calcium and magnesium shortages have been corrected by liming programs and it has not been necessary to add them when a suitable pH level is established. Sulfur deficiencies showed up on corn in California in 1968. Seedling plants were yellow and stunted but most fields grew out of the condition. In a few fields stunting and interveinal chlorosis continued to the pre-tassel stage.

What Can Be Done Now?

In spite of the problems just mentioned, great progress has been made in assembling information about micronutrients.

The following micronutrient practices can be followed now:

• Apply corrective treatments if you live in an area where deficiencies are common.

• Learn to recognize the deficiency symptoms, and watch your fields closely during the first 4 to 6 weeks after corn comes up.

• Look for deficiency symptoms on other crops that are more sensitive than corn. This will give you warning before the nutrient is lacking for corn. Indicator crops are given for each nutrient in table 11.

• Learn the soil situation where deficiencies are most likely to occur and watch for them if you have such soils. General soil situations are described in more detail below.

• Test your soils for those micronutrients on which suitable tests have been developed. Your state agricultural extension service or commercial soil testing laboratory can advise you on this.

• Send samples for plant analysis by spectographic apparatus.

• Conduct field trials and compare results with other trials in your area.

• Avoid injury from improper placement. Follow instructions from your county extension service or fertilizer dealer. Corn is very sensitive to some micronutrients placed too near the seed.

Soils Where Deficiencies Are Most Common

Most of the serious micronutrient deficiencies in the United States occur on the following soils:

• *Strongly weathered soils* are more often low in micronutrients because they are old soils in terms of their amount of chemical and physical changes. More nutrients have leached out of the plant root zone. This condition is common in the southern states where rainfall is high and leaching occurs all year because the soil is rarely if ever frozen.

• *Coarse-textured soils* are inclined to be low in micronutrients because the rock ma-

Table 11

Occurrence and treatment of secondary and micronutrient deficiencies. For several of these nutrients, other crops are more sensitive and thus can be watched for warning signs before the soil becomes low enough for a deficiency for corn. For details, see Section 9 on Corn Troubles.

Nutrient	Soil Conditions Where Deficiency Is Most Likely	Most Sensitive Field Crops	Deficiency Symptom Observed in Corn in the Field	Suggested Corrective Treatment After Deficiency Shows
Boron	High pH, drouth Sandy Low organic matter	Alfalfa Sugar beets	No	Borax broadcast or soluble brand name products
Calcium	Very low pH	Alfalfa Clovers	Rare	Limestone according to soils tests
Chlorine	None		No	None
Copper	High organic matter	Peanuts	Yes	Copper oxide or copper sulfate in the fertilzer band
Iron	High pH, wet poorly-aerated soil, cool temperature	Beans Millet, Milo	Yes	Spray 1% iron solution, may need to be repeated. Ferrous sulfate, chelates, or brand name products
Magnesium	Low pH High K Sandy soils	Corn	Yes	Apply 25 lbs. per acre (28 kilos per hectare) of soluble form in the row, spray 20 lbs. per acre (22 kilos per hectare) magnesium sulfate (Epsom Salts), use dolomitic limestone for next year
Manganese	High pH and high organic matter	Navy Beans Oats Soybeans	Doubtful	Spray manganese sulfate or other water-soluble form at 1 lb. per acre (1.1 kilos per hectare)
Molybdenum	Low pH, strongly weathered	Alfalfa Peas	No	None
Sulfur	Low organic matter cold, wet soil	Alfalfa	Yes (California)	Sulfur in row fertilizer or in preplant nitrogen application
Zinc	Exposed subsoil, high pH, very high P, cool wet soil, sugar beets as preceding crop.	Corn	Yes	Spray ½ to 1% zinc solution; several organic and inorganic compounds. Check with local fertilizer dealer

terials from which they formed were low. Sand-size particles are mainly quartz which contains only silicon and oxygen and will not supply micronutrients even when further weathered down to the size of clay particles. Furthermore, nutrients leach rapidly from sand and gravelly soils compared with loams, silt loams, and silty clay loams.

• *Alkaline soils* tend to be low in *available,* though not in total micronutrients; the solubility of several important nutrients goes down as pH goes up (figure 124. page 181). The best balance in availability of needed micronutrients and an acceptable level of certain elements that may be toxic in large amounts (manganese, aluminum, and iron) is found between pH 6.0 and 7.0. Therefore, one of the most important steps in managing soils with respect to micronutrients is to control the pH. This can be done effectively by liming acid soils, but trying to lower the pH of alkaline soils for field crops is seldom feasible.

• *Organic soils* are often low in micronutrients, especially if they are high in pH.

Use the Results of Field Trials with Caution

If your soils have no proven deficiencies, and you apply micronutrients, the chances are good that you will not see or measure an increase in yield. Failure to get a yield does not prove that you do not have a micronutrient problem. It only shows that you did not get an observable increase this year from the particular way in which you tried the micronutrient. Another nutrient or combination of nutrients, applied at a different rate, on a different date, or in another way (in the row, or as a foliar spray to avoid soil fixation), in some different formulation (more or less soluble, chelate, or fritt), or in another season might produce a yield increase. These discouraging comments do not mean that field trials should not be run. They are meant to show the need for putting together information from basic research from plant analyses, and from a number of field trials over a period of years.

One further point needs emphasis. In the hidden hunger zone, responses to a micronutrient, if any, may be only one or two bushels. No single field trial can possibly measure such small increases with accuracy.

Prevent Deficiencies or Correct Them?

There are two points of view on the use of micronutrients where deficiencies have not been proven. One is that they should be applied regularly in amounts as a preventative. Used in this way, they postpone the time when deficiencies may occur. A complex mixture of small amounts of several nutrients is mixed in with N-P-K fertilizers for row or broadcast application (see "Premium" grades, page 96). This approach to micronutrients probably gives a farmer more peace of mind than money in his pocketbook. Micronutrients applied in this way are a partial insurance policy against *slight* deficiencies. The insurance value must be balanced against the cost of applying nutrients that are not now and perhaps will not be deficient in your soil in the forseeable future.

The other point of view is that it is more economical to locate soil areas of specific deficiencies and then apply the deficient nutrient or nutrients rather than to apply a "shot-gun" mixture. Those who support this line point out that farmers with good soils have already grown 150 to 175 bushels per acre (94 to 110 quintals per hectare) without a micronutrient mixture; also, a complex mixture often dosen't contain enough of any nutrient to correct a real deficiency.

The situation for many farmers will not

be cleared up until more research has been conducted. In the meantime, farmers must decide each year which point of view to accept as they plan their fertilizer program.

Micronutrients Are Not for Average Farmers

Except in soil areas with proven deficiencies, average farmers should be discouraged from trying micronutrient applications. After all, some of their neighbors may be growing 20 to 50 bushels (13 to 31 quintals per hectare) more than they are. Farmers with average yields need to look at N, P, K, lime, hybrids, plant population, weed control, tillage, and timeliness of operations. They should catch up with the best farmers in those practices before worrying about micronutrients.

Formulations: Soluble, Chelates, Fritts

Micronutrient deficiencies are often due not to a shortage of the nutrients in the soil, but rather to the fact that they are fixed in unavailable form (see figure 124, page181). When soluble forms are added to some soils, fixation is likely to occur, canceling the intended effect.

One way to reduce fixation by the soil is to combine micronutrients into an organic molecule. Organic ring compounds that hold metal ions this way are called *chelates*. Thus far, iron and zinc are the only ones that seem practical for corn, but the situation may change at any time with further research and improvements in technology.

Chelates cost more per pound than other sources but fewer pounds may be needed to correct a deficiency. Since this phase of soil fertility is subject to sudden change, each farmer should get the latest information from his state college of agriculture soil testing laboratory or fertilizer dealer. Instructions for use must be followed closely because some chelates are very toxic to seedlings.

Fritts are made by adding micronutrients to molten glass. After hardening, the glass is ground. The principal advantage of fritts is that they dissolve slowly and therefore an application may last several years, whereas more soluble forms would be used up, leached out, or reacted with soil and thus become unavailable. There has been little research on fritts as a source of micronutrients for corn.

Broadcast, Band, Foliar Sprays

Broadcast applications are suggested for micronutrients that don't quickly become unavailable when in contact with soil. Zinc and boron are well suited to broadcasting.

For micronutrients that are soon made unavailable by chemical reactions in high pH soils, banding with fertilizer is preferred to broadcasting. This reduces the amount of contact with soil and also keeps the micronutrients in the slightly-acid zone created by the fertilizer where they stay in more available form.

Micronutrients are well suited to foliar spray applications because the amounts needed are small. Besides, the critical shortage often lasts only a few weeks and a single spray treatment can sometimes satisfy the need. However, no state at this time recommends foliar application as the way to fully treat a micronutrient deficiency, though some recommend it as an emergency treatment for zinc deficiency. Spray treatment is recommended as a method for determining whether a deficiency symptom is due to a particular nutrient.

You will find additional suggestions for applying micronutrients in the section on deficiency symptoms and how to treat them (pages 256 to 259).

Figure 99.

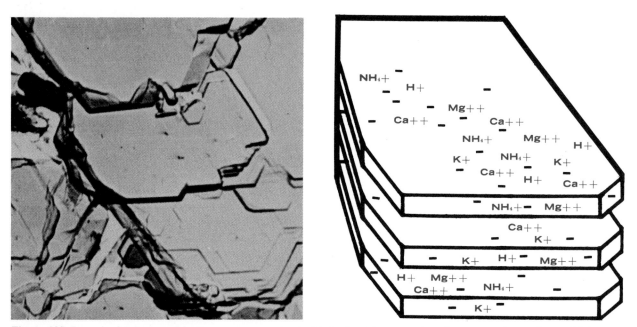

Figure 100. In a single clay particle there are many sheets. Each sheet has negative charges on the surface, which attract and hold positively charged ions. Some of the important plant nutrients, calcium (Ca^{++}), magnesium (Mg^{++}), ammonium (NH_4^+) and potassium (K^+), are held on the clay sheets, Hydrogen (H^+) is the ion that causes soil acidity.

2. KNOWING SOILS AND HOW TO USE THEM

A handful of fertile, productive soil is vastly more complex than it appears. Broadly speaking, it consists of minerals, organic matter, water and air plus a wide variety of bacteria, fungi, insects, and small animals. The mineral particles range in size from inert sand and rock fragments which do not supply plant nutrients, to medium-sized silt, and finally to microscopic clay particles which supply many of the plant nutrients and strongly influence structure, internal drainage and workability. Clay particles are extremely complex internally, figure 100. The organic matter includes fresh and partly decayed plant stalks, roots and leaves (both living and dead), molds, fungi and bacteria, small insects and animals, and humus — the end product of the decay of organic materials. Scientists are still trying to unravel the mysteries of organic matter.

This conglomeration, put together in different proportions, forms all soils, which in addition differ in slope, drainage, aeration, fertility, structure and acidity. Furthermore, except when frozen or completely dry, it is teeming with life and constantly changing as temperature rises and falls, moisture ebbs and flows and fresh plant residues, animal manures or fertilizers are added.

Yield Guides

Yield guides estimate the crop yields that top farmers can produce over a ten-year period with good growing practices. These guides do not tell you how to farm, but they can alert you to the fact that you are missing opportunities to grow higher yields. If you don't have soil maps of your farm, you can get advice from your county extension agent (farm advisor or extension director in some states) or from the Soil Conservation Service about which soils to use for reference standards.

It Helps to Know Soils by Name

In the future, more and more of the research results that farmers are looking for will be pinpointed for specific soils! Interpretations and suggested fertilizer treatments will be increasingly based on soil type.

Every modern farmer should know his major soils *by name*, not just as a sand, a "dark loam" or a "black clay." Sometimes soils that look alike on the surface are so different in the subsoil that they require completely different fertilizer and management. In other words, farms have a third dimension — depth — to go with length and width, figure 101.

Farmers don't have to go over their farms with 6-foot soil augers to check the third dimension. Soil classification experts who mapped the farm or the county have already done it. Their description of each soil includes a detailed statement on color, texture, structure, pH, and available phosphorus and potassium.

General Suggestions for Different Soils

Each soil has certain advantages and disadvantages over all others. The most successful farmer *capitalizes* on the *advantages* and *minimizes* the *disadvantages* of his soil. The following sections discuss this concept.

Sands

Sandy soils are easy to work, may be worked dry or wet, take in water rapidly, are less erosive than silts and clays, and can be worked very early in the spring and soon after summer rains.

On the other hand, they are drouthy, naturally low in fertility, have low storage capacity for applied nutrients in fertilizer, and leach more rapidly than other soils. Extremely sandy soils have not been used much for field corn unless irrigated; on these soils it is more practical to grow vegetable or market garden crops and fertilize as often as necessary.

145

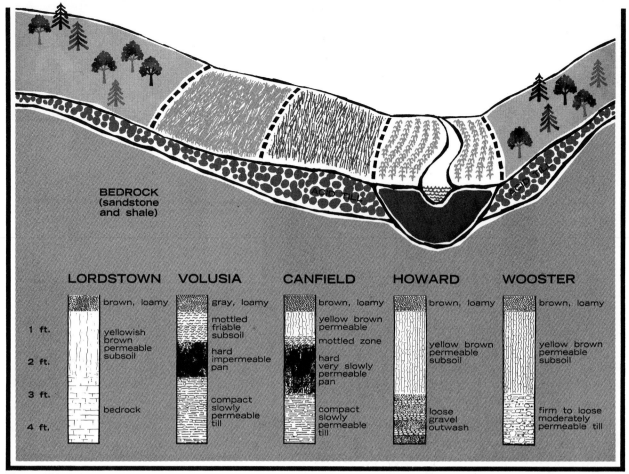

Figure 101. Soils have three dimensions — length, width, and depth. It is important to understand the third dimension, depth, because this controls the storage of available water, strongly influences rooting depth, and the supply of available P and K.

With these points in mind, what adjustments are needed for maximum profit on sandy soils?

• Plant unusually early to make the best use of stored moisture and spring rains. Early planted corn makes more growth and has a deep root system before being hit by late summer heat and drouth.

• Follow minimum tillage practices since there is no need for harrowing to firm the seedbed or break clods.

• Conserve crop residues — corn stalks, straw, legume hay, cover crop — so they will decay and improve the soil's ability to supply nutrients throughout the season. Surprising as it may seem, trying to raise the basic humus level of the plow layer will not pay (see page 149). Raising the level of organic matter in sands increases *total* water holding but has little effect on the capacity to store *available* water.

• Plant cover crops mainly to hold nitrogen from leaching during fall, winter and early spring and to prevent soil blowing. This will also add to the supply of fresh residues.

• Apply nitrogen as close as possible to the time when the crop needs it, in order to reduce loss by leaching. Sidedressing is first choice; applying just before planting is second choice. Avoid fall and early spring applications.

• Plan frequent potassium applications.

• Watch for signs of micronutrient shortages, especially (1) on soils with pH of 7.0 and (2) on strongly-acid sandy soils after they are limed heavily for the first time.

• Check the feasibility of irrigation.

• Keep the plant population 2,000 to 4,000 per acre (4,942 to 9,884 per hectare) below that on soils with better water-supplying power.

146

Silt Loams

Silt loam soils often have the best combination of water-supplying power, nutrient storage, ease of working, good drainage and aeration. They are the best soils in the Corn Belt. However, they are more easily eroded by wind and water than either sands or clays. They crust readily when overworked or allowed to become low in organic matter. Special suggestions:
- Guard against erosion.
- Reduce tillage to conserve tilth.
- Avoid working silt loams when wet because they will become cloddy in the surface and compacted under wheel tracks.

Clays and Clay Loams

These very fine-textured soils are higher in fertility than silts and sands. They are usually high in available water, less acid (in depressions they are often alkaline where surrounding knolls are medium to strongly acid) and higher in organic matter.

But they have several problems. They become cloddy when plowed either too wet or too dry. They must be worked at the right moisture content. They dry slowly in the spring and after rains. They pack badly under wheel tracks when too wet. Unless good crumb structure is maintained clays erode readily on slopes because water enters the surface more slowly and hence more runs off. Moving water easily carries off the tiny clay particles unless they are bound together into aggregates, or tiny clods.

To reduce these problems:
- Work only at the right moisture content.
- Till as little as possible to avoid breaking up the aggregates.
- Return all possible residues in order to supply freshly decomposable organic matter which provides binding material and holds the aggregates together.

If good tilth cannot be maintained with the residues from high corn yields together with reduced tillage, a sod crop should be grown once every four to six years.

Organic Soils

When the organic matter of a soil is 20 percent or more, it dominates the characteristics of the soil. Organic soils (figure 102) are easily worked, never become cloddy or crusted, are high in available water, and are originally high in available nitrogen. They do not have to be limed above a pH of about 5.5.

Frost late in the spring and early in the fall is a major problem since cold air is dense and flows into the low-lying areas where organic soils are found. Moreover, the specific heat of organic soil is less than that of mineral soil. Micronutrient deficiencies are common, especially on alkaline organic soils (see page 141). Potassium is inherently low.

A point often overlooked is that organic soils weigh only one-half to one-fourth as much as an equal volume of a mineral soil. Therefore, the root system of a corn plant is in contact with much less weight of soil; test levels may have to be maintained at a higher level than on mineral soils.

Some chemical weed killers are affected by high organic matter; farmers with organic soils should check for special recommendations before applying herbicides.

To make the best use of organic soils:
- Plant corn a little later than on mineral soils to reduce the risk of frost injury.
- Plant a little thicker than on mineral soils because organic soils usually have a high water supply.
- Watch the potassium soil test closely; organic soils are naturally lower in potassium than loams, silts and clay mineral soils, though higher in K than sands.
- Watch for micronutrient deficiencies.

Alkaline Soils

These soils are pH 7.0 or higher.
- Plan more frequent phosphorus applications to meet the needs of corn. Put less emphasis on building up high test levels of available P because an excess of phosphorus will react with calcium to form relatively

Figure 102. Organic soils (locally called muck or peat) are common in low-lying areas in all states bordering the Great Lakes. They are easy to work and have high water-holding capacity, but are subject to frost injury. Micronutrient problems are common when the pH is near neutral. Organic soils are low in potassium.

unavailable tricalcium phosphate (see table 10, page 132).

• In the row, use phosphorus fertilizers that are at least 50 percent water soluable.

• Watch for new research information on micronutrient needs. Though corn is less sensitive than certain other crops, zinc, iron, and even copper, manganese, and boron may be needed in some unusual situations.

Benefits from Proper Organic Matter Level

On Loams, Silts and Clays

• You can plow with less power.

• You can fit a better seedbed with less cloddiness.

• Rainfall enters the soil at a high rate. More water is stored for crops in drouth periods. Excess water moves through the soil quicker in the spring, allowing you to plow and plant on time, and quicker during the growing season so you can cultivate and harvest on time. Run-off which causes erosion and carries fertilizer nutrients with it is reduced.

• Prevention of crusting which hinders seedling emergence, increases run-off, and may reduce air movement into the soil.

• Fine-textured soils are less sticky when wet.

A good supply of actively decaying organ-

Figure 103. The tiny soil particles in fine-textured soils are bound together in little clumps, or aggregates, *only by the products of decaying organic matter.* Synthetic soil conditioners are available but they are too costly for use on a field scale.

ic matter produces these benefits because it supplies binding compounds which hold the fine soil particles together in little clumps or aggregates (figure 103). Clumps of particles don't pack so closely as individual particles. They make a soil crumble when worked. They increase the number of large pores or openings in the soil that provide pathways for excess water to drain rapidly. Large pores trap air to increase the oxygen supply for crop roots and to meet the needs of the soil organisms that decay residues and those that produce nitrate nitrogen.

On Sands

The reasons just given for keeping up the supply of active organic matter in loams, silts and clays don't apply for sands. But there are important reasons to concern yourself with organic matter in sandy soils. It will insure your soil enough exchange capacity to hold plant nutrients against leaching by heavy rains and supply the nutrients at a uniform rate throughout the season. Crops on well-fertilized sands that are very low in organic matter and clay are subject to "feast or famine" conditions, especially for nitrogen. Crop residues on or mixed into the surface reduce wind erosion.

Toxic Substances from Decaying Residues

Georgia researchers report poor growth when corn is planted following lespedeza sericea. They theorize that toxic organic substances may form during decomposition of some residues. No injury occurred when 4 to 6 weeks intervened between turning under the residues and planting. Similar observations have been made when certain weeds are permitted to grow in crops.

Raising As Opposed to Maintaining Organic Matter Level

It is neither practical nor necessary to significantly raise the organic matter level of your soil on a field scale. This requires an explanation because it contradicts what most people have heard.

First, let's clear up the meaning of the terms *organic matter, plant residue,* and *humus. Plant residues* are dead roots, leaves and stems not yet decayed beyond recognition. *Humus* is the relatively stable end product of decay of residues. If you could examine it under a microscope, there would be no recognizable plant tissues. *Organic matter* is the broad term we will use to include plant residues, humus and living and dead bacteria, fungi and other materials that traced at some time to living organisms.

Before land was cleared for farming, the soil's organic matter was in balance. This means that organic matter was being destroyed about as fast as it was added by the native plants. Man stepped in and changed the balance by plowing, harrowing and cultivating which increase aeration and tipped the balance toward destruction of organic matter. Pioneer farmers grew their crops on the nutrients that were released, especially nitrogen and phosphorus, by the accelerated decomposition of organic matter.

Allison estimates that the organic matter declines 40 to 50 percent in the first 25 years

Table 12

Three-year corn yields when one crop is sacrificed for green manure. (J. W. Pendleton, University of Illinois)

	Regular Corn			High population Corn (3 bushels of seed planted per acre, 188 kilos per hectare)		
		Bushels/A.	Quintals/Ha.		Bushels/A.	Quintals/Ha.
1960	(100 lbs. N)	100	63	(300 lbs. N)	0	0
1961	(80 lbs. N)	106	66	(80 lbs. N)	126	79
1962	(0 lbs. N)	142	89	(0 lbs. N)	144	90
3-Year Total	(180 lbs. N)	348	218	(380 lbs. N)	270	169

of cultivation from the virgin condition. Then the rate of decline becomes much less with equilibrium being reached in 50 to 100 years.

After equilibrium is reached, soil humus no longer serves as a source of nitrogen. Net nitrogen is available for crops only when humus is being depleted. After equilibrium, you must add a unit of nitrogen for each unit you expect to have for the crop.

By now, most agricultural soils have reached or are moving toward a new, somewhat lower organic matter balance. Modern farmers have offset the organic matter lost from tillage and crop removal by adding fertilizers, especially nitrogen. To restore the original level or even markedly raise the present level would require adding enormous amounts of crop residues, no crop removal, and little or no plowing and fitting, since this burns up organic matter. Plowing under 5 tons (10,000 pounds) of residues that contain 1.5 percent nitrogen will theoretically raise the level of the surface 7 inches (17.5 cm) only 1/10 of one percent after the residues are completely decayed. In practice the gain may be even less. An experiment on a sandy soil in New York showed the great amounts of residues needed to raise the organic matter level. In that experiment, 1000 tons of stable manure per acre over a 25-year period raised the organic matter level less than 2 percent.

A few years ago, there was interest in planting corn very thick (100,000 to 200,000 plants per acre, 247,100 to 494,200 per hectare), fertilizing it heavily and plowing it under for green manure. The data in table 12 shows why this is completely uneconomical.

The soil improving value of the green manure crop was shown mainly in the first year after plowing it under. At the end of three years the yield deficit for giving up the entire crop for one year was 78 bushels per acre (48.9 quintals per hectare). There is no way that this could be made up in later years.

Why isn't it necessary to raise the organic matter level? Because you can achieve the same end by regularly turning under large amounts of fresh residues — and keeping the nitrogen level high enough to assure a steady, rapid rate of decay. As residues rot, they supply compounds that do the job which high organic matter accomplished in virgin soils; they bind soil particles into clumps, improve tilth and water intake, and make a more uniform supply of nutrients available to crops through the growing season.

This may seem to be a play on words, but technically there is a big difference between trying to raise the general level of soil organic matter and in making sure you have plenty of fresh residues actively decaying in the soil. No practical farming system will raise the level much, if any, but in spite of that, modern farming with high yields, optimum fertility, and reduced tillage will increase crop yields.

Organic levels can, of course, be raised

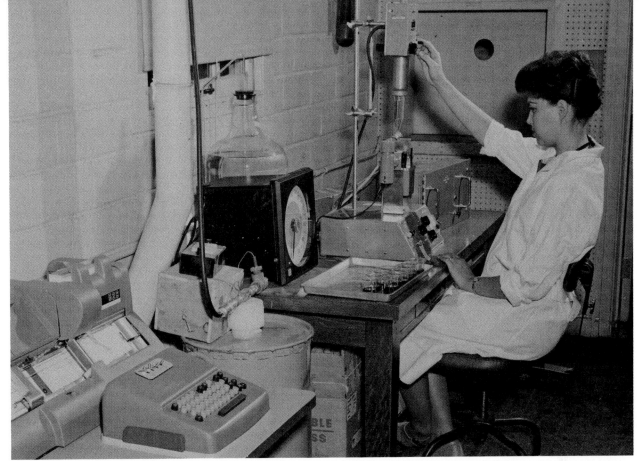

Figure 104. Soil test results from a qualified laboratory are an important step in planning profitable fertility treatments. This laboratory uses a punch-card system to enable a machine to analyze information and develop suggested treatments. The test has meaning only in relation to calibrations based on research showing responses to applied fertilizer.

in small areas — gardens, flower beds, around shrubbery — by bringing in large amounts of residues.

3. USING SOIL TESTS AND FERTILIZER RECORDS

Though soil tests are not a perfect solution to the problem of determining a given soil's needs, there is no substitute for them. The following unit of this section explains soil tests, tells how to take samples, and how to interpret and use the test results.

What Tests Can Be Made?

Tests can be made for most nutrients and for some soil characteristics that influence fertility requirements. However, all tests are not equally useful. Table 13 indicates the reliability of the tests for various nutrients. Some laboratories determine the amount of organic matter as a guide to nitrogen supply-

Table 13

The reliability of soil tests for predicting various nutrient responses. For several of the micronutrients, and perhaps some secondary nutrients, spectrographic analyses of plant tissues will be more useful than soil tests to indicate future treatments.

Test	Good	Fair	Poor
Lime requirement	X		
Phosphorus	X		
Potassium	X		
Calcium		X	
Zinc		X	
Magnesium		X	X
Copper (organic soils)			X
Nitrogen			X
Chlorine			X
Iron			X
Manganese			X
Molybdenum			X
Sulfur			X

ing power (discussed in following paragraphs) and to aid in herbicide recommendations. Base exchange capacity is tested mainly as an aid to liming and potassium needs.

What Tests Do You Need?

For the vast majority of farmers the most important tests are those for lime, phosphorus and potassium requirements. For certain soils and crops a magnesium test is helpful. In a small but growing number of cases, a zinc test can be recommended. Other micronutrient tests are being improved and will have a growing place in the soil testing program. Your state extension service or commercial soil testing laboratory can give you up-to-date information on the status of the various tests for your conditions.

Asking a laboratory to run tests for all of the major, secondary and micronutrients probably won't help you, since a test is of no value unless it can be interpreted. No test can be interpreted until research has been conducted to show the response obtained when the nutrient is added. Because many people misunderstand this point, laboratories are asked to make tests for which they cannot give an interpretation. These tests are costly to the farmer and serve no useful purpose.

Nitrogen tests are worthy of some special explanation. A lot of research effort has gone into the development and calibration of nitrogen tests but the efforts have been quite unsuccessful. This is because nitrogen that will be supplied by the soil is mainly in the soil organic matter and must be released by biological processes before it can be used by crops. These processes are influenced by temperature, moisture, aeration, pH, compaction, and the previous crop. Also, nitrogen, when it becomes available, is subject to loss by leaching and denitrification. A soil test, unfortunately, cannot predict several of these factors.

In recent years, several states have discontinued nitrogen tests as a guide to nitrogen fertilizer suggestions. Some laboratories continue to measure the amount of organic matter and then estimate available nitrogen from general knowledge about the different rates at which organic matter releases nitrogen in sands, silts and clays.

It should be apparent from this brief survey of testing methods that no generally acceptable nitrogen test has been developed. Most states prefer to estimate the optimum nitrogen to apply from information on soil type, previous crop, and recent fertilizer and manure applications. The states that make nitrogen tests also rely heavily on these factors when they prepare suggestions for nitrogen fertilizer. In conclusion: farmers should not expect a nitrogen test to be as reliable as those for lime, phosphorus, and potassium.

A new approach adapted to irrigated soils is to take a sample to the depth of rooting and determine the amount of nitrates in solution as a guide to the amount of nitrogen fertilizer to apply. One state suggested, for example, where the yield goal is 160 bushels per acre (100 quintals per hectare), to apply 240 pounds of nitrogen per acre (269 kilo per hectare) for a nitrate test below 50, and only 100 pounds (112 kilos) with a test of 250 to 300.

Research has begun to see whether this approach is useful in humid areas. The technique is to sample between the time of planting and the latest date that would supply results for sidedressing the nitrogen indicated. It cannot be as precise as under irrigation because farmers have less control over the amount of water that enters the soil to cause loss by leaching or denitrification.

Take Samples Correctly or Not At All

Unless samples are properly taken, the results obviously cannot lead to a correct plan; poorly-taken samples are often worse than no test results because they cause you to take the wrong action.

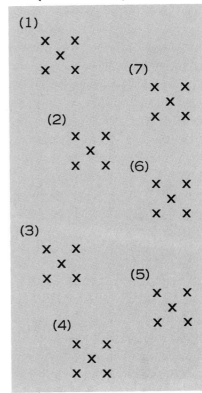

40-acre (16 hectare) Field

20-acre (8 hectare) Field

Figure 105. This regular pattern of sampling is suggested by one state for fields that apparently have uniform fertility and have been uniformly cropped and fertilized in recent years. Each numbered sample consists of 5 separate small samples mixed together. The location of each sample should be carefully recorded on a field map so that different limestone and fertilizer treatments can be applied if called for by the test results. In fields that are obviously not uniform, each different type area should be represented by one or more samples (each made up of several subsamples) depending on the size of each area.

Here are some general guides for taking samples in various situations:

Soils tests even *in the most uniform-looking fields* vary as much as 50 percent if the fields have been limed and fertilized several times. One teaspoonful of soil in the test tube may represent 4,000 tons or more. It had better be the right teaspoonful! Therefore, it pays to take a few more samples than necessary rather than risk undersampling. Saving money by taking only a few samples is being penny wise and pound foolish. The cost of taking and testing extra samples once every four to six years is small compared to the money that will be spent for fertilizer and limestone based on the test results. The cost is even smaller compared with the value of

larger crop yields resulting from proper fertilizer treatments.

Figure 105 shows the patterns recommended by one midwestern state for fields that appear to be uniform. Different soil areas should always be sampled separately.

Don't combine samples from parts of a field that have been cropped, fertilized, limed or manured differently in the past few years. Why? Because the composite test won't give you the information you need to put different amounts of fertilizer or lime on parts of the field with different needs.

On fields that have been heavily fertilized in the previous few years, you should take more samples and combine them less than on fields that have received little fertilizer.

Several states have research showing that test results vary more following recent heavy fertilizer treatment. This is due partly to uneven spreading but even more to incomplete mixing of fertilizer through the plow layer. This results in more variability among samples, so you need the results from more samples to evaluate the fertility situation.

Avoid sampling in the crop row or in the fertilizer band. Nutrients will be low in the row and extra high in the fertilizer band.

What is the proper depth to sample? Stay within the plow layer which may be from 6 to 10 inches (15 to 25 cm), depending on how you plow. In non-plowing systems 6 inches (15 cm) is likely a suitable depth. Difference in sampling depth is a major cause of variation in test results among samples that are taken in a single day, but is an even more important cause of variation when tests are compared with those taken in previous years by a different person. The explanation is simple. Phosphorus, potassium and limestone stay mainly within the layer of soil that is mixed by tillage. Suppose the plow layer is seven inches (10.5 cm) deep. If you sample to that depth you are entirely within the fertilized zone. Samples that are taken to a depth of ten inches (25 cm) will consist of nearly one-third soil that was below the fertilized zone and so test results will probably be much lower.

When fields are chiseled in place of plowing, some surface applied fertilizer is mixed to the depth of chiseling but *most remains in the top 3 inches (7.5 cm)*. With zero tillage phosphorus and potassium remain mostly within the surface inch (2.5 cm).

What about subsoil samples? As pointed out earlier, the complete soil description includes general information on subsoil fertility. If that information is not available, it is a good idea to take a few samples between twelve and twenty-four inches deep (⅓ to ½ meter) the first time a field is sampled. Tests won't change much in that zone over the next twenty years and, therefore, it is not necessary to sample the subsoil each time the plow layer is retested.

In summary, here is an ideal sampling and testing program:
- The first time a field is tested, sample very completely and composite very little. Take a few subsoil samples.
- Make a map of the field showing where each sample was taken.
- With your samples send a complete record on soil type, previous crops, recent fertilizer, lime and manure application. Indicate any special problems you are having. The person who interprets test results urgently needs this background information in order to make the best interpretation for you.
- Keep a yearly record of fertilizer, manure and lime applications.
- Retest in 4 to 6 years. Continue keeping both the test results and treatment records for each field.

What if the test results do not agree with those taken four to six years ago? The usual procedure is to blame the laboratory. In some cases, that is where the blame belongs, but often there is another explanation. The laboratory may be using new and better chemical techniques which produce a different, more accurate test. Or the test levels that were called high, medium and low have been redesignated. Most frequently the correct explanation lies in one of the following: a difference in depth of sampling, the effect of fertilizer applied in intervening years, a variation in the time of year (pH and potassium tests tend to be lower in midsummer), or the effect of the previous crop.

Interpreting Soil Test Results

The only purpose for testing soil is to help decide on the correct fertilizer and limestone treatments either for the current year or for a long-term plan. Ideally, an experienced agronomist would take the test results back to the farmer and discuss his whole crop and fertility plan with him. In some cases, the county extension agent can do this. More and more fertilizer dealers are helping to perform this service. But it's not always possible.

In order to handle the growing number of samples tested, several laboratories in state agricultural colleges are using electronic computers to "digest" all of the information on soil type, field history, and test results, and then supplying a set of fertilizer suggestions. These suggestions are sent directly to the farmer, his county extension agent or fertilizer dealer.

What if the tests for a single field range from low to high? Most laboratories recommend that a few of the high tests be discarded because they probably represent samples from a fertilizer band or similar nontypical situation. If high, medium and low tests appear to fall into regular patterns in a field, this indicates that they came from different soil types or from areas that had received different previous treatments. Where such areas are large enough, they can be fertilized or limed separately, each according to the optimum rate. If the high, medium and low tests are mixed within the field, probably the average of the lower half is the best guide for fertilizing and liming.

An interesting way to report soil tests is to show where they fall on the crop yield curve (figure 106). This method of reporting has the virtue of showing what potential there might be for improvement.

Most laboratory reports suggest fertilizer treatments for above-average management.

The potassium tests on a soil that is low in potassium-supplying power may drop from 250 on March 1 to 150 by July 1. Part of the change is due to crop removal of potassium but part may also be due to changes within the soil itself. Obviously, the help of a trained soils specialist will be needed to make the proper interpretation of tests on soils that change markedly through the season.

People who are unfamiliar with testing

Where Are You on the Yield Curve?

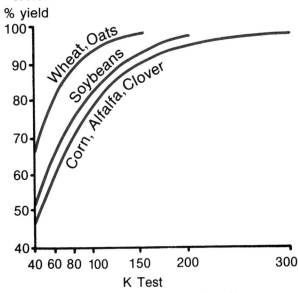

Figure 106. These yield curves are part of a soil test report. Yield curves show the percent of possible yield at different K soil test levels. The person who reports the soil tests marks the point on each yield curve that represents the farmer's soil test level for available potassium. An appropriate curve is also used for phosphorus. The farmer can immediately see how far he is from optimum yields with his current fertility level.

often mistakenly believe that the test results are shown in actual pounds or kilos of nutrients that will be available throughout the growing season. Soil tests are all too often used to set up an accounting system for fertilizing corn. It goes like this: a 125-bushel crop requires x pounds of a nutrient. The soil test shows y pounds in the soil. Plant residues and manure will furnish z pounds. Therefore the amount to be added in fertilizer is x minus the sum of $y + z$, taking into account, of course, that corn can get only part of the fertilizer nutrients (15 to 20 percent of the phosphorus, for example) that are applied.

Soil tests cannot be plugged into such an equation. Using phosphorus as an example, the following sentences explain why this is true:

— The extracting solution dissolves *some* but not all of the chemical compounds that contain phosphorus. The amount of each that is dissolved depends on the strength of the extracting solution, how much of it is used per gram of soil, and how long the dissolving process is allowed to continue.

— Laboratories use different chemical extracting procedures and therefore get different amounts of phosphorus from the same soil.

— The test is run for only a few minutes on a soil sample which is taken only from the plow layer, whereas the corn plant feeds for several months, as deep as 5 to 7 feet (1⅔ to 2⅓ meters) and in subsoils that are different from one soil region to another.

What then does the test mean? *The test takes on meaning only when it is calibrated for different soils and crops according to their responses to the applied nutrient.*

The correct way to use soil test results is to look at the calibration of the test by soil type which was developed mainly by your state experiment station and then, based on your own field experiments showing response to applied nutrients, choose the amount of fertilizer that you think will be most profitable.

Who Tests Soils and Interprets Results?

County agents and vo-ag teachers:

In some states, the county extension agents (also called farm advisors or extension directors) supervise soil testing laboratories, report and interpret results, and suggest treatments. In other states, samples and test results are channeled through the county office but the tests are made in a central state laboratory where computers can be used to print the results and interpretations. In either case, the main purpose of the extension agent is educational. Many county agents like to use the soil tests as a means of reviewing the whole farming program with the farmer and offering a broad educational service to him.

Although vocational agriculture teachers work mainly with and through their students, some have broadened their efforts to include help in interpreting soil tests and developing fertility plans.

Fertilizer dealers and manufacturers:

An increasing number of fertilizer dealers are offering a soil testing service to their customers. Some dealers have their own laboratory and a person trained to interpret the tests and suggest fertilizers and lime. Others send the samples to a private commercial laboratory or to a laboratory operated by the manufacturer from whom they buy their fertilizer. These laboratories are usually modern and well equipped.

Fertilizer dealers have learned that they have to earn the confidence and respect of farmers in the interpretation of the test results and the fertilizer treatments that they suggest. They have to overcome the natural inclination of farmers to be suspicious of their recommendations. As a result, their testing services are generally quite reliable.

Farmers often *look too much at the price* and *not enough at the helpful services* that a well-informed dealer can supply. Many local dealers have plant food specialists trained in agronomy who keep up-to-date visiting experiment fields and attending training schools run by the cooperative extension service and company agronomists.

These trained men help farmers with their crop growing problems throughout the season. Some keep field records on fertilizer applied to each field. It's hard to put a dollar value on these services and reliable information, but can anyone doubt that lack of information or the wrong information can be very costly?

The most progressive local dealers sell "solutions to problems" rather than merely tons of fertilizer. Alert farmers can benefit from seeking out these dealers.

Commercial soil testing laboratories:

Because farmers are requesting more complete services in soil sampling, and testing, and plant analyses for fertility planning, there are increasing numbers of commercial laboratories that provide these services.

Some of them prepare elaborate reports and keep complete fertilizer records for each field. This can be an extremely valuable service, which will allow the farmer to give more attention to other important decisions in his farming operation.

Base Exchange Capacity

Exchange capacity is a measure of the number of positive ions that can be retained by a unit amount of a soil. The *base* exchange capacity of your soil is important because it reflects inherent fertility, ability to retain ammonium and potassium fertilizers, and the quantity of limestone needed to correct acidity. Exchange capacity is a result of the activity of negative electrical charges on soil clay and matter (figure 100). If you draw a comb quickly through your hair, it will attract bits of paper or dust. In a like manner, clay and organic matter in soil attract positively charged ions such as potassium (K^+), ammonium (NH_4^+), calcium (Ca^{++}), magnesium (Mg^{++}), and hydrogen (H^+).

For practical purposes, the coarser particles in soil (gravel, sand and silt) do not affect exchange capacity or soil fertility because they have so little exposed surface and do not have a charged surface compared to clay and organic matter.

Clay particles are not just ground more finely than silt and sand. Clay minerals are composed of many layers, like a deck of cards (figure 100) held together by tiny, invisible strings — electric charges. Thus, they not only have exterior surfaces but also internal surfaces like the front and back of cards; these attract and hold, then later release, positively charged ions. If it were not for this property, soils could not store large amounts of nutrients and you would have to fertilize more frequently. This is the situation on sandy soils that are low in organic matter.

Some soil testing laboratories measure base exchange capacity and then suggest the *ideal* proportion of potassium, magnesium, calcium and hydrogen for the soil. However, there is controversy over the usefulness of this approach: those in opposition to it feel it is not widely applicable because optimum yields can be obtained over a wide range in the relative proportions of nutrients. Moreover, many researchers feel that careful calibration of soil tests for fertilizer responses make it unnecessary to use the base exchange capacity as a guide to fertilizer applications.

Also, the base exchange capacity of soil cannot be an absolute figure because it depends somewhat on the laboratory procedures used to measure it. Nevertheless, the approximate exchange capacity is a helpful guide to the amount of anhydrous ammonia that can safely be applied to a particular soil and the quantity of limestone that is needed.

4. THE NUTRIENTS YOUR SOIL CAN SUPPLY

The object of applying fertilizer is to supplement *in the most profitable way* those nutrients that the soil itself can supply. It should be obvious that no one can run a soil test, push a slide rule, and come up with the pounds or kilos of plant nutrients that the complex soil system will supply to a corn crop. Remember that the soil test is usually based on samples from the plow layer only, whereas the root system of corn extends deep into the subsoil. Furthermore, the soil test is made at one time, but the corn plant feeds for 100 to 180 days.

"What nutrients can a soil supply this year?" A reliable, though still imperfect, answer lies in looking at the results of agronomic research conducted to calibrate soil tests by kinds of soils. In time, calibration will progress from general soil areas to important specific soils and lastly to less important soils. To use information based on calibration of soil tests, you must know the names of your soils, preferably from having a detailed map of your farm.

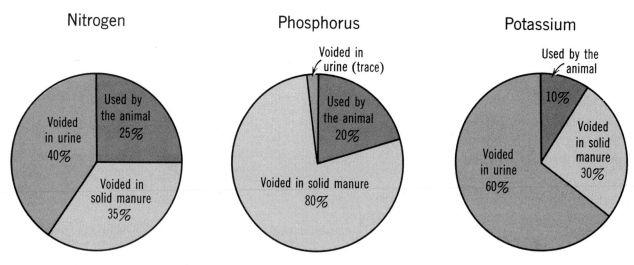

Figure 107. The fate of N, P, and K in feed eaten by livestock.

Table 14

Tons of manure produced each year by farm animals per 1000 pounds (455 kilos) of live weight (L. I. Van Slyke, "Fertilizers and Crop Production," Orange Judd Publishing Co., New York, 1932, pp 220 and 225.)

	Solid		Animal Excrement Liquid		Total		Bedding		Bedding Plus Excrement	
	English Tons	Metric Tons	English Tons	Metric Tons	English Tons	Metric Tons	English Tons	Metric Tons	English Tons	Metric Tons
Horse	7.2	6.5	1.8	1.6	9.0	8.2	3.0	2.7	12	10.9
Cow	9.5	8.6	4.0	3.6	13.5	12.3	1.5	1.4	15	13.6
Pig	9.15	8.3	6.1	5.5	15.25	13.9	3.0	2.7	18.25	16.6
Sheep	4.15	3.8	2.1	1.9	6.25	5.7	3.5	3.2	9.75	8.9
Hen					4.25	3.9				

Table 15

The composition of fresh animal manure. (L. I. Van Slyke, "Fertilizers and Crop Production," Orange Judd Publishing Co., New York, 1932, p. 218.)

Animal	Manure	Water	N	P₂O₅	P	K₂O	K
Horse	Solid, 80%	75	0.55	0.30	.13	0.40	.33
	Urine, 20%	90	1.35	Trace		1.25	1.04
	Whole manure	78	0.70	0.25	.11	0.55	.46
Cow	Solid, 70%	85	0.40	0.20	.09	0.10	.08
	Urine, 30%	92	1.00	Trace		1.35	1.12
	Whole Manure	86	0.60	0.15	.07	0.45	.37
Sheep	Solid, 67%	60	0.75	0.50	.22	0.45	.37
	Urine, 33%	85	1.35	0.05	.02	2.10	1.74
	Whole Manure	68	0.95	0.35	.15	1.00	.83
Swine	Solid, 60%	80	0.55	0.50	.22	0.40	.33
	Urine, 40%	97	0.40	0.10	.04	0.45	.37
	Whole Manure	87	0.50	0.35	.15	0.40	.33
Hens	Whole manure	55	1.00	0.80	.35	0.40	.33

Replace the Nutrients Removed by the Crop As a Guide to Fertilizer Rates?

This sounds easy and therefore is very attractive, but the idea is not sound in principle. It ignores the great differences among soils in their capacity to supply nutrients. Besides, it is not based on the economics of fertilizer use — and these are what determine profit.

For profit from fertilizers, farmers need information not included in an assessment of the nutrients removed by a crop. It has already been pointed out that soil tests calibrated by field research provide usable estimates of the contributions of soil minerals and soil humus. These contributions are not shown on soil test reports in pounds or kilos of nutrients supplied by the soil but rather as (a) percent of possible yields or (b) most profitable amounts of nutrients to add at different soil test levels. These approaches are not designed to evade the issue, they simply recognize the fact that no test can measure the supply of nutrients throughout the root zone over the whole growing season.

What further information can be developed on the nutrients that are available in the soil? Usable estimates can be made on the nutrients from stable manure, plant residues, and carryover fertilizer from previous years.

Manure

Scarcity of fertilizer and higher prices beginning in 1973 have made manure more valuable. Farmers are more concerned about conserving it and even hauling it greater distances for field spreading. At the same time regulations are in force or pending on manure storage and application.

Figure 107 shows what happens to nitrogen, phosphorus and potassium in feed consumed by large animals.

Table 14 shows the amount of manure produced by livestock.

Table 15 gives average composition of manure when voided by the animal. When

Figure 108. Many types of spreaders are available to handle liquid manure from livestock operations.

manure is spread each day as produced, all of the phosphorus and potassium are returned to the soil except in the case of winter applications on sloping, frozen fields where some soluble nutrients are carried off. Nitrogen is lost to the air as ammonia, NH_3, whenever fermented manure lies on the soil surface and dries out. The longer it has been stored before spreading, the greater the loss. Manure that has been stored should be worked into the soil right after spreading, if possible.

In an Ohio study, manure that was left in an open barnyard during January, February and March lost 30 percent of its nitrogen, 24 percent of its phosphorus and 59 percent of its potassium before being spread.

In a covered shed or feedlot, losses are about one-half as great as in open storage for nitrogen, one-fourth as great for phosphorus, and one-twelfth for potassium.

Losses in feedlots in the Great Plains area are considerably lower than in the Midwest because of less rainfall.

To estimate the nutrient contribution of manure to the overall farm fertility plan, see table 16. Information is not yet available on nitrogen losses from manure stored in lagoons or underground pits. Because the ni-

Table 16.

Estimated percentages of nutrients in farm manure that are actually added to the soil under different management in areas with annual rainfall of 36 to 40 inches (about 1 meter).

	% Actually Returned to the Soil		
	N	P	K
Spread daily (all liquid saved)	75	100	100
Open barn lot 3 months	50	75	40
Open barn lot 6 months	30	60	20

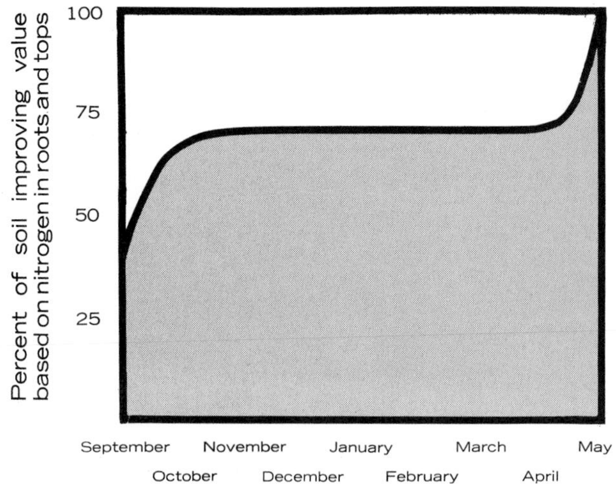

Figure 109. The approximate soil improving value of spring-seeded alfalfa and clovers for green manure from September 1 to May 1 in the central Corn Belt. Note that you could obtain nearly 75 percent of the soil improving value by plowing after October 1 in the seeding year. In this Ohio study there was a further increase of nitrogen from May 1 to May 15. But delaying plowing for this extra nitrogen is not recommended because the additional legume growth reduces subsoil moisture and results in later than optimum planting dates.

trogen converts to ammonia in this type of storage, much will be lost unless some "preservative" such as superphosphate of phosphoric acid is added to combine it into nonvolatile compounds. If not lost in storage, the ammonia will be lost when spread on the land unless worked in or covered at once. Phosphorus and potassium will be saved.

The commonly used figures for nutrients in a ton of fresh cattle manure with a moderate amount of bedding are 10 pounds (4.5 kilos) of nitrogen, 2.2 pounds (1 kilo) phosphorus (5 pounds or 2.3 kilos P_2O_5), and 8.3 pounds (3.8 kilos) of potassium (10 pounds or 4.5 kilos K_2O).

Manure also provides small amounts of all micronutrients; the source of these is feed and bedding. Micronutrient deficiencies are seldom found on fields that regularly receive liberal applications of manure.

Not all the nutrients in manure are available in the first year. Wisconsin agronomists suggest that an English ton of average manure can replace 4 pounds of fertilizer nitro-

gen, 1.54 pounds of phosphorus (3.5 pounds P_2O_5) and 5.8 pounds of K (7 pounds K_2O) during the year in which it is applied. The equivalent in kilos would be these figures divided by 2.2.

Most research information shows that manure should be valued in terms of the nutrients it contains rather than for unknown and obscure growth promoting factors.

Nutrients from Stalks, Straw and Green Manure Crops

No one can predict exactly how many nutrients will become available for this year's crop from plant residues from last year's crop. The amounts are affected by the kind and amount of residues, whether the residues are worked in or left on the soil surface, the time of plowing (figure 109), and soil conditions. Some general guides for nitrogen (table 17) may be helpful when compared to situations in specific fields. When very high yields of legumes are obtained, the amounts of nitrogen are much higher. At Dixon, Illinois the 12-year average effect

160

Table 17

A guide to the average amount of nitrogen available during the growing season from different preceding crops. If this data is used as a guide for the amount of nitrogen fertilizer to apply, it should be adjusted for above or below average growth, for unusually warm, cool or wet weather in the late fall and early spring which influence nitrification, denitrification and leaching.

| | Nitrogen that may be available by: | | | | | |
| | May 1 | | July 1 | | September 1 | |
Crop Residue	Lb./A.	Kg/ha.	Lb./A.	Kg/ha.	Lb./A.	Kg/ha.
Biennial sweet clover, seeding year, excellent growth, plowed October 1 to April 1	40	45	60	67	70	78
Alfalfa, red clover, ladino clover (same conditions as listed under sweet clover)	30	34	40	45	50	56
Alfalfa harvested for hay 1 year or more, plowed before April 1	30	34	60	67	80	90
50% legume — 50% grass meadow, plowed before April 1	20	22	40	45	60	67
Corn stalks, wheat or oat straw from a well-fertilized crop. Plowed early fall (before October 1)	0	0	10	11	20	22
Plowed late fall to April 1	-20	-22	0	0	20	22
Soybeans, navy beans	0	0	15	17	20	22
Sugar beets	0	0	15	17	20	22
Average stable manure (10 English tons, 9 metric)	20	22	30	34	40	45

from a legume catch-crop was equivalent to 125 pounds of nitrogen fertilizer per acre (140 kilos per hectare) on first year corn and ⅔ as much for the second corn crop.

Iowa agronomists have raised their estimate of the fertilizer equivalent from growing soybeans from 20 pounds of N (22 kg per hectare) up to 30 for a 40-bushel bean yield and 40 for a 50-bushel yield (33 and 44 kilos). Note that the time of plowing or otherwise killing the plants and the relative nitrogen content of residues affect the time at which nitrogen becomes available through the season. This is related to the carbon-nitrogen ratio (see also figure 84, page 117).

All of the potassium in crop residues is available during the first season because the potassium remains in water-soluble form within the plant. Its release is, therefore, not dependent on decay of the residues. Corn stalks and small grain residues supply considerable amounts of potassium for the following crop. But, of course, when looked at from the long-term viewpoint, they only return what they took from the soil in the

first place. In other words, those crops help to rapidly recycle available potassium through the crop and soil but do not actually add to the soil supply.

The availability of phosphorus in plant residues is determined by how fast they decay because phosphorus, like nitrogen, is an integral part of the plant tissues and is not water soluble as potassium is. The phosphorus in legumes, therefore, is quickly made more available than P in corn stalks, straw and mature grass. Research workers have often noted that corn responds less to phosphorus following alfalfa or clover, than following corn. However, this is a temporary effect limited to the first succeeding crop. In the long run, it is the amount of nutrients leaving the farm which determines the drain on soil fertility.

How Much Carryover of Nutrients?

The amount of plant nutrients carried over to the following year in forms which can be used by corn is impossible to estimate with precision. But you should make use of the

Table 18

Estimated average carryover of nutrients in fertilizer and manure in Iowa from application in the previous year. The figures are based on normal rainfall and normal crop residues in the previous year. (Iowa State University). To convert P to P_2O_5 multiply by 2.29; K to K_2O multiply by 1.2

Nitrogen				Phosphorus				Potassium					
Applied		Carryover		Applied		Carryover		Applied		Carryover			
										Only Grain Removed		Whole Plant Removed	
lbs/a	kg/ha	lbs/a	kg/ha	lbs/a	kg/ha	lbs/a	kg/ha	lbs/a	kg/ha	lbs/a	kg/ha	lbs/a	kg/ha
40	45	4	4.5	18	20	7	8	33	37	13	15	0	0
60	67	10	11	26	29	13	15	50	56	23	26	3	3
80	90	20	22	35	39	21	24	66	74	35	39	10	11
100	112	33	37	44	49	29	33	83	93	49	55	20	22
120	135	47	53	53	59	37	41	100	112	63	71	32	36
140	157	60	67										
160	179	72	81										

best available estimates. Table 18 gives the estimates used by Iowa State University when reporting soil tests and suggesting fertilizer treatments. If unfavorable weather prevented normal crop growth in the previous year, larger amounts of potassium and phosphorus would be carried over.

Where leaching (sands) or denitrification (poorly drained, high pH) are large, there may be little carryover from fertilizer nitrogen, figure 110.

Whether extra carryover should be allowed for nitrogen after a dry growing season depends on the weather conditions that influence leaching and denitrification during the fall, winter and early spring. In other words, the conditions *after* the crop was harvested may be as important as conditions during the growing season last year in determining the carryover of nitrogen!

If both the growing season and post-harvest period were very dry, then the amount of nitrogen carryover can be increased beyond that given in table 18.

You can adjust the nitrogen carryover figures for your own situation on the basis of where you are on the map, page 114.

5. APPLYING FERTILIZER WHERE AND WHEN IT COUNTS

On Responsive Crops Like Corn

More and more farmers plan to use all the fertility that pays on all of their crops. But if you have to choose which crop to fertilize fully and which to skimp on, put the fertilizer on the crop that best combines high acre value and good yield response. To illustrate this point: corn should get fertilizer before oats because a bushel of corn is worth nearly twice as much as a bushel of oats. It also gets fertilizer before soybeans because beans respond less than corn to direct fertilization when the fertility level is medium or above.

The situation is different, of course, when corn is compared with other high-value, responsive crops like suger beets, tobacco, tomatoes, and in some cases alfalfa. Those crops may have a higher priority for fertilizer than corn. At the present time, corn receives more fertilizer than the next four crops combined.

There is a common mistaken impression that nitrogen delays maturity in all crops.

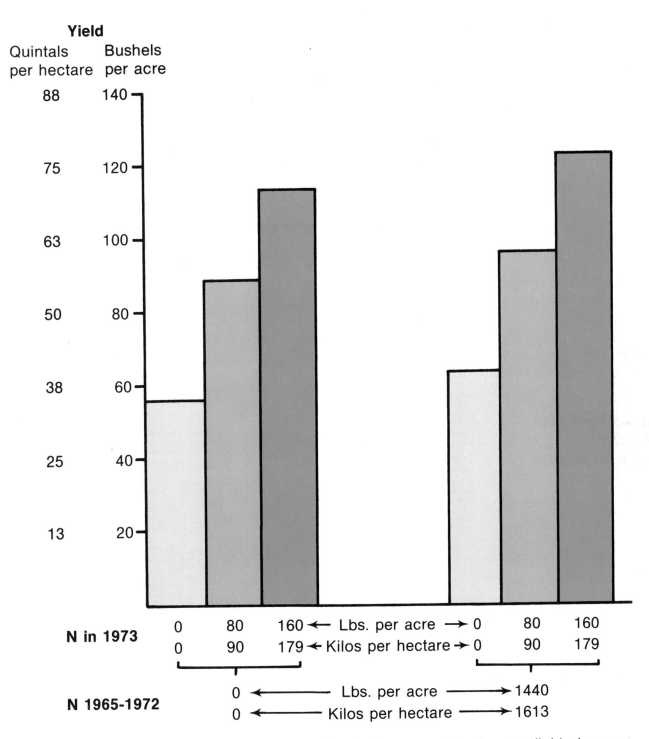

Figure 110. Effectiveness of residual nitrogen from 8 annual applications compared to nitrogen applied in the current year for corn. DeKalb, Illinois, 1973. The soil is imperfectly drained and near neutral in pH and loss by denitrification evidently was very large.

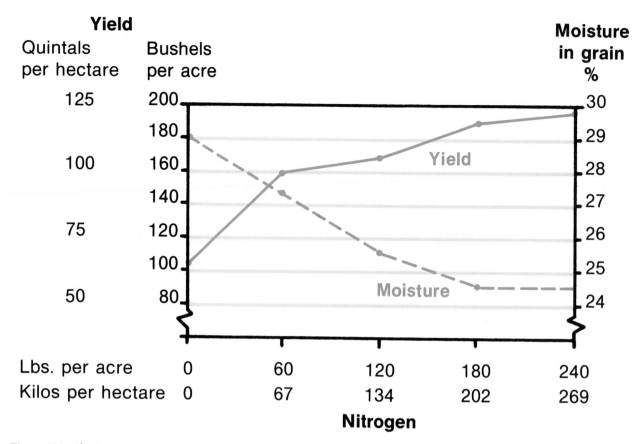

Figure 111. Effect of nitrogen fertilizer on yield and moisture in corn grain. Kewanee, Illinois, 1966.

That is true mainly for plants with an indeterminate habit of growth. Needed nitrogen hastens maturity in corn, figure 111.

On Soils That Give Large Responses

It is more profitable to apply fertilizer liberally on near-level, deep, well-drained soils of medium texture, that have high water-holding capacity and that can be farmed at the right time, than on soils with yield-limiting physical factors.

Some soils have factors beyond the farmer's control that limit their response to fertilizer. It is frequently poor business to put the most fertilizer on the "poorest land" if it fits the following descriptions that jeopardize response to fertilizer:

• Drouthy soils in low rainfall areas (without irrigation).

• Low-lying fields along streams that flood often, or low spots in fields that drown out.

• Poorly-drained fields where it is often impossible to plant or cultivate on time.

Recently purchased or rented fields that have good soil which has not been fertilized during the past several years is a good place for extra fertilizer. These fields are on the steep part of the yield curve and therefore will give excellent returns per dollar spent for fertilizer.

Placement Considerations
for Row Fertilizer ("Starter")

Row fertilizer *promotes rapid* and *uniform growth,* especially when the soil is cool and wet. Theoretically, if the general fertility level of the whole plow layer is high enough, there will be no starter effect from extra fertilizer applied through the planter. But for a quick early start, seedlings need a higher concentration of nutrients, especially phosphorus, than they need for normal growth

164

Row Placement of Fertilizer

A

Split Boot
both sides
slightly above seed

Good starter effect. Good Placement for an insecticide. May cause injury to germination and young seedling if rate is too high. Probably 25 pounds of N+ K per acre (28 kilos per hectare) is the safe limit in the western corn belt and twice as much in eastern (more rainfall). Loses effectiveness if surface 2-3 inches (5 to 7.5 cm) dry out.

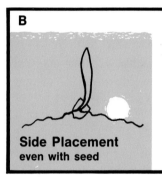

B

Side Placement
even with seed

Best starter effect. Loses some effectiveness when surface 2 to 3 inches (5 to 7.5 cm) dry out. Mainly for starter effect. Not suited for insecticide as only one side is protected.

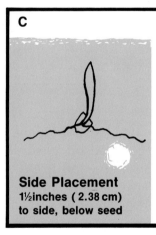

C

Side Placement
1½ inches (2.38 cm)
to side, below seed

Seedling roots enter fertilizer band a few days later than in A or B position. Fertilizer remains available through longer dry period than with A or B. Safe to apply any amount that is economical. Not suited for insecticide because the volatile gas which kills insects is heavy and moves down, away from the seed.

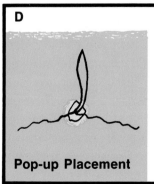

D

Pop-up Placement

Good starter effect but limited to a small amount of fertilizer preferably with a low "salt index" (see table 19). "Greatest danger of fertilizer "burn".

Figure 112.

later in season. Usually, therefore, there will be a noticeable increase in early growth from row fertilizers. Since row fertilizer effect is greatest in cool soil, the farther north you are and the earlier you plant, the greater the chance of seeing early growth stimulation.

Where weeds are to be controlled by cultivation rather than chemicals, extra-early growth may be an advantage. It helps to offset the fact that some weeds grow better under cool, wet conditions than corn. Row fertilizer is placed for quick use by the corn and is less available to weeds except those close to the band of fertilizer.

Row fertilizer may hasten maturity by a few days. This is especially important for avoiding soft corn in the northern corn-growing regions.

Row fertilizer is generally recommended in Minnesota, northern Iowa, Wisconsin, Michigan, northern Illinois, Indiana, Ohio, New York and Pennsylvania even where soil test levels for P and K are high.

In a period of shortage and high fertilizer prices, an application through the planter can replace larger broadcast applications for one or two years if the soil test is medium or above.

Pop-up Placement

In 1964 farmers began reading about "pop-up" fertilizers. This was the result of experiments to reposition the hopper tube so it would discharge 40 to 50 pounds per acre (45 to 56 kgs/ha) of a 6-24-12 or similar analysis in contact with the seed (D in figure 112).

Many people have built fertility levels so high that at planting time they are mainly interested in applying a small amount of fertilizer for early growth stimulus, while depending on high fertility throughout the plow layer to meet later needs. About ⅓ to ½ of the normal sideband amount placed close to the seed gives this early stimulation.

It is doubtful that there is a substantial difference between results from "pop-up" fertilizer and applications placed in a band to the side and below the seed, since root systems will intercept the conventional fertilizer band no more than two days later than they reach a "pop-up" application. The main advantage of the pop-up technique is to reduce the number of fertilizer fill-up stops during the planting operation.

After the soil has been built to a high general fertility level, a small amount of nutrients through the planter will give the desired starter effect.

On highly fertile soils in the central and southern Corn Belt row fertilizer, though it promotes early and even growth, usually increases yields only in cool, wet seasons. It is, therefore, a type of insurance policy. Some farmers feel it's worth the trouble of row fertilizing to have the best-looking field of corn in the community.

Soils with Low to Medium Fertility

On these soils, row fertilizer is just another way to supply nutrients that are lacking. Even though you broadcast large amounts of fertilizer, row fertilizer is strongly recommended in order to make certain that the young corn plants have ample nutrients.

Can Row Fertilizer Reduce Corn Yield?

Sometimes a small to moderate amount of fertilizer near the row cuts yield. The explanation is usually found in one of the following:

• The row fertilizer stimulated early growth and produced large plants but there were not enough nutrients in the soil to carry larger plants through to maturity.

• In most cases, it was dry early in the season. The row fertilizer produced larger plants that used up the moisture supply at a faster rate. By midseason, fertilized corn had larger plants that needed more water than unfertilized corn would have, but more of the water had already been used.

• Drouth continued until after the fertilized corn had silked, the most critical stage for drouth effect! The unfertilized corn did not silk until after the drouth broke. If drouth had occurred a week to ten days later the corn without row fertilizer would have been hurt more because it would have been in the most critical stage, whereas fertilized corn would at least partly have the kernels already set.

What lessons can be learned from these observations on unfavorable responses to row fertilizer? *First,* be sure that there is enough overall fertility to carry the crop through to maturity after row fertilizer gives it a good send-off. *Second,* forget about years in which an early drouth injured row-fertilized corn more than unfertilized. In the long run, the time that dry weather occurs will balance out. The odds are that your row-fertilized corn will stand dry weather as well as or better than a crop without row fertilizer.

Influence of Row Fertilizer on Depth of Rooting

For some reason, many people have the mistaken idea that putting fertilizer in a band near the row causes a shallow root system. To be sure, row fertilizer stimulates extra roots within and around the fertilizer band, but it also promotes a large and deep root system.

Nutrient Ratios For Row Fertilizers

Research in many states has shown that a combination of nitrogen and phosphorus is the first requirement for row fertilizer. A ratio of one part of nitrogen to each three or four parts of P_2O_5 (1.3 to 1.8 of P) is ideal. Nitrogen in this ratio, especially in the ammonium form, promotes the uptake of phosphorus by the young seedlings.

What about potassium in the row fertilizer? For several years, farmers were advised by some authorities to leave potassium out of the row fertilizer because they thought (a) it might injure or delay germination, (b) the chloride in muriate of potash would reduce the uptake of phosphorus, and (c) K wasn't needed in the starter fertilizer anyhow.

This reasoning no longer holds up. Side placement can eliminate the danger of injury. The phosphorus within the growing part of corn cells is determined by the supply that is available to the root hairs and not by the amount of chloride. Research in several states shows small yield increases generally, and larger increases in cool, wet seasons, even at medium to high soil test levels for potassium. A few states report better standability when potassium is included in the row fertilizer.

In conclusion, if row fertilizer is applied it should contain N, P and K. On soils that test high in K, a ratio of 1:4:2 of N, P_2O_5 and K_2O (1:1.8:1.7 of N, P and K) is suggested. On soils low in K, a 1:4:4 (1:1.8:1.3 of N, P and K) is preferred.

The Importance of Water-Soluble Phosphorus

For row fertilizer, at least 50 percent of the phosphorus should be water soluble. On alkaline soils — pH 7.0 or above — 80 percent water-solubility is preferred, but no advantage has been shown above 80 percent. For row application on slightly to moderately-acid soils that test high in available phosphorus, the degree of water-solubility has little effect on yield.

Rates for Row Fertilizer

For starter effect only, the following amounts are enough to promote rapid early growth:

	Pounds per acre	Kilos per hectare
N	8 to 10	9 to 11.2
P	8 to 12	9 to 13.4
P_2O_5	18 to 27	20.2 to 30.2
K	10 to 20	11.2 to 22.4
K_2	12 to 24	13.4 to 26.8

For maintenance amounts of P and K, after you have built P and K to high soil test levels, enough P and K can be safely applied through the planter with side placement to maintain the high tests. Fifty pounds

Figure 113. A worn split boot resulted in the fertilizer being placed in direct contact with the seed. The normal seedling, right, was from the other row where fertilizer was about an inch (2.5 cm) from the seed.

of P_2O_5 (23 pounds of P) per acre (56 and 26 kilos per hectare) will maintain the phosphorus test. Most agronomists feel that corn can benefit from only 30 to 40 pounds per acre (34 to 45 kilos per hectare) of P_2O_5 in the band because corn plants feed effectively on banded phosphorus only during the first 6 to 8 weeks. The phosphorus above those amounts serves as maintenaince rather than supplying P for this year's crop.

Sixty pounds of K_2O (50 pounds of K) will replace the potassium in the grain from a 150-bushel yield of corn (23 kilos K per 94 quintals).

When corn is harvested for silage, about 60 percent more phosphorus and 2½ times more potassium are removed. Over a period of years, a considerable amount will be returned in manure, but maintenance needs in a silage system always exceed those in a grain system because of losses from manure.

Can all of the nitrogen be applied through the corn planter? The answer is yes, according to research in Indiana and Wisconsin. Rates up to 200 pounds with side placement caused no injury and were as efficient as broadcast fertilizer in the trial years.

It is doubtful, however, that large applications through the planter are practical for most farmers. First, large applications slow down planting considerably. Second, when a large amount is to be applied, it can often be bought and applied at lower cost in bulk, in liquid or straight materials than as a mixture for planter application.

Fertilizer "Burn" and How to Avoid It

High rates of fertilizer applied through old-style worn, split-boot applicators at high planting speeds can cause fertilizer injury (figure 113). The same thing can happen with "pop-up" placement if the rate is too high. Injury from N, P and K is mainly due to high salt concentration in the solution around the seed or young root system. Water moves from zones of low to high salt concentration. Therefore, when the salt concentration *within* the root is low compared with the concentration *around* it, water does not enter the root and the young corn plant wilts and dies from lack of water if the whole root system is affected. If only part of the roots are in the zone of high salt concentration caused by fertilizer, the plant may survive and recover. At very high concentrations the roots die.

The various fertilizer materials have different "salt indexes" (table 19). The measure of salt index is osomotic pressure which indicates the strength of the salt solution in competition with plant roots for water. The salt index, then, indicates the likelihood of "fertilizer burn" when the fertilizer is in contact with the germinating seed or young roots.

The salt index for a mixed fertilizer can be calculated when you know the materials and amounts of each used to make the mixed

Table 19

Relative salt concentration of chemically pure fertilizer materials compared to nitrate of soda. (Adapted from L. F. Radar, Jr., L. M. White and C. W. Whittaker, "Soil Science," 1943.)

Fertilizer	Relative Salt Index per unit of $N + P_2O_5 + K_2O$
Nitrate of Soda, 16.5% N	100.0
Ammonium Sulphate, 21.2% N	53.7
Ammonium Nitrate, 35% N	49.3
Sulphate of Potash-Magnesia, 21.9% K_2O	32.5
Muriate of Potash, 60% K_2O	31.9
Urea, 46.6% N	26.7
Nitrate of Potash, 13.8% N, 46.6% K_2O	20.1
Sulphate of Potash, 54% K_2O	14.1
Ammonia, Anhydrous, 82.2% N	9.4
Diammonium Phosphate 21.2% N, 53.8% P_2O_5	7.5
Monoammonium Phosphate, 12.2% N, 61.7% P_2O_5	6.7
Superphosphate, 20% P_2O_5	6.4
Superphosphate, 48% P_2O_5	3.5
Mixed fertilizer	(depends on ingredients)

fertilizer. As a rule, the higher the analysis, the *lower the salt index per unit of plant nutrients.* In other words, it is usually safe to apply more nutrients (but not more total weight of fertilizer) near the seed in high analysis fertilizers than in low analysis.

Salt injury is worst when a dry period

FERTILIZER POSITIONS

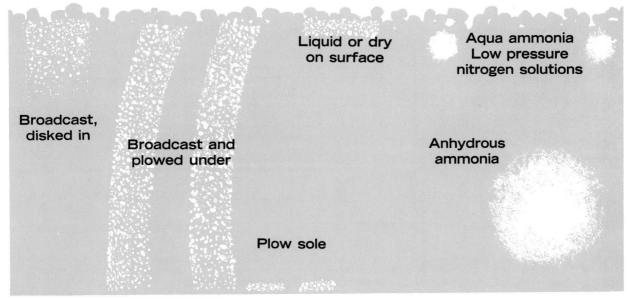

Figure 114.

follows a planting period with normal moisture. Moisture evaporating from the soil leaves a highly concentrated solution.

The best way of avoiding injury is by insuring correct placement. Salt injury can be avoided by side placement, 1 to 2½ inches (2.5 to 6.25 cm) from the seed, or application of reduced amounts.

Another cause of injury is free ammonia gas, NH_3. Free ammonia in amounts large enough to cause injury can come from anhydrous ammonia, high or low ammonia pressure nitrogen solutions, and from diammonium phosphate. To avoid ammonia injury, keep it an adequate distance from seeds and young roots or apply it a week or more before planting.

Some micronutrients, among them boron, copper, molybdenum and cobalt, are extremely toxic to germinating seeds even at very low levels; extreme care is needed in their use.

Chelates that carry micronutrients may also be directly toxic. Follow the manufacturer's instructions carefully!

Broadcast Fertilizer, Liquid and Dry

There are several reasons for the increased use of broadcast fertilizer:

• Less labor is required to broadcast than to apply equal nutrients through the planter.

• The job can be done before or after the rush of planting time.

• Plant nutrients are often priced lower in the forms that are used for broadcasting or sidedressing. This may be due either to handling in bulk which saves bagging cost, or to lower processing cost.

• Fertilizer that is broadcast and plowed under is placed deeper than that which is applied through the planter (figures 112 and 114). For large amounts of P and K, this is preferred over row application because the nutrients are more likely to be available throughout the season. Deep placement of nitrogen is more effective in a dry season. But, on the other hand, surface placement is more effective in a very wet period because roots need oxygen in order to absorb nutrients — those near the surface have a better supply of oxygen from air.

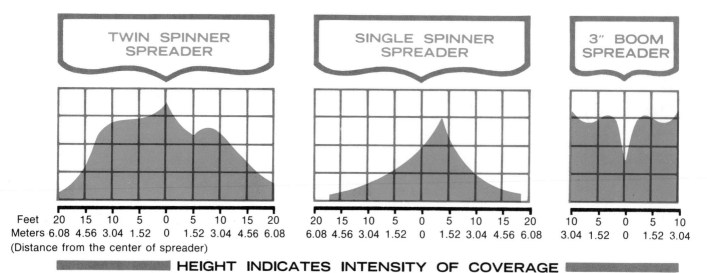

| Feet | 20 | 15 | 10 | 5 | 0 | 5 | 10 | 15 | 20 |
| Meters | 6.08 | 4.56 | 3.04 | 1.52 | 0 | 1.52 | 3.04 | 4.56 | 6.08 |

(Distance from the center of spreader)

HEIGHT INDICATES INTENSITY OF COVERAGE

Figure 115. Patterns of fertilizer behind three spreaders of different types. Careful overlapping would be needed in order to get an acceptably even application from the spinner spreaders. Patterns can be modified by spreader adjustments and particle size of the fertilizer, but some unevenness is characteristic of any bulk broadcast application.

Disadvantages of Broadcasting

• It results in more soil-fertilizer contact (figure 114) which is undesirable for phosphorus in alkaline soils (see page 132), and for many micronutrients which are rendered unavailable by chemical changes in alkaline or strongly-acid soils. On the other hand, maximum soil-fertilizer contact is preferred for rock phosphate because rock depends on soil acids to change it chemically and increase the available P. This is best accomplished when rock is intimately mixed with the soil. It is not suited to alkaline soils.

• It often results in truck or tractor tracks in plowed ground but this can sometimes be avoided by application before plowing.

• A small amount of fertilizer is less efficient when broadcast than it would be if applied in the row.

• Broadcast application is often less evenly spread over the field.

How Important Is Even Spreading?

Broadcast fertilizer can never be spread at an absolutely even rate. High prices for both fertilizer and corn increase the importance of even spreading. Three questions logically come to mind:

— Just how uneven are nutrients distributed over the field?

— What is the effect of uneven spreading on yield?

— What can be done to improve evenness of spreading?

Every piece of broadcast spreading equipment has its own spreading pattern. Figure 115 shows the pattern of dry fertilizer from twin-spinner and single-spinner trucks and from a spreader with 3-inch boom. Other spinner and boom spreaders would have different patterns.

In addition to unevenness across the spreader swath, there are two causes of unevenness in all broadcast applications, both dry and liquid. First, the problem of driving the spreader so it overlaps just the right amount with spinner-type spreaders and barely touches the previous strip with boom spreaders. This isn't easy since the driver can't always see where fertilizer was applied on the previous trip. People who have studied broadcast applications in the field are agreed that the care and skill of the driver is a major factor in even spreading.

A second cause of uneven spreading is the variation of ground speed near the end of

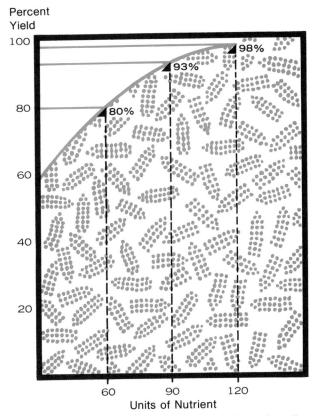

Figure 116. A typical response curve to show the effect on yield when the nutrient is applied evenly and unevenly. In this chart an application of 90 units evenly distributed produces a yield of 93 percent. If the same amount of nutrients are unevenly spread with one-third of the area receiving 60 units, one-third 90 units, and one-third 120 units, the yield will be the average of 80, 93 and 98 percent or 90.3 percent. The yield loss for such uneven spreading (starting at a very low yield level of only 55 percent) is 93 minus 90.3 = 2.7 percent. If the yield without fertilizer had been 80 percent, the yield loss from similar uneven spreading would have been 1.7 percent.

a field, in extra-soft places, and going up and down slopes. Modern spreaders are designed to minimize these effects, but they can't be completely eliminated.

Much of the unevenness from broadcast fertilization is undetected by the farmer or the dealer. It is a built-in part of broadcast application. Variations from ½ to 1½ times above and below the average rate often occur on small areas.

Spreaders of better design can be and are being made. The important point is that spreaders must be carefully adjusted, and the driver has to be alert and do the most careful job he can.

This discussion applies equally to single nutrient carriers, pelleted mixed fertilizers, dry bulk blends and liquids. Many persons have mistakenly associated unevenness only with bulk blends.

Even spreading is easier with liquids than with dry fertilizers. Problems are likely to be from "salting out" in the tank, clogged nozzles, inaccurate spacing on passes across the field, and changes in pressure.

Agronomists in several states have studied the effect of uneven broadcast application on crop yields. They have concluded that it is *much less than one might expect* (figure 116). You can easily see uneven growth in a field, especially in small grains, before you can measure an effect on yield.

Important conclusions from this research are:

• The lower you are on the yield curve, the greater the effect of uneven spreading on yield. When you farm far up the yield curve, unevenness won't show but, of course, it still means some loss in efficiency.

• Dry bulk-blends will theoretically result in greater yield loss than homogenous pelleted or liquid fertilizers because of incomplete mixing or different spreading patterns of the ingredients caused by varying particle size, shape, or density.

• Unevenness of spreading is less important on corn than on small grains because an extra heavy rate usually does no damage to corn, whereas it may cause wheat, oats or barley to lodge. If uneven spreading results in extra high N and low K, corn might lodge, but this is unlikely in most fields.

• Farmers should require dealers and custom spreaders to use care in the choice of materials, in mixing, in spreader adjustment, and in driving pattern. No rigid set of rules can be set for this; much depends on the sense of responsibility and good judgment of the people involved.

• Up to some point, loss in yield from uneven spreading is more than offset by the lower cost of bulk fertilizer, but there is a

171

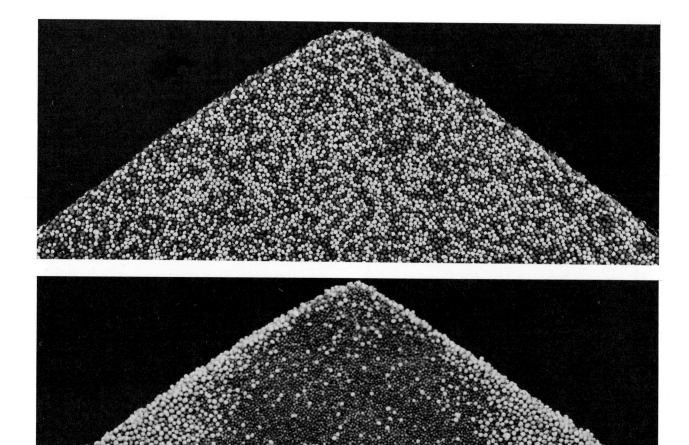

Figure 117. Similar-sized particles, above, result in a more uniform mixture than particles of different size, below. The segregation due to differences in size, shape or density of particles is greatest when the fertilizer falls in a cone and rolls down the inclined sides.

point beyond which this is no longer true.

Those who researched this matter, and considered the results and their practical implications, came to the conclusion that bulk application and bulk blending *when properly done* are efficient approaches to fertilizer application. Most major companies that produce dry fertilizers are now supplying them in bulk, both homogenous pelleted and bulk blended.

Improving Bulk Spreading

Most of the points have already been discussed in the preceding paragraphs. Here is a complete list for reference:

• In dry mixed fertilizers, use granules of similar size so they will be thrown the same distance by the spreader's revolving fans. Avoid material with fine particles or dust.

• In bulk-blends, select ingredients of as near the same particle size and density as possible (figure 117), mix thoroughly, load evenly, and avoid having the fertilizer fall onto a cone in the trucks. Studies show that the separation of fertilizer ingredients of different particle shapes and sizes is greatly reduced if the fertilizer does not fall on a peak and roll down the sides.

• In liquids, avoid settling out in the tank, check nozzles for clogging, and maintain uniform delivery by constant pressure.

• Adjust the spreader properly for the

fertilizer being spread.

• Carefully follow the correct driving pattern.

• Make sure that the fertilizer delivery rate is adjusted as much as possible for changes in ground speed.

Bulk Blending (Custom Mixing)

Bulk blending, also called custom mixing, is a system of storing dry ingredients in bulk at local points and mixing them on order for each farmer. The fertilizer industry can often supply some plant nutrients at lower cost this way than by other systems.

In addition to a cost advantage, the bulk-blender can make any ratio of plant nutrients a farmer wants. This is an argument for bulk blending because many farmers have their soils tested regularly and they like the idea of a fertilizer mixture being made to their own specifications. The point has often been oversold, but it is sound in principle. In practice, the overall soil testing procedure from field sampling to interpretation is not precise enough to distinguish, for example, between a "factory mix" 10-20-20 and a bulk blend that analyses 10-19-23. Field experiments would probably not show a significant difference in yield.

Bulk blending has grown by leaps and bounds since its small beginning during the early 1950s. In the Midwest, where it got its start, there were 633 bulk blenders in 1962, 965 in 1963, 1250 in 1964, and over 2000 in 1974.

Laws to regulate methods of taking samples from blends, guaranteeing analyses, and setting tolerances for deviation from guarantee were developed in the late 1950s and early 1960s. In some states, blenders had been by-passing the usual inspection procedure for mixed fertilizers by selling the farmer individual ingredients and giving him title to them. Then the blender mixed the ingredients together *on request — as a service to the farmer.* In most states, this is no longer possible. Bulk blends generally are required to undergo inspection by state fertilizer control officials and to meet tolerance standards.

Bulk Blend through the Planter?

In the beginning bulk blends were used only for broadcast applications. Farmers soon began asking why they should not use them through the planter. Little research information is available to answer the question. The decision rests on two points:

• How uniformly can the ingredients in the blend be spread along the row?

• For best P uptake, must the N and P be in the same pellet or can they just be close together?

Homogenous pelleted fertilizers (A and B in figure 74, page 101) or liquid mixed fertilizer would be preferred to bulk blends (C) if the price was the same. But that is not usually the case, so the farmer has to decide how much it's worth to have all nutrients in each pellet or in solution. Any saving in cost with blend would, however, be small because the amount applied is not large.

Volatilization Loss of Surface-Applied Nitrogen

Anyhdrous ammonia, as well as nitrogen solutions that contain free ammonia, cannot be applied to the surface because nitrogen will be lost as a gas.

But what about liquid and dry fertilizers that do not contain free ammonia?

Urea and solutions that contain urea may lose nitrogen to the air (page 111) when urea hydrolyzes to ammonia unless the fertilizer is in direct contact with the soil so it can hold the NH_4^+.

Some volatilization loss of nitrogen is likely to occur whenever fertilizers with the ammonium (NH_4^+) form are left on the surface of soils with a pH above 7.0. The NH_4^+ ion reacts with carbonates or bicarbonates in alkaline soils and NH_3 gas is readily evolved from ammonium carbonate. Little data are available from field trials to indicate precisely how much N is likely to be lost. Conditions are so varied that research data from one place and time could not be reliably used elsewhere.

Both nitrate NO_3^- and ammonium NH_4^+ carrying fertilizers can be surface-applied on soils below pH 7.0 without fear of loss. This means that for the majority of Corn Belt soils, volatilization losses are negligible for ammonium nitrate, ammonium sulfate, ammonium phosphate, diammonium phosphate, nitrate of soda, calcium nitrate, potassium nitrate, and either dry or liquid mixed fertilizers that contain these sources or are made by ammoniation of superphosphates or reaction with phosphoric acid.

Foliar or Leaf Feeding

The most efficient way to supply certain micronutrients to some crops is through the leaves. The specific advantages of leaf "feeding" is that it bypasses the capacity of soils to fix certain nutrients in chemical forms unavailable to the plant. (The fixing capacity of certain soils can also be bypassed by "chelating" the nutrient.)

Leaf feeding is mainly suited for micronutrients which are needed in very small amounts and which are efficiently absorbed by the leaves.

Leaf feeding has thus far not been economical for applying major nutrients to field corn. Corn requires nitrogen, phosphorus and potassium in such large amounts that it would take 10 to 20 separate applications to provide enough nutrients without causing leaf burn. Iowa researchers reported good increases in preliminary trials in 1973 with pure polyphosphates on soils where the yield without foliar applications was 160 bushels per acre (100.4 quintals per hectare). Corn tolerated high rates of application.

When corn plants are 6 inches (15 cm) tall, not more than 5 percent of the spray is held on the leaves; at 24 inches (⅔ meter), the figure is probably less than 25 percent. In other words, most of the fertilizer in a

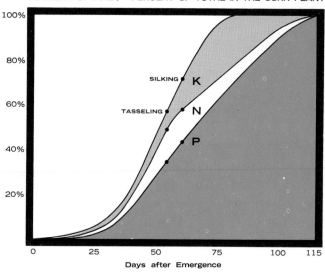

Figure 118. Curves showing the use of N, P and K by corn. These curves, however, do not indicate periods of most critical need. For detailed information on this, see figure 77, page 106; figure 87, page 123; and figure 92, page 134.

foliar spray actually falls on the soil and that is a poor place for efficient uptake of P and K.

Select the Best Time to Apply Fertilizers

Corn takes up nitrogen and phosphorus throughout its growth cycle, but potassium needs level off somewhat sooner (figure 118). The nutrient uptake curves are interesting, but they do not indicate specifically when fertilizer should be applied.

The importance of having a good supply of available nitrogen and phosphorus immediately after germination is discussed on page 166. The plant uses a lot of P but the absorbing root surface is small and the rate of P uptake is slowed by cool soil. After plants are knee high, P deficiency symptoms are rare. The soil warms up, organic matter decays more rapidly and releases phosphorus, and the enlarging root system contacts more available P as it expands through the soil.

The main need for K is not in the seedling stage as for P but is still early in the growth of corn. It is helpful in the starter fertilizer at low soil test levels and in cool, wet periods

174

even at high tests. The big surge of potassium into the plant is before tasseling.

When to Apply P and K

Since phosphorus and potassium are not lost over winter or during the growing season by leaching or volatilization, the best time for the main application is *any time before planting*. Plowing them under is preferable to mixing them in the surface soil. (See special comments about phosphorus on alkaline soils, page 147.) Starter and maintenance amounts may be applied through the planter.

Claims have been made for good increases, especially in dry weather, from foliar application of phosphorus at silking time but this has not been confirmed by experiment station research.

Surface application in no-till, sod planting systems is a special case. Research indicates that P and K are used efficiently by corn even though not worked into the surface. The explanation likely is that the surface mulch keeps the soil moist so roots can function effectively even during midsummer.

Sidedressing P and K is still a dubious practice though research in Iowa showed acceptable response to phosphorus. After fertilizers containing P and K react in the soil, these nutrients move very little. Therefore, when sidedressed, they are poorly placed and applied too late for early growth stimulation. If the soil stays dry in the zone where they are applied, they will not be used efficiently.

Sidedressing may be encouraged for trial on very low testing soils when enough row fertilizer was used to get the plants off to a good start but was obviously not enough to meet the later, larger needs of the crop.

Sidedressing Nitrogen

In the main corn growing areas sidedressing has a slight yield advantage over preplant and somewhat more over fall application, figure 119.

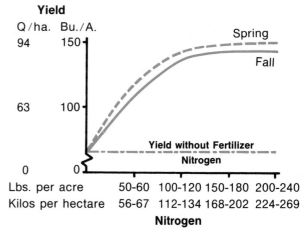

Figure 119. Comparison of fall and spring application of nitrogen for corn, 18 experiments in Illinois.

Special advantages are:
• You can apply nitrogen in years when you most need it and omit it in other years. If you have an unusually good stand and plenty of moisture in the subsoil to produce top yields, you can profitably sidedress at an extra-heavy rate. But if you have a very poor stand of corn or large areas drown out, you can save the nitrogen you planned to sidedress.

• Sidedressing gets the nitrogen on *after* you've controlled the weeds, so you fertilize corn, not weeds.

• There's less time for nitrogen to leach from sandy soils or to volatilize — following denitrification — in poorly drained soils.

• You have more flexibility in switching to another crop, soybeans for example, if you have not already applied nitrogen.

You can sidedress nitrogen any time from planting time until the corn is too tall to get equipment through. However, delay will increase root damage and a prolonged rainy period could prevent timely application. So, on balance it is best to sidedress *before* the plants are knee-high.

Sometimes the slit made by the applicator blade results in a wide crack in soils that shrink markedly upon drying, figure 120.

To avoid root damage, sidedress in the *middle* of the corn row. You'll gain nothing

Figure 120. The narrow slit made by the ammonia applicator blade became a line of weakness where a wide crack formed when the soil dried. Some live roots bridged the crack.

by sidedressing close to the row since corn roots meet across the row by the time the crop is knee-high. And you reduce the risk of root pruning.

All of the common nitrogen fertilizers are acceptable for sidedressing, but anhydrous ammonia, aqua ammonia, and nitrogen solutions are most popular. Get sidedressed nitrogen down into the soil. Nitrogen on the soil surface won't be effective until rain moves it down into the root zone. Nitrogen moves into corn only in moist zones. It is preferable to sidedress dry and liquid forms 1 to 2 inches (2.5 to 5 cm) deep. Some nitrogen carriers must be discharged under the soil surface to prevent volatilization losses, so place anhydrous 6 inches (15 cm)

or deeper. Put solutions that contain free ammonia at least 2 inches (5 cm) deep.

Aerial Applications
When Corn Is Too Tall to Cultivate

What should you do if rainy weather prevents you from sidedressing on time and the corn gets too tall for ground application equipment? Airplane application up to tasseling time is acceptable if your soil is low in available nitrogen. Up to 125 pounds of nitrogen per acre (140 kilos per hectare) can be applied in dry pelletted carriers.

A few pellets may lodge in the whorl or leaf axils and a small amount of leaf "burn" might result. But the increase from supplying needed nitrogen should far more than offset

176

any minor leaf damage. The only precaution is not to apply the nitrogen when the leaves are wet with dew or rain because the pellets would stick to the leaves. Liquid fertilizer would not be suitable for a major nitrogen application.

Researchers Dibb and Welch in Illinois intentionally placed urea pellets in the whorls of young corn plants at rates equivalent of 0 to 600 pounds per acre (672 kilos per hectare). There was superficial leaf tissue damage at the highest rates but growth was little affected. Damage was severe from an ammonium nitrate-urea solution. Delayed aerial application should be considered an emergency measure rather than a substitute for usual ground application.

The Effect of Fertilizers on Corn Maturity and Lodging

The effect of early planting and choice of hybrid on maturity are well-known. But what about the effects of fertilizers? The best time to compare the moisture content as a measure of relative maturity from different treatments is when the grain is just mature, between 30 and 35 percent. If you wait until the grain has dried to 20 percent or below, differences will have largely disappeared. This is because the wetter corn dries faster after maturity. Hence, grain from two fertility levels that differed by 5 percent in moisture when they were in the 30 to 35 percent range may differ only 1 or 2 percent when they dry to 20 percent.

Data from experiments in many different states leads to these conclusions:

• Applying a fertilizer with NPK through the planter hastens maturity from a few days to about one week, if there is a large visible response to the fertilizer early in the season. In seasons when the weather is warm after planting, row fertilizer causes only slight growth stimulation and has little effect on maturity where soils are high in fertility.

• Adding the nutrient that is in shortest supply advances maturity, whether it is N,

P, or K, and regardless of whether it is applied through the planter or broadcast. The greater the growth and yield response to the nutrient, the more maturity is hastened.

• Adding a surplus of nitrogen when *other nutrients are limited* has, in a *few* cases, delayed maturity but this is the exception rather than the rule.

• Adding an excess of any nutrient when others are plentiful has no effect on maturity.

Many people believe that high nitrogen usually delays maturity, but this is incorrect! The evidence is very convincing. Nitrogen at 300 pounds per acre (336 kg/ha) has not delayed maturity in research trials when P and K were at optimum levels, table 20.

The popular opinion that high nitrogen delays maturity developed because corn that is heavily fertilized with N stays green longer, whereas corn that lacks nitrogen turns yellow and the lower leaves die, giving the *false impression* that it is maturing. A close look at the ears shows that the well-fertilized corn is just as nearly ripe even though the plants are greener.

Very high N when K is short sometimes appears to *hasten* maturity because it increases stalk rot which results in premature dying of plants but this should not be confused with an effect on true maturity.

The percent of ears silked on a given date gives an exaggerated impression of differences in maturity from fertilizer application. Here is data from an experiment in the northern Corn Belt:

Percent Silked August 5	Percent moisture at harvest
25	40.9
80	40.4
90	39.2

The plot that was only 25 percent silked on August 5 was probably 90 percent silked 3 or 4 days later and that is approximately the difference in maturity indicated by the moisture contents of 40.9 versus 39.2 percent.

Table 20

The influence of nitrogen fertilizer on corn maturity in Minnesota. Results from 11 separate replicated trials in two years with harvest just before the grain was physiologically mature. Nitrogen up to 300 pounds per acre (336 kilos per hectare) did not delay maturity. Small amounts of P and K in the row had little effect on maturity. (University of Minnesota).

| | | Moisture in the Grain, Late September | | | |
| | | 1955 (6 Trials) | | 1956 (5 Trials) | |
Nitrogen Applied		N only	N + P + K[1]	N only	N + P + K[1]
Pounds per Acre	Kilos per Hectare	%	%	%	%
0	0	36	37	40	40
60	67	36	–	38	37
120	134	37	36	38	39
180	202	36	35	39	39
300	336	37	35	39	39

Phosphorus at 17 pounds P and K at 33 pounds per acre (19 and 45 kilos per hectare) in the row.

Though fertilizers usually have relatively little effect on maturity, they often greatly influence lodging (figure 121).

6. EVALUATING FERTILIZER COSTS AND RETURNS

Fertilizer Prices

From 1940 to 1973 fertilizer prices in the United States remained low compared to land, machinery and wages, figure 122. The situation changed dramatically in 1973-74. Price controls in the U.S. on phosphorus fertilizer resulted in a large increase in export of phosphates. This caused shortages followed by substantial increases when controls were lifted. Nitrogen increased as much as 300 to 400 percent in the spring of 1974 compared to the low point in 1970-71 because of higher cost and real shortages of natural gas, the main feedstock used to manufacture anhydrous ammonia. Besides, farmers planned a large increase in corn acreage, thus creating greater demand.

The future trend in fertilizer prices is uncertain but, barring a general recession, will rise because of growing world demand for food which depends heavily on fertilizer.

U.S. production of nitrogen fertilizer is based almost entirely on natural gas in contrast to use of naphtha and other petroleum products in other parts of the world. Natural gas reserves are small at this time and there is no likelihood that the price of it will return to the highly favorable situation of 1940 to 1972. During that period the price was held artificially low by government regulations.

Economics of Fertilizer Use

For many years when the price of fertilizer was relatively low you could hardly go wrong by fertilizing liberally.

As a result, farmers substituted fertilizer for acres of land in order to farm more profitably (figure 122). Some farmers are still far enough down the yield curve that they can get back $1.50 to $3.00 for each dollar spent on the right fertilizer. Money put into stocks, bonds and savings seldom produce returns equal to money spent for the right fertilizers.

From an economic point of view, the three factors to consider in selecting kind and amount of fertilizer are:

1. Cost of fertilizer
2. Expected yield response
3. Expected price of the crop

Plants Lodged

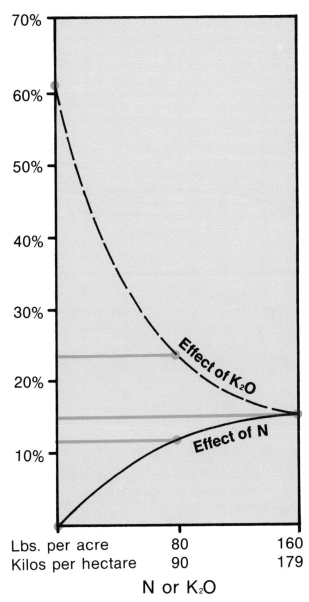

Lbs. per acre	80	160
Kilos per hectare	90	179

N or K₂O

Figure 121. Curves to show the effects of nitrogen and potassium on lodging — each in the presence of ample supplies of the other two major nutrients. Increasing potassium reduced lodging in part, at least, because it reduced stalk rot. Increasing nitrogen increased lodging. The effect of nitrogen when P and K were adequate may have been due to higher yield with larger ears rather than to predisposing the plants to disease.

Unfortunately the first item is the only one that you know at the time you have to make your decisions on fertilizer to apply. Your choice depends a great deal on item number 2. No one can give simple ready-made guidelines on this matter, but agricultural colleges, soil testing and farm management services and a growing number of fertilizer companies have computer programs that integrate information on soil type, soil test, previous crop, and fertilizer and manure applications in relation to proven responses from research. But there is no substitute for the judgement of each farmer because only he has full information on his financial situation and what he prefers to spend his money for. The computer gives only an economic judgement based upon data fed into it.

Fortunately the profit curve does not rise to a peak and then drop off sharply. It reaches a plateau where each additional dollar added in extra fertilizer returns one dollar in additional yield so that you may be at least 10 percent above or below the absolute optimum without much change in profit.

The time eventually comes when you near the top of the fertilizer response curve, and must decide whether to continue to raise your fertilizer rates still higher or use the money for other purposes. In addition to off-farm investments, you may consider buying more land, new machinery, more livestock, or improving your buildings.

There are, of course, some drawbacks to investments in fertilizer. There is always a slight risk of crop failure or of a poor crop. But likewise there is a risk of stock prices falling or of other investments failing to return a profit. Another consideration is that, once added to the soil, you cannot convert the investment in fertilizer into cash in an emergency.

There are two important noneconomic points to consider in fertilizing:

• Unwanted environmental effects, especially excessive nitrate and phosphorus in

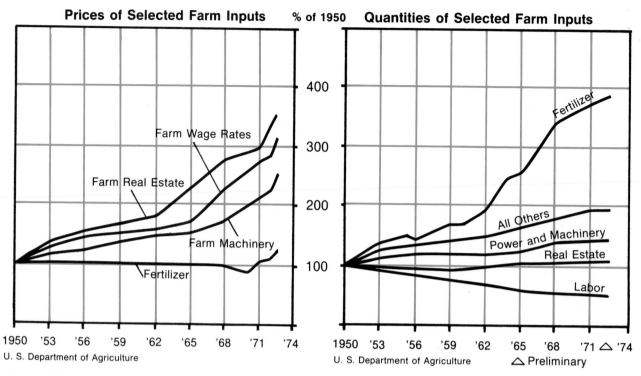

Prices of Selected Farm Inputs   % of 1950   **Quantities of Selected Farm Inputs**

U. S. Department of Agriculture

U. S. Department of Agriculture   △ Preliminary

Figure 122. Trends in selected cost items (left). Other prices rose much faster than fertilizers from 1950 to 1972. The sharp increases in all items in 1974 to 1975 is not shown but fertilizer was still relatively favorable in price.
    Trends in amounts of selected items used (right). Farmers are using relatively more fertilizer, the lowest cost item, and less land and labor.

some waters (see pages 343 to 348).

• Unwise use of fertilizer reserves

Because P and K can to some extent be "banked" in the soil through buildup programs, farmers can often take advantage of low fertilizer prices to buy extra amounts and then they can "coast" in years when fertilizer prices are high or the weather prevents planned application.

In years of unusually favorable profit, you may save on your income tax by banking extra P and K in your soil.

Adjusting to Higher Prices

When fertilizer prices change suddenly as in 1973-1974 you may be tempted to drastically alter your fertilizer plans. The first reaction to higher fertilizer prices is likely to be to reduce the rate of application. This should not be done without careful study.

• The price of corn may have increased as much as the price of fertilizer. This occurred in 1973-1974.

• The optimum amount of fertilizer is

influenced less than you would expect by the relative price of corn and of fertilizer, figure 123. This is because costs other than fertilizer (land, seed, labor, machinery, tillage) are assumed to remain the same and thus the effect of fertilizer price is reduced.

In years of shortages or of unusually high prices consider the following adjustments:

1. Follow soil tests as a guide to P and K applications.

2. If soil tests for P and K are medium to high you can postpone a broadcast maintenance application for a year or two.

3. At medium P and K soil tests, fertilizer applied though the planter should allow near optimum yield.

7. LIMING ACID SOILS

Why Liming Pays

Liming medium to strongly acid soils improves most crops because:

• It reduces the solubility of manganese and aluminum which are present in strongly

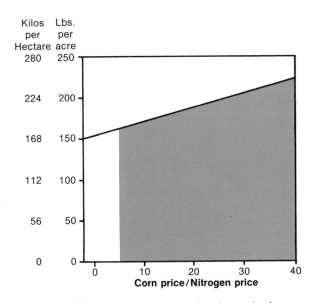

Figure 123. The sloping line shows the change in the most profitable nitrogen rate when the price of corn relative to the cost of fertilizer nitrogen ranges from 5 to 40.

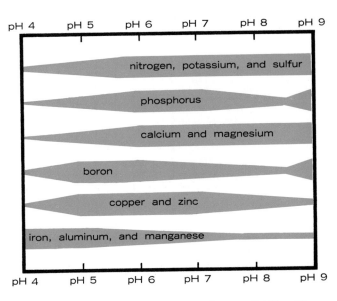

Figure 124. The effect of pH on nutrient availability. The wider the shaded bar, the more of the nutrient available. The best overall balance of availability is between pH 6.0 and 7.0.

acid soils in large enough amounts to be toxic, especially to alfalfa and clover (figure 124).

• It improves the soil for micro-organisms which speed the decay of plant residues and release nitrogen, phosphorus, secondary and micronutrients for crop plants.

• It favors the growth of nodule-forming bacteria on alfalfa, clover and soybeans, which permit them to get nitrogen from the air and add it to the soil.

• It increases the availability of some micronutrients.

• It frees phosphorus in the soil and keeps newly applied phosphorus more available to plants (table 10, page 132).

• It corrects calcium and magnesium deficiencies, although they are rare on any but the most acid soils.

Best pH for Corn

Research indicates that with high fertility, maximum corn yields can be grown in the range of pH 5.6 to at least 7.5 (figure 125).

Somewhere below pH 5.6, on mineral soils corn begins to suffer. At pH 4.0, it will barely survive.

When limestone is first applied to soils below pH 5.0, they appear to take on new life. A temporary surge of plant nutrients is released due to a speed-up in the decay of organic matter caused by an increase in the growth of soil organisms. Also, the availability of soil phosphorus and some micronutrients is improved.

For continuous corn or a corn-soybeans cropping system, pH 6.0 is a suitable goal on acid soils. But an extra initial investment of $6 to $12 an acre for lime will raise a silt loam to pH 6.4 or 6.5 and it won't cost any more to maintain it at 6.5 than at 6.0. Profit will probably be about the same in the long run.

In a cropping system that includes alfalfa or clover, the goal should be pH 6.5 to 7.0.

In recent years, some farmers have been advised to apply up to 20 tons of limestone per acre (44.9 metric tons per hectare) and

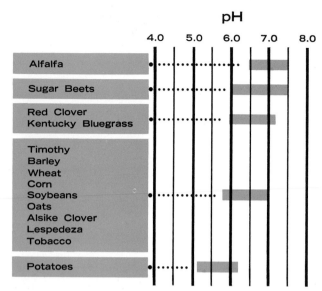

pH

| | 4.0 | 5.0 | 6.0 | 7.0 | 8.0 |

Alfalfa

Sugar Beets

Red Clover
Kentucky Bluegrass

Timothy
Barley
Wheat
Corn
Soybeans
Oats
Alsike Clover
Lespedeza
Tobacco

Potatoes

Figure 125. The most favorable pH range (green bar) for some important field crops. Well-fertilized corn is not adversely affected by acidity until the pH falls below about 5.6.

even to put limestone on fields that are not acid. Neither research results nor theory about how limestone works indicate that this is profitable, except to the person who sells the limestone.

Kinds of Liming Materials

Several materials will neutralize soil acidity but *agricultural limestone* is most economical except for special situations. Aglime, as it is commonly called, is calcium carbonate ($CaCO_3$) with varying amounts of magnesium from a trace to as much as 45 percent magnesium carbonate ($MgCO_3$). Limestone with a significant amount of magnesium (perhaps a minimum of 5 to 10%) is called dolomitic limestone.

The value of limestone is determined by (1) its capacity to neutralize soil acids (total neutralizing power or calcium carbonate equivalent), and (2) the speed at which it acts (mainly due to fineness). Pure calcium carbonate has a neutralizing value of 100, pure dolomite about 108.

Fineness is important because the rate at which limestone reacts with soil acids depends on the amount of surface that is exposed by the particles. Fine grinding increases the surface. For very fast action, an extra-fine ground limestone is best, but it costs more. Farmers will find that for field crops, it is usually most economical to buy limestone that has an average fineness for their state and to apply it at the rates suggested by their agricultural extension service and responsible local dealers.

Two other liming materials are worth mentioning:

Hydrated lime has a neutralizing value of about 135 and is a fine powder. It reacts completely with soil acids within a few weeks, but is generally too costly except for high-value speciality crops.

Marl is found as a natural carbonate deposit of marine animal shells in swampy areas. It always has some clay and organic matter as impurities. By the time marl is mined, dried and ground, it costs more than agricultural limestone, except in a few areas.

Gypsum As a Substitute for Lime

Gypsum is an excellent source of calcium, but it is doubtful that calcium is ever deficient for corn on any soil that is pH 5.6 or above, unless the pH has been raised by some unusual soil treatment. The problems on most acid soils are related to pH rather than directly to a deficiency of calcium as a nutrient. Gypsum is not effective in improving yields on acid soils.

Gypsum improves alkali soil (high pH) in low rainfall areas because the problems are caused by excess sodium. The calcium in gypsum replaces sodium on the soil clay and organic matter: the sodium is then leached out by rainfall or is flushed out with irrigation water. Excess sodium is not a problem on high pH (alkaline rather than alkali) soils in Iowa, Illinois, Indiana, Ohio, Michigan, New York, and other states in the humid region (except "slick spots" in southern Illinois). They have excess amounts of calcium and magnesium rather than sodium.

Leaching and Crop Removal

Limestone applied to *acid soils* leaches to only a small extent, except on sands. When

Figure 126. A very uneven application of lime resulting in overliming some areas and failure to correct acidity in others.

calcium and magnesium carbonates in limestone go into solution, they take the place of hydrogen on the exchange sites on clay and organic matter particles (figure 100, page 144), and thus are held against leaching.

The data from lysimeter studies for losses of calcium by leaching is actually not valid for acid soils — it shows too high a loss. This research was conducted mainly on soils that had high-lime subsoils. Calcium and magnesium found in the drainage water came mainly from the subsoil rather than from limestone applied to the plow layer.

Table 21 gives the amounts of limestone needed to offset acidity caused by the removal of calcium and magnesium is some cropping systems.

Continuous corn crops for grain remove only moderate amounts of calcium and magnesium but the nitrogen fertilizer applied in such a system requires extra limestone.

Amounts of Limestones to Apply

The agricultural extension service in each state can supply liming recommendations based on the kind of soil and quality of limestone used.

8. CHECKING THE CROP THROUGH THE SEASON

It's a good idea to walk into each field every week during the early part of the season and every two or three weeks thereafter in order to spot troubles when they begin! Postmortems are poor substitutes for knowing what happened and when it happened.

Experts on crops, soils, fertility, insects or diseases can help to diagnose troubles early, but not when the crop is nearly mature.

Farmers now have several tools which they or others can use to diagnose troubles. Tissue tests and plant analyses for N, P and K, spectrographic analyses for micronutrients, deficiency symptoms, photographs of insects and diseases are covered in Section 9.

Deficiency symptoms are good tools for farmers with average and below-average crops to use when analyzing what's wrong with their corn. But top farmers must deal mainly with "hidden hunger" where nutrients may be lacking for top yields but are not short enough to show as deficiency symptoms. As a rule, deficiency symptoms indicate a rather severe shortage.

183

Table 21.

Approximate amounts of high quality limestone needed to offset acidity due to calcium and magnesium removed by different cropping systems. High yields (corn 150 bu., alfalfa 5 T., wheat 60 bu., soybeans 50 bu., oats 90 bu., clover 3.5 T.) (94 q. corn, 11.2 T. alfalfa, 40 q. wheat, 34 q. soybeans, 32 q. oats, 7.8 T. clover) are assumed — corn stalks and grain straw are left in the field or returned in manure. (See page

Cropping systems	Limestone to Offset the Removal of Calcium and Magnesium Each Year		Years Before 1 Extra Ton is Needed
	Lbs. per Acre	Kgs per Hectare	
Corn-Corn-Oats-Alfalfa-Alfalfa	240	269	8
Corn-Corn-Soybeans-Wheat-Clover	148	166	14
Corn-Soybeans	103	115	19
Corn every year	146	164	14

Tissue tests and plant analyses, as pointed out on page 298, can help to spot "hidden hunger." But field strip testing is another way that is likely to be more useful in the long run. The main reason to identify hidden hunger is to learn whether extra fertilizer should have been used. Why not, then, learn directly by having a couple of 8-row strips in one or two fields every year which receive 50 to 100 percent more fertilizer than the rest of the field?

Test strips must be away from the edge of the field. Machine harvest the center four rows or hand-pick and weigh the corn from representative areas to compare with the rest of the field. Results in a single year aren't very reliable, but with yields from strips in one or two fields each year, you'll soon have a good idea about the effect of extra fertilizer.

You don't need to run your own research farm on all fertilizer problems. Your state agricultural experiment station and the United States Department of Agriculture are charged with this responsibility, and they, as well as the fertilizer industry and soil testing laboratories, can supply the general guides to proper rates. But many leading farmers wonder whether the suggested rates are high enough. Extra-high fertility strips on your own farm are a good way to help you find out.

9. USE CAUTION IN TRYING UNPROVEN MATERIALS

In their eagerness to try new things, leading farmers sometimes fall for the fast talk of fertility "quacks."

How to Spot the Fertility Quack

• He often claims mysterious benefits from "conditioning" the soil and unlocking the nutrients already in the soil, often with material from some unusual "natural deposit." The emphasis on natural deposits is for two reasons: (1) to appeal to people who mistakenly believe that it is wrong to use chemical fertilizers; (2) to avoid having to compete with legitimate fertilizer dealers.

• He makes no guarantee for nitrogen, phosphorus or potassium and thus avoids the fertilizer laws. Sometimes the benefits claimed are for micronutrients (trace elements), but the micronutrient content is often not guaranteed. What's more, you have no way of knowing whether the nutrients, if present, are available. Usually the analysis shows several elements that are *not used at all in plant growth*. The percentage of certain micronutrients is often less than that of your soil!

• His home office and the source of the product he peddles are so far away you can't easily check on them.

• He has no research results from an unbiased source to back up his claims. Instead he uses testimonials from farmers in other states. You have no way of knowing whether the conditions under which the observations were made would produce reliable results or whether the results apply to your soil.

• When asked what the county extension agent or reliable fertilizer dealers think of the product, the quack often says, "Don't ask them. They probably wouldn't know the value of our product and therefore wouldn't recommend it."

• He usually runs down the agronomists at the state university and often says, "They won't test our product."

Legitimate but High Priced Fertility Services

Most farmers are at some time contacted by persons who have a legitimate fertilizer product but make exaggerated claims for it. They often offer an elaborate soil testing and fertility planning service which, of course, includes their product. Their programs, of necessity, usually contain some ideas that are different than those of the local extension adviser.

Each farmer has to decide how much their advice is worth and whether it justifies the added cost. We have pointed out elsewhere that the essential compounds in fertilizers are usually well known to all and none has a monopoly on effective chemicals.

Sources of Reliable Information

By following fertilizer practices based on the research of colleges and the USDA, farmers have increased their yields of corn and other crops at fantastic rates during the past 25 years. If you need information or advice on fertility practices, contact your county extension agent or legitimate fertilizer dealer. Always seek advice before you sign up for a dealership with an unproven product.

Agronomy departments regularly test new products that show some promise, although not all new products can be tested immediately because of budget and manpower limitations.

10. COMBINING SUPPORTING PRACTICES WITH HEAVY FERTILIZATION

Today *lots of farmers do a good all-around job* of growing corn. Others do an *excellent job* with *some practices*, such as using plenty of fertilizer, but are only fair in others. Bumper corn yields are the reward to the farmer who puts together the best complete package of all practices. Fertilizer is only partly effective when any other factor limits the yield; for example too low population or late planting, figure 127.

Looked at another way, whenever you improve plant population, or the hybrids you use, or weed control, or soil tilth, you get more profit for each dollar spent on fertilizer. But have you thought of the fact that when you improve any practice you raise the possible yield and thus raise the amount of fertilizer that it will pay you to use? In other words, it pays the best farmers to use more fertilizer than their neighbors.

11. MUNICIPAL WASTES; SLUDGE AND EFFLUENT

Cities are turning increasingly to land application to dispose of the material from their sewage treatment systems. There is much misunderstanding of the amount and nature of the material.

Most of the material from *large cities* will likely be liquid digested sludge. The digestion process will have killed most if not all disease organisms. There is no known disease hazard at this time from applying digested sludge on cropland. Corn is a good crop to receive it.

Research is underway to determine the safety of grazing livestock on land where digested sludge has been applied including

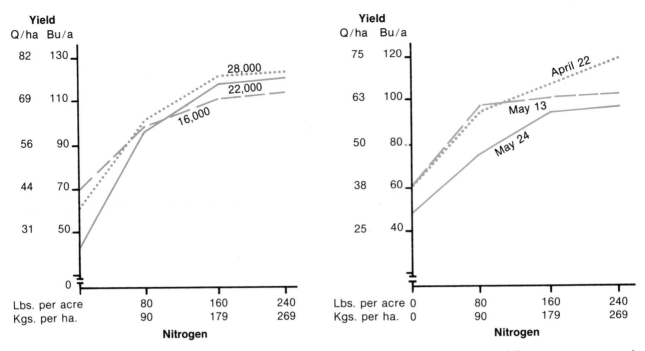

Figure 127. Proper supporting practices illustrated by population (left) and date of planting (right) are necessary to take full advantage of nitrogen fertilizer. The most successful corn growers combine all good practices so that none inhibits the full response of the other factors. (University of Illinois).

spray application on forages.

Liquid sludges vary from about 1 to 10 percent solids. For that reason all statements made here are based upon the common denominator — *dry weight*. The dry weight is made up of about ½ organic material (mainly microbial cells and compounds which they synthesized in their grown processes) and ½ inorganic — mainly metals.

Typical sludge contains about 2.5 percent N in organic form and 2.5 percent as ammonium (50 lb. of each per English ton, about 20 kilos per metric ton). If the sludge is applied to the land surface and allowed to dry, much of the ammonium N will volatilize into the air. This can be reduced by plowing as soon as the moisture content will permit. About ½ of the nitrogen in ammonium form (¼ of the total) may be presumed to have volatilized.

Sludge usually contains about 3 percent P (6.8 percent P_2O_5) on a dry weight basis. This is 60 pounds P or 137 pounds (27 kilos P, 62 kilos P_2O_5) per ton.

Potassium content is low — 0.4 percent or

8 pounds per ton (3.3 kilos per metric ton).

Sludge contains these secondary and micronutrients: calcium, magnesium and sulfur; copper, manganese and zinc. Sodium, though sometimes used by plants, is not indispensable.

Sludge also contains elements that are not essential: cadmium, chromium, lead, mercury and nickel.

Seven years of sludge application with a cumulative total of 186 dry tons per acre (418.5 metric tons per hectare) on an Illinois soil caused yield increases of 15%, 23% and 32% for the three rates as compared with no sludge. No reductions resulted on corn from excessive metals, micronutrients or salt concentration. Inasmuch as the no-sludge plot received a liberal treatment of N, P and K, the yield increases may be due to the water added rather than to the nutrients. There is no doubt, however, that sludge can replace fertilizer.

Soybean yields were seriously reduced in one year under the heaviest sludge treatment. This was attributed to high salt concentration.

The upper limit for sludge application in a single year is controlled by available nitrogen — about 300 pounds per acre (336 kilos per hectare) is a reasonable maximum. If the sludge is surface applied and plowed under when dry enough, the rate would be 6 tons per acre or 14.6 metric tons per hectare. (This assumes that one half the ammonium nitrogen is lost by volatilization and the remainder is available plus one half of the organic nitrogen.)

For repeated applications, the amount of phosphorus is likely to control the feasible rate. Six dry tons adds 822 pounds P_2O_5 per acre or 920 kilos per hectare (359 lbs., 401 kgs. P). This rate is too high from either efficient utilization of phosphorus or possibly for acceptable yields of some crops.

Sandy soils can make better use than finer-textured soils of the available nutrients and of the accompanying water. On the other hand, both nitrates and phosphates are more likely to move into drainage water from excessive applications on sands.

The heavy metal content of corn stover increased in seven years though not to a point of concern for animal feed. Grain composition changed very little.

The plant nutrients in sludge can to advantage be recycled for crop production. Contrary to popular opinion this would have little effect upon the need for commercial fertilizer in the U.S. because the total nitrogen content of human wastes is only 3 to 5 percent of that added in fertilizers. High prices for fertilizers make sludge more acceptable for land application.

Inasmuch as *everything* has to go *someplace*, it is untenable to take the position that until we have complete and perfect research information, sewage sludge cannot be put anywhere. Decisions for the present must be made on the basis of the best known available alternatives including health, economic and environmental considerations. Incineration causes air pollution and may place some toxic elements in more hazardous location with respect to health than in the soil. Heavy metals that remain in the ash after incineration must still be disposed of somewhere. Applying sludge to wooded areas in Illinois may be acceptable but many wooded areas are quite sloping so perhaps runoff would be greater than on agricultural land.

We do not now have, nor will we have in the near future, complete information on cadmium and other heavy metals on which to finally assess all possible present and future risks from the application of sludge to agricultural land. No injury has been established from applications of sludge consistent with a limit of 300 pounds (336 kilos per hectare) of available nitrogen repeated for several years. Therefore, it seems reasonable to proceed with carefully planned land application and to provide for monitoring of the effects on receiving soils, waters, and crops and to conduct needed research on health and environmental effects.

In summary, cropland is a suitable place to apply sludge of typical analysis.

Some persons complain about odors from land application of sludge. Properly digested sludge has far less odor than an application of animal manure and in many cases there is little if any odor.

Sludge is not the only municipal waste material that may be offered for land disposal. Effluent from tertiary treatment systems (screening, biological digestion, and a final screening often by a filter bed) is clear liquid that contains only soluble materials. The operator of the system should supply data on the composition of the effluent.

Liquid from settling lagoons is a third material. It is usually low in solids but varies because of different amounts of stirring of the settled material.

Both effluent and supernatant liquid from settling lagoons contain considerable amounts of nitrogen, phosphorus and potassium. An analysis is needed of each source when used as a substitute for fertilizer.

7

Water Management

On non-irrigated farms where good growing practices are followed, lack of water is often the greatest limiting factor to higher corn yields. This is hardly surprising when you consider that corn requires as much as 5,000 gallons of water per bushel (750 hectoliters per quintal) of grain. Rainfall from planting to maturity is rarely enough to supply the 18 to 24 inches (½ to ⅔ meter) of water needed for 100 to 175 bushels per acre (63 to 94 quintals per hectare) of corn. In fact, during the 100 to 130 days that corn is growing, rainfall in the Corn Belt normally amounts to only half of that needed and part of that is lost by runoff, drainage and evaporation. Furthermore, the rainfall doesn't always come when plants most urgently need it. Therefore, making the best use of rainfall pays off every year. Some years it will make the difference between profit and disaster.

Managing excess water so that it does not interfere with timely planting, cultivating and harvesting, drown out the crop, cause excessive loss of nitrogen by denitrification, or result in severe erosion may be as important as managing it to maximize use by the crop.

Corn has a high water requirement but is one of the most efficient field crops in producing dry matter with the water it uses (figure 128). The water that is available to

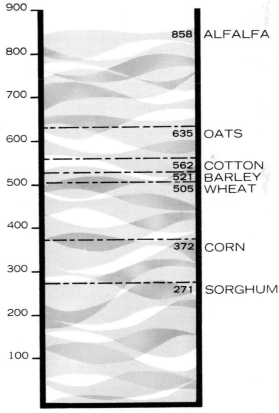

WATER transpired by plants for each unit of above-ground dry matter produced

(lbs. water per lb. dry matter or kilos water per kilo dry matter)

858 ALFALFA
635 OATS
562 COTTON
521 BARLEY
505 WHEAT
372 CORN
271 SORGHUM

Figure 128. Water used by several field crops to produce one pound of dry matter in stems, leaves and seeds. Among these crops, corn is more efficient in use of water than any other crop except sorghum. These are typical amounts, but the actual amounts are higher in very hot, dry regions and lower in cooler, more humid regions. This data does not include water that is evaporated from the soil surface.

189

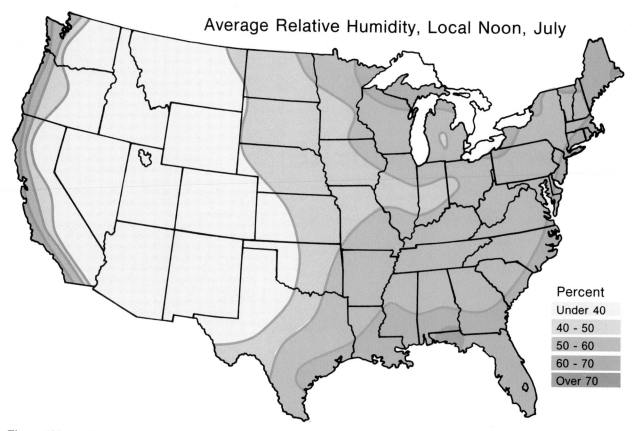

Average Relative Humidity, Local Noon, July

Percent
Under 40
40 - 50
50 - 60
60 - 70
Over 70

Figure 129. As the relative *humidity goes down*, the *evaporation* of water from the soil and plants *goes up*. Evaporation is also affected by temperature. The effectiveness of rainfall is lowest when temperature and radiation are high and humidity is low.

your crop is the amount of rainfall, minus the amount that evaporates or runs off. Rainfall in the United States between April 1 and September 30 varies from about 3.5 to 36 inches (9 to 90 cm.) (see map, page 23) A unit of rainfall, however, is not equally effective in all regions. It is most effective for growing crops in regions that are cool and where the humidity is high (figure 129). In the dry areas of the western third of the United States, high temperatures and radiation, and low humidity evaporate large amounts of water from the soil and crop leaves during the growing season.

The water balance in soils through the year in humid regions is pictured in figure 130. In subhumid regions, the subsoil is seldom fully recharged and, therefore, the crop has less total water available during the growing

season than if the subsoil is full of water at the beginning of the season.

In the Corn Belt there are usually periods of a week or longer when the moisture from rainfall and subsoil is less than optimum for corn. It's a rare year when moisture is not below optimum at least once. You can't do much about the weather but there are many things you can do to effectively use the rainfall the weather gives you.

Soil scientists measure available water in different soils by saturating them, letting them drain, and then growing crops without any more water until the plants wilt and die. When the plants die, there is still some water in the soil (about 5 percent in sand and 20 percent in clay by weight) but it is in such small pores and thin films around the soil particles (figure 131) that the roots can't get

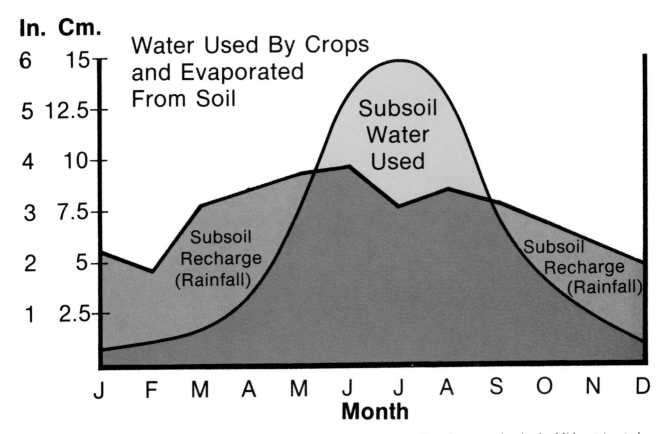

In. Cm.

Water Used By Crops and Evaporated From Soil

Subsoil Water Used

Subsoil Recharge (Rainfall)

Subsoil Recharge (Rainfall)

J F M A M J J A S O N D

Month

Figure 130. Normal rainfall and the monthly loss of water through crop growth and evaporation in the Midwest (central Illinois). The curves will vary in other regions but the general picture is the same — rainfall *during the growing season* is inadequate for maximum yield of corn. The worst drouths occur in years when incomplete recharge of subsoil moisture is followed by below-normal rainfall during the growing season. On the western edge of the Corn Belt, the subsoil is seldom fully recharged and irrigation is practiced for satisfactory yields.

it fast enough to keep the plant from wilting and dying.

From measurements on many soils, the following data has been developed for available water in soils:

Soil	Available water	
	In. per foot	cm. per meter
Coarse sand	0.5	4.2
Very fine sand	1.2	10
Very fine sandy loam	1.9	16
Silt loam	2.1	17.7
Silty clay	2.6	21.9
Clay	2.8	23.5

In humid regions the total water available for corn is often as high on silt loams as on clays or clay loams because the subsoil often has better structure, is less compact,

and is better aerated than clays hence roots penetrate deeper.

Can you raise the capacity of soil to supply available water by making a deeper topsoil, chiseling, or adding organic matter? The answer is that these practices have little direct effect on the soil's capacity to store *available* water.

• Depth of topsoil is not an important factor because the roots soon penetrate far below any topsoil you can build.

• Chiseling in humid regions is at best temporary (page 62) and does not affect available water unless it breaks through a root barrier into available moisture in the subsoil. In poorly-drained clay soils the soil layers below chisel depth are often no better in structure than those within chisel range, figure 46, page 63.

Sand
(Coarse texture)

Silty clay
(Fine texture)

Soil's capacity to store water

Available water

Capillary water in medium to large pores

Capillary water in tiny pores

Hygroscopic water held in thin layers on soil particles

Unavailable water

Capillary water in medium to large pores

Capillary water in tiny pores

Hygroscopic water

Figure 131. Diagrammatic representation to indicate how tightly water is held by soil and the great difference in both total and available moisture in coarse and fine-textured soils.

• Adding organic matter increases the water holding capacity but unfortunately most of this increase is in water held so tightly that corn can't get it (figure 131). For this reason, adding organic matter has almost no effect in sandy soils which do not form crumbs or aggregates. In loams, silt loams and clays, organic matter by increasing aggregation raises the available water-holding capacity slightly. This increases the total porosity and also adds some large pores because the pores in and around aggregates are larger than those in a poorly aggregated soil.

The really important effect of adding organic matter is that it increases the amount of rainfall that gets into the soil because of better soil tilth on the surface!

These rather discouraging comments about raising soil water-holding capacity do

192

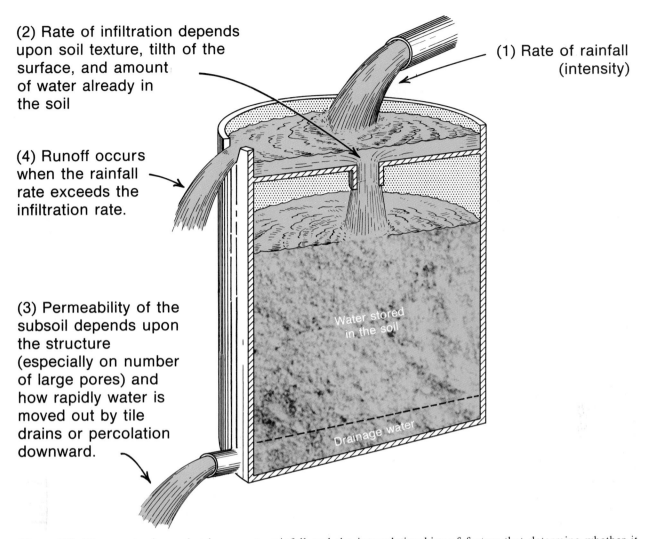

(2) Rate of infiltration depends upon soil texture, tilth of the surface, and amount of water already in the soil

(1) Rate of rainfall (intensity)

(4) Runoff occurs when the rainfall rate exceeds the infiltration rate.

(3) Permeability of the subsoil depends upon the structure (especially on number of large pores) and how rapidly water is moved out by tile drains or percolation downward.

Water stored in the soil

Drainage water

Figure 132. Diagram to show what happens to rainfall and the interrelationships of factors that determine whether it (1) runs off thus contributing to erosion and floods or (2) enters the soil and helps to meet the water requirements of plants and to recharge the subsoil and ground water. Farming practices greatly influence the rate at which rainfall enters the surface.

not mean there is nothing you can accomplish through soil management to increase the available water for your corn crop.

The key to raising the amount of available water is to manage the water that falls on your fields so that you get the most out of it. Here are five steps that deserve a close look:

1. Increase the rate at which water enters the soil surface, thus reducing runoff (figure 132).

2. Get more grain or silage for each inch or centimeter of water through fertilization and other good practices.

3. Adjust the planting rate to your specific conditions.

4. Kill weeds to prevent them from competing with corn for water.

5. In low rainfall regions, leave residues on the surface.

Effect of Nitrogen on Efficiency of Water Use

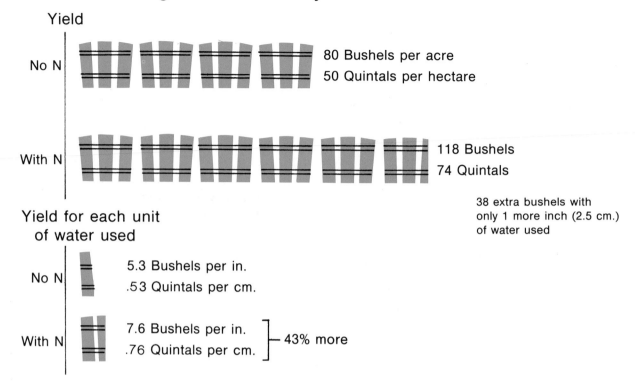

Yield

No N | 80 Bushels per acre
50 Quintals per hectare

With N | 118 Bushels
74 Quintals

38 extra bushels with only 1 more inch (2.5 cm.) of water used

Yield for each unit of water used

No N | 5.3 Bushels per in.
.53 Quintals per cm.

With N | 7.6 Bushels per in.
.76 Quintals per cm. — 43% more

Figure 133. Yields from 33 irrigation experiments in Nebraska show that well fertilized corn averaged 38 bushels more corn with only 1 extra inch (2.5 cm) of water used. Fertilized corn was 43 percent more efficient in using the water.

Stretch the Water Supply with High Fertility and Other Good Practices

Surprising as it seems, research proves that the total amount of water used by high yielding crops is only slightly more than that used to produce low yields. In other words, when you improve your methods in any way — weed control, hybrid, plant population — you grow more bushels with a given amount of water.

High fertility is especially important in stretching the water supply, figure 133.

At low fertility each inch of water made 5.3 bushels (each cm. made .54 quintals) of corn; at high fertility each inch made 7.6 bushels (each cm. made .77 quintals), a gain of 43 percent.

When *any* nutrient is lacking, plant growth is retarded, but the amount of water lost through transpiration from leaves, plus evaporation from the soil, continues at about the same rate as if the plants were thrifty. C. B. Tanner, University of Wisconsin, states that evapotranspiration (evaporation from the soil plus transpiration from leaves) with 50 percent or more leaf canopy stays about the same when fertilizer is added, even though the yield increases.

Not only does well-fertilized corn use water more efficiently, but it also gets more water through (a) deeper roots — if there is water in the subsoil (figure 134), and (b) a slightly greater capacity of the roots to extract water from fine pores and thin films that surround soil particles.

However, if the deep subsoil has not been recharged with moisture during the fall, winter and spring, extra-deep roots are of little help. This was shown by Missouri research in which high fertility increased the yield of corn 61 bushels per acre (38.3 quintals per hectare) in the first of two drouth

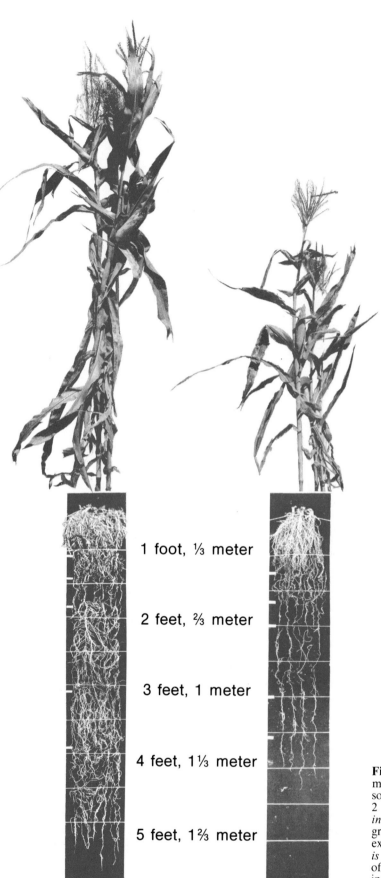

1 foot, ⅓ meter

2 feet, ⅔ meter

3 feet, 1 meter

4 feet, 1⅓ meter

5 feet, 1⅔ meter

Figure 134. Well fertilized corn, left, has a deeper and more extensive root system. On loams, silt loams and clay soils, each additional foot in rooting depth means about 2 extra inches (5 centimeters) of water *if there is moisture in the deep layers.* This extra water can keep the corn growing through a dry period and may result in 10 to 20 extra bushels for each 2 inches of water. *If the deep subsoil is dry, deeper rooting has little advantage.* A long history of good management and high fertility is far more effective in giving drouth tolerance than is a very heavy application of fertilizer in the preceeding year or two.

Figure 135. The strip on the left was overworked with the result that rainfall penetrated much slower.

years, but in the second year, with subsoil moisture used up, high fertility had much less effect.

When subsoil moisture and rainfall in the current season are both short, the extra growth early in the season promoted by fertilizer can reduce yield. The larger plants have not only used more moisture early in the season, but they also need more later on because of their greater leaf area. While this happens occasionally, it is not reason enough to reduce the amount of fertilizer that you apply. *In a dry year, the odds strongly favor high fertility increasing yields in areas where the subsoil is normally recharged with water by corn planting time.*

A good supply of potassium is especially important for efficient use of water by plants. Potassium helps to keep the leaf pores (stomates) more nearly closed and it is through these pores that water is lost by transpiration.

Get the Water Into Your Soil and Reduce Runoff

It's not the amount of rainfall but how much you get into your soil that counts. Here are four things you can do to get more water into your soil:

• When possible, protect the soil surface from the beating action of rain that breaks soil crumbs and causes the soil to run together. One of the best ways to accomplish this is to shred stalks right after picking and leave them on the surface.

• Cut down on seedbed preparation (figure 135). Tillage destroys soil aggregates. Two days after a rain the surface of a regular seedbed may still be muddy while the subsoil is moderately dry. A plow-plant field will be dry on the surface but more moist in the subsoil.

• Cultivate to break a crust (figure 136). It won't have a lasting effect but will increase

196

Figure 136. Cultivating to break a crust increased infiltration from .23 inches (.58 cm) to .34 inches (.86 cm) in one experiment.

the rate at which rainfall enters during the first part of the next rain.

• Farm across the slope or on the contour and don't overcrop sloping fields with row crops. Even with good soil management plus special erosion control measures, you can't grow corn every year on strongly sloping fields.

Adjust Plant Population to Your Conditions

Contrary to popular belief, the need for water does not go up directly with increasing plant population, figure 137.

More plants per acre, of course, do need slightly more water but the point is that water use goes up slower than population. Why? The answer is that water is removed from the soil both by transpiration from corn leaves and by evaporation from the soil surface. Thicker planting shades the ground earlier and more completely and thus reduces the amount of water that is wasted by direct evaporation while the surface is moist.

Moreover, in thick stands the plants shade each other more than in thin stands. This reduces the temperature in the leaves and thus cuts down the amount of water that is transpired from the leaves.

Planting in narrow rows is another way to reduce moisture loss from direct evaporation early in the season.

Until the last 20 years, "firing" of lower leaves of corn in dry weather was mistakenly blamed on lack of water, but is now known to be nitrogen deficiency aggravated by dry weather. With this new information, it is clear that you do not lose as much yield from your normal plant population in a dry season as was formerly thought. (See page 199 in Section 5 on optimum plant population.)

197

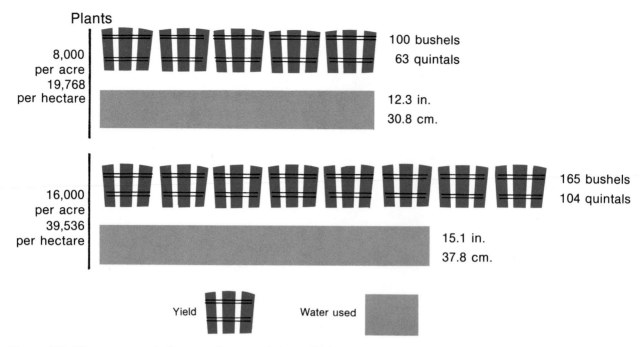

Figure 137. Water use graph for two plant populations. With good management practices, yield goes up faster than the increased need for water.

Plant Earlier

Early planting makes more efficient use of a limited water supply for three reasons:

• The crop *shades the soil* earlier in the season, thus reducing the water lost by evaporation. Two weeks of extra sunshine on the soil surface evaporates a lot of water. Remember that radiation from the sun is increasing daily as the sun moves more directly overhead until June 21.

• Early-planted corn reaches the most critical stage of silking with more water still left in the subsoil. This often makes a large difference in yield, even though the total water used by early and late plantings is approximately the same.

Farmers should not be mislead by the occasional season when early-planted corn yields less because rains come too late for it. The odds favor early planting.

• Early-planted corn has its roots as much as a foot deeper (⅓ meter) into the subsoil when hot, dry weather usually hits. This extra rooting depth means 1 or 2 more inches (2.5 to 5 centimeters) of available water.

Special Suggestion
for Dry Years Without Irrigation

With normal rainfall, the subsoil is recharged before corn planting time (figure 130, page 191) except in areas where corn is grown under dryland farming practices. But what should you do if there was not enough rain to fill the subsoil reservoir.

• Optimum fertilization increases the efficiency of a short water supply. Therefore, the standard rates of preplant and row fertilizer are likely to be most profitable. Farmers who plan to sidedress most of their nitrogen should consider shifting from heavy rates to moderate rates if it is still dry at sidedressing time and the *long-range forecast* at that time is for *below-average rainfall.*

• Water use is not directly proportional to population (fig. 137). High populations shade the soil more completely, and thus less moisture is lost by evaporation.

• The drop-off in yield above the optimum population for any given moisture supply is less rapid than you might expect (table 22).

Table 22
Effect of plant population in a season with less than normal rainfall. Urbana, Illinois, 1964. (J. W. Pendleton)

Plant Population at Harvest		40" Row Spacing (1 meter)	
Per acre	Per hectare	Bu./A.	Quint./ha.
16,000	39,536	122	76.6
20,000	49,420	123	77.2
24,000	59,304	119	74.7
28,000	69,188	119	74.7
32,000	79,072	112	70.3
Average		119	74.7

A few extra thousand plants won't have much effect on your yield. However, aiming for extra high population is more hazardous than in years when the subsoil is recharged.

• The odds are fairly good that in the better corn-growing areas you will receive substantial rainfall (though not necessarily optimum amounts) during the growing season. Usually the corn crop gets about half its needed water from stored reserves and half from rainfall during the growing season in the central Corn Belt.

• Early planting (if there is enough moisture for germination) will be a great advantage if rainfall is short *all summer*; it will not be an advantage if the dry weather ends after early-planted corn has silked, but before later-planted corn has reached this most critical period for water.

• Effective weed control is particularly important in dry years.

• If you have not already plowed for corn and thus still have a choice between (a) plowing up a good stand of alfalfa, or (b)

Figure 138. If your soil has large cracks, and the corn is still small enough, it is advisable to cultivate and fill the cracks. This will slow evaporation from the deep subsoil.

leaving the alfalfa another year and putting corn on the same field another year (or on fields that grew any row crop last year), remember that the moisture supply is greater in the field that grew corn or a row crop. Alfalfa continued to use up subsoil moisture in the fall, long after corn or row crops were harvested.

• If you are going to plant corn after a meadow crop, plow early before the sod has a chance to use up subsoil moisture.

• On fall-plowed fields, try to get by with only one disking just before planting. Extra harrowing speeds drying of the surface soil.

• If your soil develops large cracks early in the season (figure 138) it may be helpful to cultivate to fill them. The disadvantage of filling the cracks is that water will not enter the soil as rapidly during a heavy summer rain.

Chemical and Plastic Covers to Save Water

Illinois and South Dakota researchers have grown 100 bushels per acre (63 quintals per hectare) yields of corn with only the water stored in the soil by planting time (figure 139). No rainfall was allowed to enter the soil and no evaporation was permitted from the soil surface during the growing season. This research showed that drouth could be eliminated in most corn growing areas if a practical method is found to reduce moisture loss by evaporation.

If plastic were used to conserve moisture, only the area between rows would be covered. Rain would be allowed to enter the soil in the row. Plastic covering is already being used to grow high-value vegetable crops, but the purpose in this case is more to control weeds and raise soil temperature than to save moisture. At present this technique is not feasible for corn; when used experimentally it has cost more than the value of the increased yield.

Hexadecanol and related chemicals have been used for several years to make a film one-molecule thick to reduce evaporation from the surface of ponds and reservoirs. These chemicals also reduce water loss when applied to soil but it takes so much of them that the cost is prohibitive. Thus far, research has failed to show any practical way to use chemicals to stretch the water supply in corn fields.

Soil scientists are also treating soils with chemicals that reduce the surface tension of water so that it enters the soil more rapidly, thus storing more water from summer rains. No treatment has been found that can be recommended to farmers, but research is continuing, and may soon bear fruit.

An Asphalt Barrier

Agricultural engineers at Michigan State University in cooperation with International Harvester and American Oil Company pioneered an entirely different approach — installing plastic at about 2 feet (⅔ meter) in sandy soils to conserve water from rainfall or irrigation. A specially designed machine is needed to lay the plastic. Power needed to pull the machine is very great. The economic feasibility depends upon the price of corn, the cost of installing the plastic and how long it remains effective. The researchers hope for an effective life of 15 years. At the present time the system is not economical for corn.

Water Movement to Roots by Capillarity

It is commonly believed that capillary movement of water from a free water table in the subsoil is an important source of water to plants. But soil physicists have shown that water moves too slowly through this pathway to be of great help to the plant. Instead, corn roots in soils with good structure tend to follow the moist soil zone as it moves downward during dry weather. *In other words, root extension is the main way that corn plants survive long periods of inadequate rainfall.*

When the soil is very dry, a small but perhaps significant amount of moisture

Figure 139. Researchers have covered plots with plastic when the corn was a few inches high. In this demonstration, no rainfall was allowed to enter the soil and no moisture was permitted to evaporate from the soil surface. Over 100 bushels of corn per acre (63 quintals per hectare) have been grown on only the water stored in a good Illinois soil. South Dakota researchers grew 99 bushels on similar plastic-covered plots.

Figure 140. The enormous amount of water lost by evaporation is shown by the beads of moisture that formed on the underside of clear plastic *within one hour* after it was placed on the surface of a soil that *appeared to be dry*. Around the corn plants the evaporated moisture escaped through the small opening in the plastic made for the corn plants.

moves as vapor through large and medium-sized pores. In the daytime some vapor moves out of the soil surface and some moves downward to cooler layers where it condenses. At night the soil surface cools more rapidly than lower layers and so vapor moisture moves up and condenses near the surface. Though the amount of water involved is small, it may be quite helpful to a corn plant in a severe drouth.

Some Aspects of Water Movement in Soil

When water moves down through a dry soil and hits a sand or gravel layer, it *does not enter and move quickly through it* as you would expect (figure 141). In demonstrations by Dr. Walter H. Gardner, Washington State University, water was metered into the V-shaped depression and timed as it penetrated the soil. After 20 minutes it had wet a half circle nearly down to the sand. When it reached the sand soon afterwards, it flowed *sideways* instead of down! Why? Because the pores in the soil are smaller than in the sand and thus pull the moving water more strongly.

When the soil became saturated, additional water was free to move into and through the coarser sand. After 5 hours (lower half of the photograph), water had penetrated well into the soil below the sand layer directly beneath the water supply, but not out toward the edges which were not yet saturated above the sand layer.

When water moved through the soil and contacted the sand layer, it formed thin films around the sand particles and between them — only where they touched — as long as the water was held by forces equal to those in the small pores between sand particles. Water did not fill the large pores until the soil above was completely saturated.

Air trapped in large pores interferes with the flow of water just as effectively as do solid soil particles. After the large pores are full of water, it flows freely at a rate dependent on the cross-sectional area in the same way that a large pipe conducts water faster than a small one.

One practical implication is that in your fields, water flow — either up or down — will be inhibited rather than helped by buried sand or gravel layers until the layers are saturated.

If you have a clay soil underlain by sand or gravel, the clay just above the sand will stay wet longer than any other place, including the sand beneath it.

When water moves downward from a coarse layer to a zone of finer-textured soil, it immediately moves into the finer soil because the pores are smaller and thus they have a stronger pull (suction) on the water. Note in the lower half of figure 142 that there was no lateral movement of water at the contact point (as in figure 141) before the clay layer began to wet.

But, now a new factor in water movement enters the picture: the small size of the pores in the clay layer. Small pores mean that much of the water is held in thin films on the soil particles and in effect water tends to "stick" to them. This stickiness of the soil particles for water means that they exert a drag on the flow of the water.

Even though water begins to move immediately into the clay layer, it cannot move through it very rapidly. Consequently, in the lower half of figure 142, note that the water has moved sidewise in soil *above* the clay much farther than it has moved downward *through* the clay. This is what happens in soils that have a claypan.

This also explains why clay soils must be kept in good tilth by having the individual particles bound together into crumbs or aggregates if you want a soil that will absorb rainfall rapidly, to store more water and reduce erosion.

Some farmers have sandy soils underlain by clay at different depths. These soils have more available water than sands without clay because the excess water from previous rains tends to be trapped above the clay due to the slow movement of water through it. Besides, roots may penetrate into the more moist clay layer and get water from it.

When water moves through the soil and comes to a layer of coarse plant residues (straw, cornstalks, mature grass or legume), it acts the same as contacting a coarse soil layer, figure 143. The water will not flow into the large open spaces in the residue layer until the surrounding soil is completely saturated. Coarse layers are an impediment to water movement — either up or down — when water is moving in an unsaturated soil. Note in the left half of the photograph that when the residues are mixed through the plow layer, water flows freely through them.

In the field it would be impossible to have a solid layer of residue on the plow sole as in the right half of the photograph. But there are probably many local areas within the soil where such a layer of residues impedes the flow of water.

Air spaces are needed in clay soils; coarse residues worked into the plow layer serve that purpose.

It is often said that old legume root channels and earthworm tunnels provide little drains through compact subsoils. That is true if they are open to the soil surface. If not, they function just like the residue layer in the photograph, or the coarse sand in figure 141. The principle is the same, only the *size* of the opening is larger. In practice then, root channels and earthworm tunnels provide a water channel for excess water to move rapidly after but not until the soil around them is fully saturated.

What about the implications for tile drains? Tile drains are like very large pores. No water enters them until the surrounding soil is completely saturated.

Water Flow in Saturated Soils

After the soil pores are full, water moves down by gravity. Up to that point, it moved under suction or tension and thus could go up, down, or sidewise. Water in a saturated soil moves downward by the pull of gravity and the size of pores governs the rate of flow. As illustrated in figure 143, if a wetting front comes to larger pores in an unsaturated soil, it detours around them. But, once the zone around the larger openings is saturated and water moves into these openings, it flows faster than in the small pores.

Tile Drainage

Tile drainage systems are usually planned and installed by local contractors. Their training and local experience qualifies them to do the job properly. Therefore, no attempt is made here to describe various systems in detail.

The conventional system in the U.S. has used clay tiles placed at 2 to 4 feet ($\frac{2}{3}$ to $1\frac{1}{3}$ meter) depth and ranging from 4 to 8 rods (20.1 to 40.2 meter) apart on nearly level land. In slightly rolling fields it is common to run individual tile lines along slight draws to reach depressions which have no natural outlet.

Plastic tubes with openings to permit entry of water are of more recent origin.

Mole drains made by pulling a ball or bullet-shaped article through the soil when wet to form a continuous channel leading to an outlet ditch or hillside have been tried extensively and are used in some parts of the world. The soil must be wet and high enough in clay to form a smooth walled opening. The life of mole drains is only a few years.

The flow lines of water to underground drains of all types is much different than most people think, figure 144.

Land Smoothing

Much of the land in humid regions that is quite flat has slightly depressed areas that become potholes in the spring and after moderate to heavy rainfall. In soils with poor internal drainage these low spotss may prevent growing corn or other grain crops. Or in more permeable soils they delay timely

203

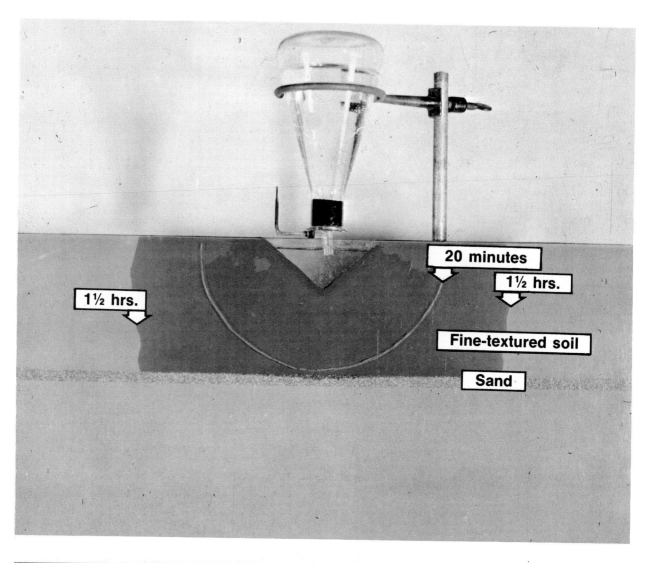

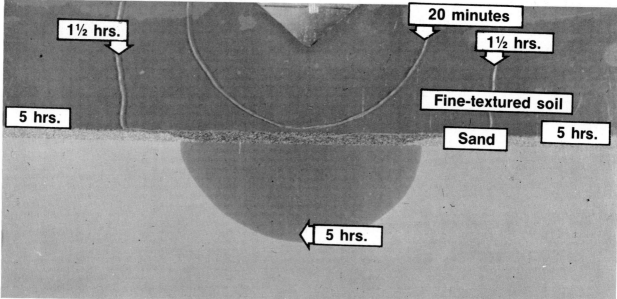

Figure 141. Water moving from a fine into a coarse soil. Note that the wetting front stops temporarily when it reaches the coarse sand layer but continues to spread laterally in the finer-textured soil.

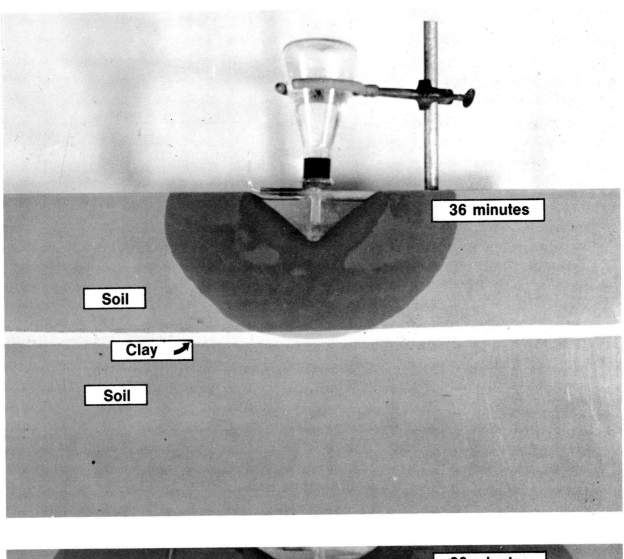

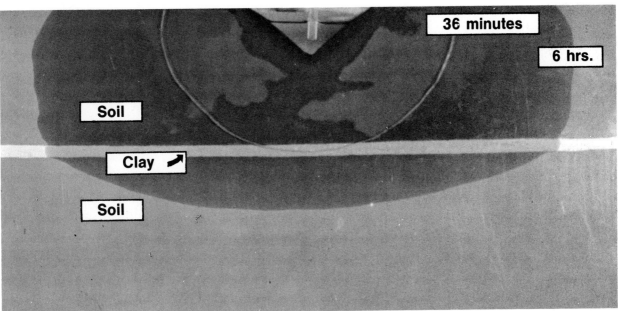

Figure 142. Water moving from a medium-textured to a finer-textured soil. There is no delay in the advance of the wetting front when it contacts a finer-textured layer.

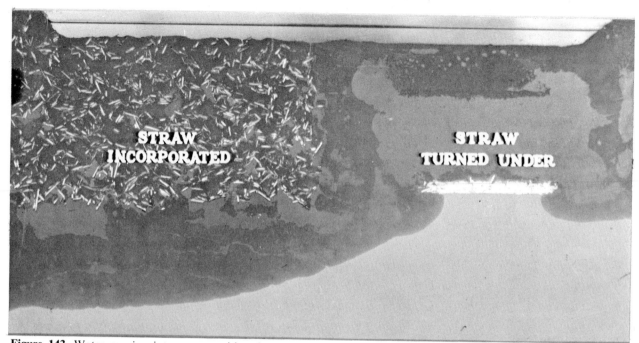

Figure 143. Water moving into contact with a layer of coarse plant residues, left residues mixed in, right residues in a solid layer.

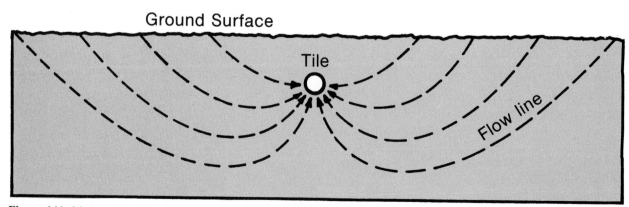

Figure 144. Lines of flow of water to a drain tile. Water from the center of the area between tiles flows upward into the tile. In a saturated soil it can move against gravity by hydrostatic pressure.

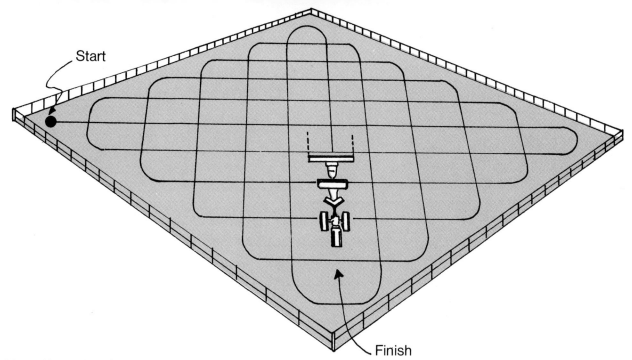

Figure 145. Preferred field pattern for operating a smoothing plane to eliminate low spots.

planting, cultivating and harvesting. In years with average rainfall they markedly reduce yields and in some years they drown out the crop altogether. It is not uncommon to plant, replant and still lose the crop.

As the value of good land and the crops it produces rise, land smoothing to eliminate low spots becomes more attractive, especially on land not suited to tile drainage. Land smoothing is a long-term investment which in many cases can be done at 1/10 to 1/20 of the value of the land.

Land smoothing is not the same as leveling. Leveling would impair surface drainage whereas smoothing improves it. Smoothing means cutting off slight knolls and filling depressions and hopefully leaving a gentle slope to assure surface run off. If the area is nearly level, you may need to make a slight hump and then plant at right angles to it so the rows become small channels for the water to follow. If the slope after smoothing is enough to cause erosion, you will want to run the rows parallel to the slope.

In all cases, you will need to develop a suitable drainage system to receive and carry away the surface water.

In most fields the best pattern for operat-ing the land plane is as shown in figure 145. The work can only be done when the soil is dry and after you have harrowed or plowed to produce loose soil that can easily be moved.

You likely will need assistance from tech-nicians of the Soil Conservation Service or of a competent local contractor in planning the smoothing and drainage system.

Irrigation

In all the non-irrigated regions where corn is an important crop, water is nearly always inadequate during short periods, even in years with good distribution of summer rain-fall.

In the United States most corn is still grown without irrigation. But as leading farmers push toward the yield limits with better hybrids, thicker planting, better weed control, and more fertilizer, they are asking whether irrigation is their next move to higher yields and profits. And, in fact, corn is the main field crop irrigated in the humid re-gions: it has a relatively high acre value, it makes efficient use of applied water and it gives large responses to rather small amounts of water applied at the critical time.

Irrigation adds a whole new dimension to farming. It isn't something you can try in a small way like a new hybrid or new chemical for weed control. You have to make a big investment to try it at all.

The question to be answered is not whether irrigation will increase yield, but *"Will the increase pay the cost of installation and return a profit?"*

Farmers in humid regions who have installed irrigation systems are often quite enthusiastic. But enthusiasm doesn't pay the equipment, labor and water bills!

Water Rights

Industries and cities need more water every year; public demands for fishing and recreation are growing, with the result that farmers in many places are finding they have competition for water. The laws governing the use of water from streams and lakes are different from state to state. In some places you can't take all the water you want from streams or lakes. Check with your county extension service or Soil Conservation Service about local water rights.

Reliable Water Supply

Most people do not realize the amount of water needed for irrigation. One acre-inch of water is 27,000 gallons (a hectare-centimeter is 100 kiloliters). A small stream that has a good supply of water in a normal year may be completely dry when you need it most — during a real drouth. The same criticism can be made of farm ponds that are filled from surface runoff. Average-sized farm ponds hold about 3 acre feet (1.11 hectare-meters) of water. If you irrigate with 2 inches (5 centimeters) of water each week for 3 weeks, this pond will supply only enough water for 6 acres (2.4 hectares) (a considerable amount will have been lost by evaporation from the surface of the pond). For example: to add 2 inches (5 cm.) of water in one irrigation on 100 acres (40.5 hectares) of corn will requires 5,400,000 gallons (204,-406 hectoliters). A farmer who irrigates a large acreage needs a tremendous water source.

Wells supply water for an increasing share of the nation's irrigation systems. In most cases, deep wells are needed, but in some sandy and gravelly flood plains special pipes can be sunk to a water supply at only 15 to 25 feet (5 to 8 meters). Where water from wells is to be used, a test well should be dug to make sure there are layers that will supply enough water of good quality. The water should be checked for salt content and carbonates. Continued use of salty water leads to a buildup of salts in the surface soil, resulting in poor yields and very poor tilth in soils that are high in silt and clay. Large areas of the world have been forced out of agriculture by improper irrigation. The problem arises in subhumid to arid regions where there is inadequate rainfall to flush out accumulated salts.

Frequency and Intensity of Drouth

A farmer's memory is not an accurate record of the frequence and severity of drouths during the corn growing season. Normal rainfall from April 1 to September 30 is shown on the map on page 23, and relative humidity, which strongly influences the effectiveness of the rainfall, in figure 129. The severity of drouth in the Great Plains where irrigation of corn is common is clearly shown in figure 146.

The number of farms with new irrigation systems increases after each dry summer in the Corn Belt.

Some farmers who have irrigation systems do not use them in years with above-normal summer rainfall. Dan Wiersma, agronomiust at Purdue University, makes an interesting point about this. He states that having an irrigation system allows a farmer who has drouthy soils to fertilize heavily and plant thicker every year. Even in years when the irrigation system is not needed, it may still be credited with part of the yield increase

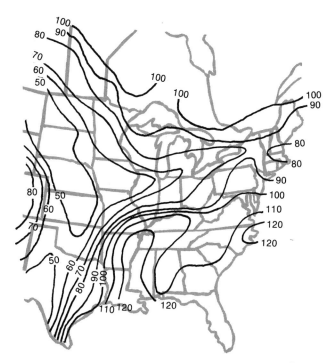

Figure 146. Pattern of percent of normal July rainfall in major drouth years in eastern U.S. Drouth is greatest in the Great Plains where both normal rainfall and percent of normal are lowest. Fingers of drouth extend eastward through the Corn Belt. In major drouth years in the Corn Belt rainfall is actually above normal in the lower Mississippi valley and southeast.

due to extra fertilizer and higher plant population *which might not have been used* if there were no irrigation system to assure an adequate water supply.

Water Absorbing Rate and Water Holding Capacity of Your Soil

Any soil that will absorb at least ¼-inch (.6 cm.) of water per hour can be irrigated. If the rate is lower, the sun on a hot day will evaporate water nearly as fast as the soil can absorb it. Irrigating with self-propelled systems can, of course, greatly reduce loss by evaporation by irrigating at night.

The difference in available water within the rooting depth of corn varies from a low of about 5 inches (12.5 cm.) on sands to a high of at least 14 inches (.36 meter) on deep silt loams. In some areas this explains the large number of irrigation systems on sandy soils and complete lack of them on nearby

silt loams. It also explains the need to irrigate at short intervals on sandy soils.

In many states the Soil Conservation Service can supply irrigation guides that give estimated water-holding capacities for the major soils.

Realistic Yield Increases for Irrigation

Because an irrigation system is a major investment, each farmer should try to estimate the yield increases that he can reasonably expect over a 10-year period.

Few experiment stations outside the western states have long-term results on yield increases from irrigation. In a high-yield experiment, Cornell researchers in New York found an average increase of about 30 to 32 bushels per acre (19 to 20 quintals per hectare) over an 8-year period.

Farmers who irrigate usually also apply more fertilizer and invest more time and money in doing an outstanding job of farming. For this reason, not all of their higher yields compared to those of their neighbors can be credited to irrigation.

What It Costs to Install and Operate Irrigation Systems

Tremendous advances were made in irrigation equipment during the 1960's.

Costs to grow irrigated corn differ among geographic regions, types of systems, and from year to year. Nevertheless data developed for a major irrigation state, Nebraska, for 1974 are a useful reference. The following is adapted from an article by University of Nebraska Extension Economist, Bitney, in Crops & Soils Magazine (ASA), October 1974.

When considering investing in an irrigation system ask yourself —

• Will it be profitable over the life of the system?

• Can I pay for it?

• Can I earn more return than from investing the same amount of money in other enterprises?

Table 23

Years required to pay off an investment in center pivot irrigation equipment with 1974 costs.

Corn Price ($/bu)	Situation 1 100% Equity No opportunity cost	Situation 2 Land interest charge of 6%	Situation 3 20% Equity at a 6% opportunity cost 80% mortgage at 10% interest
	Years		
1.70	20.8	*	*
1.80	10.6	23.9	*
1.90	7.4	11.2	16.0
2.00	5.7	7.6	9.4
2.50	2.7	3.0	3.3
3.00	1.8	1.9	2.0

* Expenses plus interest on irrigation development exceeds income in these situations and payoff is not possible.

Crops and Soils Magazine, American Society of Agronomy.

Tables 23, 24, and 25 are for developing 132 acres (53.4 hectares) with a central pivot system on one-fourth section (160 acres, 64.8 hectares) of sandy soil in Nebraska. Whether or not the specific cost figures apply to your time and place, you will find that the list of items to consider, the way to calculate costs, and the life expectancies of parts of the system are valuable information. You can likely substitute current figures and update the calculations for your situation.

The three land situations in table 23 needs some explanation.

Situation 1 would be a person who owns the land debt free and is willing to assign all returns to pay off the irrigation investment.

Situation 2 would be one who owns the land debt free but desires to take a 6 percent return on his land investment before applying the return to the new system or one who is paying 6 percent on his land mortgage.

Situation 3 represents a person who has an 80 percent mortgage on which he pays 10 percent interest, and who also desires a 6 percent return on his 20 percent land ownership.

Other considerations that affect the economics or other basis for decision include

Table 24

Estimated corn production costs per acre for sandy soil, in Nebraska, 1974.

Machinery	
Tillage & planting	$ 12.55
Harvest (custom)	17.50
Hauling & handling	2.50
Drying	13.75
Irrigation	
Variable costs	28.50
Fixed costs	40.68
Purchased Items	
Seed	9.00
Fertilizer	60.00
Insecticide & herbicide	7.25
Interest on	
operating expenses	8.70
Labor	4.95
Management	13.50
Land interest & taxes	
(Dryland basis)	17.50
Overhead expenses	7.25
Total per acre	$243.63
Total per hectare	$602.01
Total per bushel (135 bu/a)	$ 1.80
Total per quintal (84.7 q./ha.)	$ 7.09

Figure 147. Furrow irrigation is widely practiced on fields that are nearly level and especially where the water supply is a river or reservoir.

Table 25

Initial costs and annual fixed costs for center pivot irrigation in 1974.[a]

	Initial Cost	Estimated Useful Life	*Depreciation* [b]	Annual Fixed Costs as a % of Initial cost *Interest*	*Ins. & Taxes*	*Total*	Annual Fixed Cost
Well	$ 3,000	25	4	5	1	10	$ 300
Pump	3,325	20	5	5	1	11	365
Gearhead	930	10	10	5	1	16	150
Diesel Engine	4,500	10	10	5	1	16	720
Tanks and Underground Pipe	2,280	25	4	5	1	10	230
Center Pivot System	27,500	15	6⅔	5	1	12⅔	3,485
Land Shaping	2,000			5	1	6	120
Total	$ 43,535	—	—	—	—	—	$ 5,370
Per Acre	330	—	—	—	—	—	$ 40.68
Per Hectare	815						$106.52

[a] Based on a 132 acre unit, well 150 ft. deep, and a pumping level of 120 ft.

[b] Interest calculated at 5 percent of initial cost is equivalent to 10 percent interest on the average undepreciated balance (assuming zero salvage value).

Crops and Soils Magazine, American Society of Agronomy.

Figure 148. Self-propelled sprinkler systems which cover 80 or more acres (32.4 hectares) in huge circles have greatly increased irrigation in the Great Plains area of the U.S. The water supply is from deep wells in contrast to flooding and rill systems which are common on floodplains and terraces adjacent to rivers and reservoirs.

the impact on state and federal income taxes and the value of relatively stable versus more variable yields from year to year.

There is likely an inclination on the part of most farmers outside established irrigation areas to underestimate the costs of irrigation systems. The data presented here may help in making realistic estimates.

In humid regions irrigation of field crops is most profitable: where the water source can be developed at low cost; on sandy soils where yield increases are likely to be large every year because the soil is drouthy; and where hybrid seed corn is grown. If you don't grow hybrid seed, *you will likely need an average increase of at least 30 bushels* per acre (19 quintals per hectare) to pay for installing an irrigation system. To get that average increase, you will need increases of 60 to 70 bushels per acre (38 to 44 quintals per hectare) in the driest years.

Farmers who already have irrigation equipment for use on specialty crops can irrigate field corn for less than half as much as those who have to install a new system since operating costs are only about 40 percent of the total cost.

Adapt Other Practices to Irrigation

When you invest in an irrigation system you've raised the overhead costs for growing the crop. Therefore, you must do a better job in all other practices to capitalize on your investment. Looking at it the other way around, when you do an outstanding job, an irrigation system becomes an insurance policy on your investment in land, labor, seed, fertilizer, weed killers and insecticides.

A study of many publications on irrigation shows that the goal in plant population should be about 2,000 to 3,000 more plants per acre (4,942 to 7,413 per hectare) than without irrigation.

No standard rate of fertilizing can be given for all locations, but about 20 to 30 percent extra nitrogen is suggested for irrigated over non-irrigated fields.

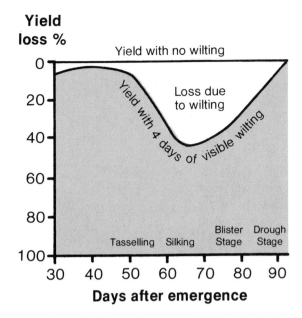

Figure 149. Yield lost when corn visibly wilted for 4 consecutive days at various growth stages. Loss was greatest when moisture stress occurred from tasselling to the dough stage. Two-year average, Iowa.

Applying Nitrogen in Irrigation Water

Many farmers have found that it is economical to apply at least part of the nitrogen fertilizer in irrigation water. It saves a special trip over the field and nitrogen can be applied when the corn is too tall for a tractor and sidedressing equipment. The possible technical problems are so complex that information should be obtained from your local irrigation equipment and fertilizer suppliers.

A question that must be answered is what to do if you receive a good rainfall at the time you had planned to irrigate and apply nitrogen? One answer is to wait a few days, then make the fertilizer-irrigation water more concentrated than normal, apply a small rate of water, and then run water alone for a short time to wash the fertilizer off the plants. That, of course, is not adapted to a continuously moving, once over system.

Nebraska researchers report substantial increases for applying about one third of the total nitrogen in irrigation water on corn growing under stress due to high temperatures, insects or certain diseases on sandy soils.

Apply Herbicides — "Herbigation"

Applying herbicides through irrigation began extensively in Nebraska and Colorado in 1974. Advantages include saving a separate operation, uniform application, and simplicity. Some herbicides that would be toxic to corn in normal concentrations are safe in the very dilute solution in irrigation water. Little herbicide actually stays on the leaves. There are some drawbacks:

• Only a few chemicals have thus far been registered for application in irrigation water.

• Irrigation is not always needed when weeds must be controlled. This is most likely to be the case early in the season.

• Volatile herbicides may not be suited.

• Herbicides that leach readily may be moved too deeply.

• Wettable powders are not suited to surface irrigation. They tend to settle out near the end of the field where the water is introduced.

The concept of applying herbicides through irrigation water should be watched closely because there will be new developments coming along rapidly.

When to Irrigate

Corn grows best when the water storage capacity of the soil is 50 to 100 percent full. Three ways to decide when to irrigate are:

1. Buy commercial meters and install them in your fields (figure 150).

2. Judge by the soil "balling" method. About 50 percent of the available water has been used at the 8-inch (20 cm.) depth when:

• a sandy loam will not form a ball when pressed in your hand;

• a loam or silt loam balls but is crumbly;

• a clay or clay loam is pliable but cracks appear in the ball. Experience is necessary to gain confidence in this method.

3. Keep a weather balance record. For this you need to know:

• How much available water your soil can hold per foot of depth. If you cannot get it in the Soil Conservation Service guide, use

Figure 150. George Bouyoucos, Michigan State University, with the gypsum block he designed to measure soil moisture through the season. The blocks are buried at different places and depths over the field and serve as a guide to irrigation. There are several other moisture meters available commercially.

Table 26
Estimated daily loss of water through evaporation plus transpiration in the Corn Belt. (Van Bavel)

| | | | | | Water Lost Per Day | | | | | |
| | May | | June | | July | | August | | September | |
	in.	cm.	in.	cm.	in.	cm.	in.	cm.	in.	cm.
Northern United States										
Dark, cloudy day	.07	.18	.12	.30	.12	.30	.07	.18	.06	.15
Partly cloudy day	.12	.30	.17	.42	.17	.42	.12	.30	.09	.22
Hot clear day	.18	.45	.22	.55	.22	.55	.18	.45	.13	.32
Central United States										
Dark, cloudy day	.11	.28	.14	.35	.14	.35	.11	.28	.08	.20
Partly cloudy day	.14	.35	.17	.42	.17	.42	.14	.35	.11	.28
Hot clear day	.19	.48	.23	.58	.23	.58	.19	.48	.14	.35
Southern United States										
Dark, cloudy day	.13	.32	.14	.35	.14	.35	.13	.32	.09	.22
Partly cloudy day	.16	.40	.17	.42	.17	.42	.16	.40	.13	.32
Hot clear day	.22	.55	.23	.58	.23	.58	.22	.55	.16	.40

the general figures on page 191.

• Rainfall amounts — which you can establish by keeping rain gauge records.

• How much water is lost each day through evaporation from the soil and transpiration from the crop, table 26.

With this information, you keep a running account of the water balance and plan to irrigate when about one-half of the available water in the root zone is gone. This is a general guide on when to irrigate but you will want to watch the crop closely and be prepared to irrigate as soon as plants show rolling or wilting on very clear, sunny days. Remember that the water stress on crops is controlled more by the intensity of sunshine than by air temperature though the two are, of course, usually closely related in midsummer. Farmers in western Kansas and eastern Colorado found that their irrigation systems were inadequate to meet the water needs of corn when the humidity was low, the days clear and the temperature reached 90° to 110°F (32 to 43°C) most days for nearly a month in 1974.

A heavy irrigation that saturates at least two feet (.67 meter) of soil is more effective and takes less overall time than several light irrigations.

Once you have made the investment in an irrigation system, should you use it as much as possible or only when the corn urgently needs water? Applying all the water that the crop can use for maximum growth would seem to give the best return on the investment, but this has to be balanced against time, labor and operational expense. The decision depends in part upon how busy you are with other work at times when the corn crop would benefit a little from extra water but is really not hurting. Note in table 27 that the yield increase for six irrigations over three applied at the critical period was only seven bushels per acre. That likely would not pay the labor and operational cost for the three extra irrigations.

Irrigating for about three weeks, beginning just before tasseling and extending through silking, should have first priority.

Table 27

Corn yield and efficiency of water use from rainfall and irrigation at different times, western Nebraska. The soil was moist at planting time; rainfall was 2.5 inches (6.25 cm.). (L. B. Nelson, USDA)

Irrigation	Yield		Water Used		Corn Per Inch of Water Used
	Bu./a.	Quint./ha	In.	Cm.	Bu.
None	69	43	10.7	26.8	6.4
3 times before silking	118	74	—	—	—
3 times: 10 days before tassel, at tassel, and at silk	143	90	15.3	38.3	9.3
6 times throughout the season	150	94	21.4	54.4	7.0

Table 28

Subsoil type strongly influences the effect of erosion on crop yields. Corn Yield on Swygert, with 49 percent clay in the subsoil is hurt much more than on Tama with 31 percent clay. (R. T. Odell, University of Illinois)

Soil	Percent Clay in the Subsoil	Average Yield with Good Management			
		With All Topsoil in Place		With Most Topsoil Eroded Off	
		Bushels/acre	Quintals/hectare	Bushels/acre	Quintals/hectare
Tama silt loam	31	101	63	80	50
Swygert silty clay loam	49	78	49	33.5	21
Difference		23	14	46.5	29

Risks from Too Much Irrigation

In subhumid and arid areas you nearly always have control over the total amount of water added if you have an irrigation system. But in humid areas it sometimes happens that you get a heavy rain soon after irrigating. On level, moderately well-drained soil, this can cause ponding, drown out corn, and produce loss of nitrogen to the air following denitrification. Good natural or artificial drainage should always be assured before an irrigation system is installed.

On sandy soils, a heavy rain on top of irrigation can leach nitrate nitrogen below the depth of corn roots.

In subhumid and arid regions unnecessary irrigation, especially several light applications, hastens salt buildup in the surface soil.

The greater the salt concentration of the water supply, the greater the danger of salt buildup. Throughout the world large areas of irrigated land have been abandoned for this reason.

Irrigation Methods

Whether furrow irrigation, flooding, or an overhead sprinkler system is best in your area depends on local conditions. For furrow and flooding systems your fields must be nearly level or gently sloping in the direction of water flow. Overhead sprinklers are suited to somewhat rolling land. For information for your conditions seek advice from your county extension agent, Soil Conservation District, and machinery dealer who handles irrigation equipment.

Soil Conservation and Water Management

(For suggestions on environmental protection and improvement see pages 339 to 351.)

No man's conscience can be clear, or his future profit secure, if he allows irreparable damage to his soil. Fortunately, profitable farming by the present generation is one way to improve soils for the future.

The engineering part of soil conservation is a job for experts. You can get general advice from your county extension agent and help in laying out strips and terraces from your soil conservation district. The services of the Soil Conservation Service technical staff are available to the district. The public shared part of the cost of some special practices through the Agricultural Stabilization and Conservation Service. This expenditure has come under increasing criticism as a production subsidy and its future is uncertain.

Much soil conservation does not involve engineering but is just good soil management and high-profit farming. What happens when a farmer neglects to follow conserving practices? What does erosion do to his farming operations?

Erosion washes away topsoil which has the most nitrogen, phosphorus, organic matter and the best tilth (figure 151) resulting in lower yields (table 28). Furthermore these materials in addition to pesticides reduce the quality of the receiving waters.

When soil erodes, a farmer has to buy more fertilizer; more water is lost and therefore his crops suffer sooner in a drouth; his fields develop gullies that can cause machinery breakdown or force him to farm around them. He can fill the gullies but they are cut again by the first heavy rain; he can leave

Figure 151. The depth of the topsoil and the type of subsoil (amount of clay, compactness, stoniness) determine the decrease in yield when surface soil is lost by erosion, and the ease with which eroded soil can be rebuilt to produce high yields. The surface soil contains most of the organic matter, nitrogen and applied fertilizer and lime. The subsoil is generally of poorer tilth and has a higher clay content.

Figure 152. Sod waterways prevent gullies and catch some soil that is carried in runoff water, and thus serve a limited purpose. On very gently sloping fields they may be enough, but on steeper slopes they treat but don't cure the "disease of soil erosion." The slopes on this field are about the maximum for which sod waterways alone can be recommended.

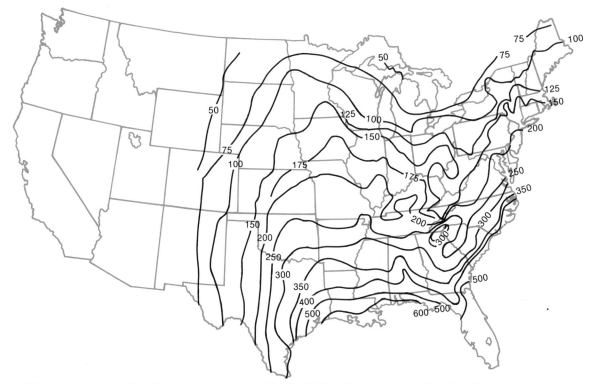

Figure 153. Erosion index values for cropland developed by the U.S. Soil Conservation Service. The figures on the contour lines represent *relative erosion due to rainfall only on continuously fallow land.* They take into account only the amount and intensity of rainfall. The higher the number, the greater the likelihood of erosion.

In actual practice, some of the areas that show a very high erosion index in southeastern states are covered with heavy crops or residues which protect them. At the other extreme, areas in the Great Plains have so little rainfall that they do not produce dense crop cover or enough residues to protect the surface. The index assumes no soil cover.

218

Table 29
Minimum tillage reduces erosion when corn follows either an alfalfa-bromegrass sod or corn. (Mannering, Meyer, Johnson, ARS, USDA, Purdue University)

	Minimum Tillage Reduced Erosion
First year corn after alfalfa-bromegrass	44%
Third year corn after alfalfa-bromegrass	34%
Fifth year corn after alfalfa-bromegrass	27%

sod waterways (figure 152) which will prevent the formation of gullies but won't keep the soil in place. What is the real solution? Following proper conservation methods is the most profitable approach.

You can't farm sloping land and keep every grain of soil in place. Fortunately, you don't need to.

Soil experts have established permissible soil losses for each soil based upon the depth of topsoil and the kind of subsoil. The intent is to limit the loss so that yields can be maintained undiminished indefinitely. In other words so that soil improving practices balance the small soil losses. Permissible losses are small on soils that are shallow over bedrock or that have a very heavy clay subsoil. They are relatively larger on deep silt loams which have favorable subsoil texture. This information coupled with the predicted soil loss, discussed next, provides a useful guide to decision making. It has in fact already been accepted by Iowa as the basis for regulations to control pollution. The Soil Conservation District office can tell you the safe limits of loss for your soils.

The Universal Soil Loss Equation

An equation has been developed which predicts the amount of soil that will be lost under various cropping and management systems:

$$A = R\ K\ L\ S\ C\ P$$

Unless you are a Soil Conservation Service technician you likely do not need to learn to use the equation, but you should be aware of the factors that influence the degree of erosion that will occur.

A is the calculated soil loss per unit area.

R is the rainfall factor which recognizes the total yearly rainfall and the number and intensity of storms, figure 153.

K is the soil-erodibility factor which recognizes differences in the ease with which erosion and soil loss occur on soils with different texture and structure.

L is the slope-length factor. The longer the slope without an impediment to water runoff, the greater the erosion.

S recognizes the degree of slope or steepness.

C takes into account the effect of different crops; for example, corn, wheat and hay.

P includes special erosion control practices such as contouring, strip-cropping and terracing.

Practices That Save Both Soil and Water

• *Fit the crops to your soil.* Keep corn and other row crops on the least sloping fields. It may be best to grow corn continuously, or at least for several years on the level fields — keeping the sloping fields in small grains and long-term hay. Indiana researchers found that narrow rows reduced early season erosion in soybeans but had little effect in corn until five weeks after planting.

• *Use plenty of fertilizer.* High yielding crops protect the surface more completely during the growing season and add more organic matter in roots and tops. This extra organic matter binds soil particles into aggregates, improves tilth, increases infiltration and reduces erosion.

• *Select a good minimum tillage system.* The key to reducing soil loss is to increase the rate at which water enters the soil. Minimum tillage leaves the surface in prime condition for water to enter and thus reduces erosion (table 29). This is one of the advantages of chiseling over moldboard plowing.

• *Leave residues on the surface if you can.* Residues on the surface preserve structure and keep it from sealing over. Leaving shredded stalks on the surface over winter greatly reduces soil loss. In the central and northern Corn Belt heavy residues on the surface are sometimes a disadvantage in the spring because they keep the soil too cool and wet for good early growth.

• *On fall plowed fields, plow across the slope and leave the surface rough.* A rough surface is composed of little basins which catch water and prevent soil particles from being rolled across the surface by wind. Also, rough ground is more porous and lets water in faster. Any secondary tillage on fall plowed ground destroys some of the aggregates. It costs money, yet does more harm than good. Freezing and thawing plus fall and winter rains will compact the plow layer enough.

• *Grow cover crops if they fit your farm.* Seeding cover crops at the last cultivation has been studied in most states, but the practice has not taken hold very well among farmers. A cover crop reduces wind and water erosion; it picks up nitrogen in nitrate form and keeps it from leaching, thus saving nitrogen for crops and reducing the amount that reaches surface or groundwater. It also improves the surface structure of clayey soils.

Several approaches to growing cover crops in corn production have been studied:

— Planting in an established sod and killing the vegetation only in the row. This has generally been unsuccessful because the sod reduced corn yield especially in a dry season.

— Seeding a cover crop at the last cultivation. This has been only moderately successful. Stands are variable. High population, high yielding corn often shades out the young seedlings.

— Aerial seeding late in the season. This method has not been extensively studied. The theory is that the young seedlings will grow after the corn begins to lose leaves hence shading will be less than in midseason.

Seeding a cover crop in the growing crop takes extra time and money. Stands are variable, and volunteer stands of some species in following years are a nuisance in some areas. In very dry years, an overwinter cover crop reduces available moisture and causes lower corn yields.

• *Try a cover crop on early fall-plowed fields.* This is a new practice that deserves much more trial on farms. Spring oats seeded at the time of fall plowing fit very well into a system of early corn harvest followed by early plowing. Whether any smoothing of the plow furrows is necessary must be decided on an individual field basis. It would not be needed on sands or sandy loams. On finer-textured soils smoothing would not be necessary if the soil was at optimum moisture for plowing.

Spring oats have certain advantages over other possible choices:

— They grow more rapidly during the cool fall weather. Oats continue to grow vigorously until frozen and do not slow in growth rate to develop cold weather tolerance as do winter grains.

— Oats are entirely killed by winter weather hence do not present the problem of a sod to be killed in the spring. Cover crops that survive the winter may be difficult to manage in wet springs when timely plowing is impossible. The development of good chemical sod killers has reduced that problem.

— Oats will not deplete the moisture supply by spring growth in a dry year. The surface mulch will, in fact, conserve moisture.

— An oat sod is not dense, so direct corn planting with little or perhaps no spring tillage is possible. The proper combination of preemergence or postemergence herbicides will have to be worked out depending upon the nature of the weed problem.

Figure 154. Strip cropping and terracing are an increasing part of the landscape in rolling areas. Strips are being designed as far as possible to produce uniform width of strips and to reduce or eliminate point rows.

Special Engineering
Soil Conserving Practices

There is good news for farmers who are dependent on contour strips and terraces. As farm machinery became larger, farmers were increasingly annoyed by uneven strips, point rows, and steep-sided terraces that they couldn't farm across.

Soil Conservation Service farm planners are now laying out fields in even-width strips and parallel terraces to reduce or eliminate point rows (figure 154). The terrace channels are being widened and flattened so they can easily be farmed across with modern machinery.

For technical assistance on engineering practices, contact your county soil conservation district office. Your local county agricultural extension agent can help you with many conservation measures that are a part of good farming.

On land that is too steep for farming even with strips and terraces on the contour, you may still be able to grow corn in very narrow strips, figure 28 , page 29.

8

Weed Control

A turning point in the history of weed control for corn was reached in 1944 when experiments showed that 2,4-D, a growth-regulating chemical, would selectively kill many broadleaf weeds without serious injury to corn. Thus it was the forerunner of many growth regulators that selectively kill certain weeds or families of weeds without damage to the crop.

Growth regulators differ in principal from previously used chemicals in that they upset the internal growth mechanism of plants rather than killing on contact. The amount of the appropriate chemical to upset the plant hormone system is far less than the amount needed to kill by salt concentration or (denaturation of the plasma membranes) solubilization by petroleum compounds. Growth regulators, therefore, began the modern era of very small dosages — sometimes only a few tablespoonsful of active chemical per acre or per hectare.

Growth regulators and certain methods for applying them (especially airplane application and low volume combined with fine mist) have increased problems of damage on nearby, nontarget plants. They also pose some threat to plants in streams and lakes and hence to insects and fish. Fortunately most herbicides used for corn are applied to the soil and many are mixed into the soil thus minimizing the amount that reaches surface waters. (See page 348 for a more detailed discussion of environmental effects.)

Specific chemicals and rates are not presented here because recommended chemicals, rates, and methods for their use are different from one region to another and change rapidly from year to year. It's a good idea for farmers to check with their local dealer and county extension agent every year for the latest suggestions.

This section gives only some important principles of weed control in corn. The tremendous toll from uncontrolled weeds in corn is indicated in table 30.

The wide variety of chemicals now available has greatly increased your options for effectively controlling weeds compared to the days when you had to depend upon the cultivator, hoe, scythe, or hand pulling. Besides, preemergence chemicals allow you to kill weeds when the soil is too wet for cultivating or hoeing.

Plan Early

The successful control of weeds in corn begins with early planning. The plans for next year's weed control program should

Table 30
The effect of pigweeds on corn: a two-year average. (E. L. Knake, University of Illinois)

Pigweed Stand in the Corn Row	Yield		Yield Loss	
	Per Acre Bushels	*Per Hectare Quintals*	*Per Acre Bushels*	*Per Hectare Quintals*
None	108	67.8		
1 per 40 inches (1 m)	101	63.4	7	4.4
1 per 20 inches (½ m)	92	57.7	16	10.0
1 per 10 inches (25 cm)	91	57.1	17	10.7
1 per 5 inches (12.5 cm)	78	49.0	30	18.8
1 per inch (2.5 cm)	67	42.0	41	25.7
Band of weeds	64	40.2	44	27.6

start soon after this year's planting season ends. The plan should begin with a weed map for the field showing where the weeds are most serious and the species involved. Soil type will influence the rate of application and even the success of some herbicides. Therefore a soil map may be helpful. Since some herbicides tend to remain in the soil for relatively long periods the crop that is to follow the corn crop may need to be a part of the weed control plan.

No single herbicide will control all weed species. Therefore a combination of herbicides may be needed. These may be combined and applied as a mixture or they may be applied separately and at different times. Another method of keeping troublesome species under control is to plan a cropping sequence that allows a rotation of chemicals page 231. For instance, species such as cockleburs are relatively easily and cheaply controlled in corn with 2,4-D. They are not so easily controlled in soybeans.

Weed control in grass waterways, fencerows and other noncropped areas are important areas to include in a weed control plan. If weeds are allowed to mature seed in these areas much of the seed produced will eventually find its way to the cornfield.

The major objective of a weed control plan should be to control those weeds that emerge at or about the same time as the corn. The success of control by mechanical means for directed postemergence herbicide applications depends on a height differential between the corn and the weeds. If the weeds emerge before or at about the same time as the corn there will be little difference in height.

Kill Weeds Early

The first 3 to 5 weeks are critical in controlling weeds in corn. Research shows that when weeds are only 6 to 8 inches tall *they have already cut corn yield* (figure 155).

If competition for plant nutrients was the only damaging effect of weeds, you could apply enough fertilizer for the corn and weeds, then let the weeds grow. Several researchers and some farmers tried this but the results were disappointing. Weeds compete for water and light as well as nutrients. In dry years the extra competition for water is enough to seriously cut corn yields. Besides, it takes so much extra fertilizer for the corn to offset competition when weeds are allowed to grow that it makes the whole proposition risky at best and quite unprofitable most years. In many years an enormous crop of weed seeds would be added to the soil if weeds were allowed to grow and this creates a still bigger problem in future years.

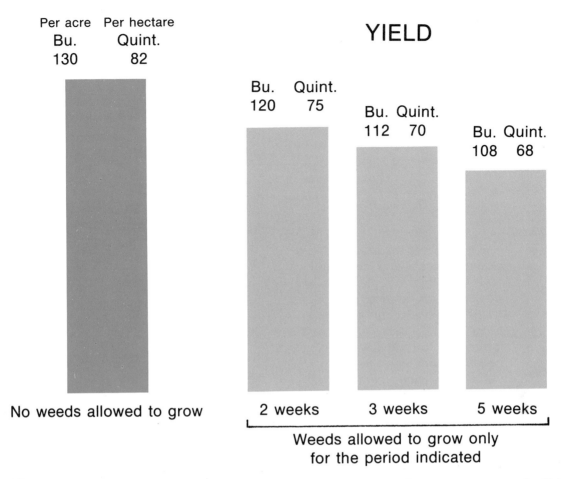

Figure 155. Early control is important; allowing weeds to grow for only 2 weeks after the corn came up caused a 10-bushel per acre (6.3 quintals per hectare) loss in yield. Allowing them to grow 3 and 5 weeks caused further losses.

Weeds that start after the last cultivation make the field look bad, but they don't hurt yields nearly so much as the weeds that grow when the corn is small. One reason for the extra damage from weeds that start early is that they *compete throughout the entire season.* Weeds that start after the last cultivation compete only part of the season. Besides, late-starting weeds tend to shade only the lower corn leaves which are already partly shaded by the upper leaves of corn itself.

Farmers know that corn needs warm weather in the spring in order to hold its own with weeds. Some seeds are able to grow quite well at temperatures that are too low for corn (figure 156). Early weed control starts with seedbed preparation and preplant or preemergence application of herbicides.

Preplant Weed Contol

Some herbicides are incorporated in the soil to avoid loss from volatilization or photodecomposition. Others are incorporated to reduce dependency on rainfall.

The most convenient time to incorporate these herbicides is prior to planting and as the seedbed is being prepared.

The advantages of preplant incorporation are obvious. Under most conditions the herbicide is placed in moist soil. Therefore it is not as dependent on timely rainfall as if placed on top of the soil. The early weeds, those that emerge with the corn, are controlled. There are also disadvantages such as the increased cost of a broadcast application. However, one of the most important

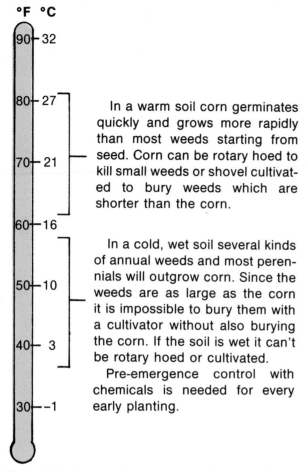

In a warm soil corn germinates quickly and grows more rapidly than most weeds starting from seed. Corn can be rotary hoed to kill small weeds or shovel cultivated to bury weeds which are shorter than the corn.

In a cold, wet soil several kinds of annual weeds and most perennials will outgrow corn. Since the weeds are as large as the corn it is impossible to bury them with a cultivator without also burying the corn. If the soil is wet it can't be rotary hoed or cultivated.

Pre-emergence control with chemicals is needed for every early planting.

Figure 156. The variation in growth of weeds and corn at different temperatures.

disadvantages is that the preplant application reduces or may eliminate your opportunity to make modifications in your cropping program if the planting season is delayed by wet weather. For instance if a herbicide such as AAtrex is applied the field is essentially committed to corn. Soybeans cannot be substituted as planting is delayed.

Depth and thoroughness of incorporation is important. Most of the annual weed seeds that are going to germinate are located in the upper 1 to 2 inches (2.5 to 5 cm) of soil so this is where the herbicide should be placed. Uniform distribution both vertically and horizontally in this area is important. Several tillage implements may be used to incorporate the herbicide. The tandem disk is one of the most common. Disking twice will usually result in more uniform distribu-

tion than disking once. The herbicide will be incorporated about half as deep as the disk penetrates. The field cultivator, another common tillage tool in parts of the Corn Belt, tends to streak the herbicide unless a harrow is used behind it. The disk followed by the field cultivator does an acceptable job of incorporation. Other implements that may be used include the mulch treader, drag harrow, rotary hoe and rotary cultivator.

Read the label and follow the recommendation of the manufacturer of the herbicide. Not all herbicides are adapted to incorporation in the soil.

If bad weather holds you out of the field until the effectiveness of the herbicide is beginning to deteriorate, a second application of the original herbicide may increase the danger of crop damage or residue problems. In addition it will usually be at variance with the registered and approved rates. The better approach will be to till the soil to kill the weeds and consider a preemergence or postemergence application of another herbicide.

Preemergence Weed Control

Preemergence weed control involves the application of herbicides as a part of the planting operation or immediately following planting. Preemergence weed control has many of the same advantages as preplant application especially the potential of controlling annual weeds that emerge at or about the same time as the corn. Additional advantages include the fact that you are left the option of switching to another crop if corn planting is unduly delayed by weather conditions. The amount of the herbicide used may be reduced by applying it in a band over the row (figure 157). However the weeds that emerge in the untreated area between the rows must eventually be controlled by mechanical means or a postemergence herbicide.

Weeds in the row cause early damage to corn. The ones between the rows have little

Figure 157. Near perfect weed control in the row from a band application. This is often a great advantage in wet springs. Cultivation can usually kill weeds between the rows, but cannot control weeds in the row that are too large to bury.

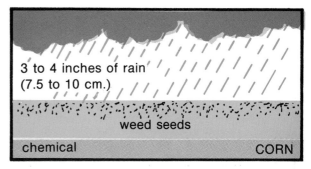

TOO MUCH RAIN.

Some of the more soluble chemicals leach BELOW the zone in which the weed seeds are germinating. Thus the weed seedlings escape injury. Some herbicides injure the corn seedlings when leached into contact with the germinating seed.

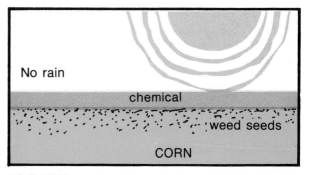

TOO DRY.

The chemical stays on the surface. Weed seeds germinate below the chemical. Many of the weed seedlings shoots can grow up through the chemical without being killed.

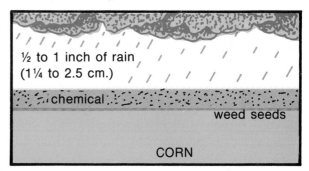

JUST RIGHT

The rain moves the chemical to the germinating weed seeds in the top 1 to 2 inches (2.5 to 5 cm.) of soil.

Figure 158. The amount of rainfall in the first week or two after treatment determines how well weeds are killed by pre-emergence application of herbicides. Soil type also influences pre-emergence chemicals. Soluble compounds move farther in sands than in silts and clays because an equal amount of rainfall penetrates farther. The amounts of clay and organic matter also influence the rate at which some herbicides are changed chemically to compounds that don't kill weeds.

effect while they are small but research at Rutgers University showed that they reduce corn yields if left only two or three weeks (figure 155). The effect is less pronounced when moisture and fertility are plentiful.

The major disadvantage of preemergence application of herbicides is that the effectiveness of the herbicide is more dependent on the weather than is the preplant incorporated herbicide.

If you have been using preemergence treatments for several years, you have probably found that results vary from year to year and sometimes from field to field in the same year. This is mainly because you need the right kind of weather, especially during the first week or two after treatment (figure 158), and you can't count on it every year.

Herbicides vary in water solubility. The more soluble the material is, the less rain you need to make it effective. But because it is soluble, it is more apt to be moved down too far below the germinating weed seeds and into the zone of the corn seedling by heavy rain.

Less soluble chemicals have a longer-lasting effect but need more rainfall to make them work.

Since preemergence chemicals sometimes fail to work, sooner or later you'll be asking how long to wait before moving in with a rotary hoe or cultivator. Here is the advice of E. L. Knake, weed expert at the University of Illinois:

"If for some reason the herbicide *is not* killing weeds, don't *wait too long* before cultivating.

"Suppose you used one of the more soluble preemergence herbicides at planting time. If it has not taken hold within two weeks and weeds are showing up, the chances are that the chemical is not going to work. In that case, it is usually advisable to move in with a rotary hoe or shovel cultivator to get the early weeds.

"If one of the chemicals with more residual effect has been used, weeds may sometimes begin to grow and then die, as the small weeds eventually pick up the chemical. But it's risky to wait too long, hoping that such chemicals will take hold, because they may not. With these longer-lasting chemicals you can go ahead and clean up the first crop of weeds with the rotary hoe or row cultivator and probably still get some benefit from the chemical on later weeds. Rotary hoeing about two weeks after planting does not appear to have much effect, good or bad, on most of the chemicals that are used.

"So, for top-yielding corn, weed control with cultivation or chemicals is imperative. Here are the main points to remember: If it is too wet to cultivate and the chemical is doing a good job of controlling the weeds, be thankful that you used it. If the chemical is not working, weeds are growing, and if it is dry enough to cultivate, it's best not to sit around waiting for miracles."

Postemergence Weed Control

The weed control plan should include an attack on weeds after the corn has emerged. The purpose may be

— to control the weeds between the row if you used a banded preemerge herbicide.

— an emergency treatment in the event that the preplant or preemerge herbicide failed.

— to supplement the preplant or preemerge application,

— or it may be all that is really needed.

2,4-D is often the first herbicide that comes to mind when one thinks of postemergence weed control but the rotary hoe, shovel cultivator and many other herbicides offer a wide variety of control methods.

In fields where broadleaf weeds such as cocklebur and morning glory are the primary problem, postemergence control may be equal or superior to preplant or preemergence control and more economical. On the other hand in fields where annual grasses are the primary problem, preplant or preemergence control is superior and postemergence control should be considered only as a supplementary or emergency control measure. This is particularly true of the directed sprays. The success of a directed spray usually depends on a height difference between the corn and the weed species to be controlled. If there is little or no height difference in the problem area or field, a directed spray may not be advisable.

Herbicide Combinations

The objective of combining two or more herbicides is to exploit their good features and reduce their faults. You may be able to control more weed species with the combination or it may reduce the risk of crop damage or residue carryover.

You may mix them yourself — "tank mix"

– or purchase them premixed. Tank mixing allows the flexibility of adjusting the ratio to fit weed or soil conditions. However, problems are sometimes encountered in mixing herbicides and you must remember that tank mixes are subject to EPA restrictions. Herbicides should not be mixed unless one or more carry information concerning the mixture on its label. If a tank mix is used the label restrictions on all products in the mixture apply just as if they were used singly.

Before mixing herbicides consult with your supplier concerning the proper mixing procedures and methods. Some emulsifiable concentrates and wettable powders do not mix well unless the proper method is followed. In general wettable powders should be added to the tank and agitated before an emulsifiable concentrate is added. The emulsifiable concentrate should usually be mixed with an equal volume of water before adding to the tank.

Liquid Fertilizer and Herbicide Mixtures

A combination of nitrogen fertilizer solution, 2,4-D, and a wetting agent has given excellent *late season* control of weeds in some areas (figure 159).

The nitrogen solution (ammonium nitrate alone or with urea) serves as a sidedressing of nitrogen and also increases the kill of weeds.

In order for this practice to work, *weeds must be controlled in some other way until the corn is about 15 inches (37.5 cm.) tall.* When the corn is 20 to 30 inches (½ to ¾ meters) tall, the fertilizer and 2,4-D combination is sprayed *at the base* of the corn plants and between the rows. At this stage, the leaves of small weeds are covered with the spray and killed; only the base of the corn stalk is covered and it is not injured. The purpose of the late spray is to control weeds until harvest time. If the corn plant population is high, late-starting weeds should not be a serious problem.

Figure 159. The left row was sprayed with a combination nitrogen fertilizer solution, 2,4-D, and a wetting agent. When corn is 20 to 30 inches tall (⅓ to ¾ meter), the spray is directed at the base of the plants and between the rows. This method is aimed at control of weeds that grow late in the season. Other means must be used to control weeds until the corn is 15 inches (37.5 cm) tall.

Here are the disadvantages of this plan:
• The nitrogen is left on the soil surface; in a long dry period it may not get washed down to the roots.
• There are lower cost sources of nitrogen for sidedressing.
• In some fields, grasses are the main weeds and 2,4-D does not control them. Combinations of nitrogen solutions and other herbicides are being studied.

Herbicides that are applied preplant may also be mixed with N, P, K fluid fertilizers or with nonpressure liquid nitrogen. Mixing the fertilizer and the herbicide can offer

229

savings in trips over the field. On the other hand the application may need to be delayed until shortly before planting if the herbicide is to be effective. In addition the equipment used to apply the herbicide-fertilizer mixture must provide an accurate and uniform application of the herbicide. Agitation must be adequate to prevent settling of wettable powders and layering of liquids.

If the right applicating equipment is available and the herbicide is compatable with the fertilizer being used, savings in both time and money may be possible by mixing the herbicide with the fertilizer.

What About the Residue Problem?

Crop rotations complicate the use of herbicides that have a long-lasting effect through the season because they sometimes remain in the soil and damage more sensitive crops in the following year. Soil conditions may be such that the chemical is not leached out, volatilized, or broken down by biological forces. Damage to oats, soybeans and sugar beets has occasionally resulted from carryover of a herbicide to which corn was tolerant. You can avoide or reduce the residue problem in several ways:

• Don't apply more of the herbicide than is absolutely necessary.

• Apply long-lasting herbicides in bands over the row to keep down the rate per acre.

• Whenever there is risk of carryover due to weather unfavorable for the breakdown of the chemical, plant corn again on the field or plant another non-sensitive crop.

• In the last year of corn before a sensitive crop, use a herbicide that has little carryover.

Crop Rotation to Control Weeds

Weeds have different life cycles. When you prepare a seedbed for a crop like corn you also prepare a seedbed for annual weeds. Unless you control them with chemicals and timely cultivation, annuals thrive in row crops. In contrast, they are not a problem in hay meadows that you leave down 3 to 4 years. After the first year, weed seedlings don't get a chance to start because of the competition from the meadow.

But some tough perennial weeds such as quack grass, bindweed, thistles and horse nettle are worse in long-term hay meadows because they can stand regular mowing as well as the hay crop. But you have a chance to reduce tough perennials when you plow, harrow and cultivate corn or any row crop;. also, there are several chemicals that you can use to kill them in corn, but not in other crops which would be killed with the weeds. Because corn acreage represents a large potential market for herbicides, chemical companies have developed a wider range of effective chemicals than for many other crops.

All in all, corn is hard to beat as a crop in which to effectively control weeds because you can use both chemicals and cultivation.

Shifts in Weed Species

Growing the same crop or one that requires similar cultural practices (seedbed preparation, date of planting and harvesting, cultivation) for several years, or applying the same chemical usually results in a shift in weed species. University of Illinois and USDA scientists studied the effects of various cropping sequences and applying the same or different chemical herbicides over a six-year period. Results are shown in table 31 and figure 160.

Several lessons were learned from this research:

• Cultivation alone resulted in more weed growth every year and a buildup in weed seeds at the end of six years.

• Growing the same crop every year helps to control certain weed species but results in an increase in those species which thrive under the same set of cultural practices as corn.

• Using the same herbicide every year controlled both grass and broadleaf weeds at the start, but in the fourth year (figure 160) weedy grasses became a

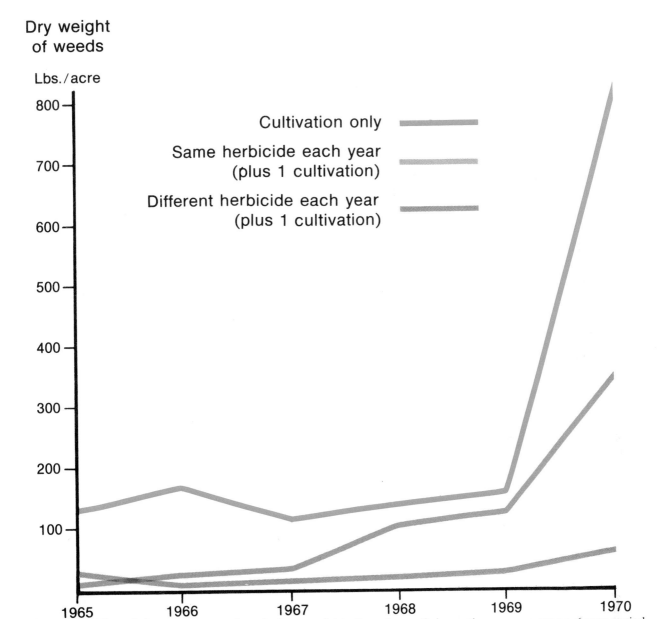

Figure 160. Effect of three weed control methods on weight of weed growth in continuous corn over a 6-year period. Urbana, Illinois, (F. W. Slife).

Table 31

Weed seed content at the beginning and after six years of various herbicide and cultivation treatments in a corn-corn-soybeans cropping system, Urbana, Illinois. (F. W. Slife)

	Grass		Broadleaf		Total	
	1965	*1970*	*1965*	*1970*	*1965*	*1970*
Same herbicide each year. Cultivated once	22	20	103	33	125	53
Different herbicide each year. Cultivated once	21	4	98	34	119	38
No herbicide. Cultivated three times	22	60	110	138	132	198

Figure 161. Effective early control of weeds without cultivation. Soil tilth is excellent and cultivation would serve no useful purpose.

Figure 162. The rotary hoe when run at high speed is extremely effective for killing small weeds both between and in the row. Hoeing is a faster and cheaper operation than cultivating. Also, it can be used to kill weeds in the row when corn is too small for cultivation.

232

problem and were very bad in the sixth year.

- Best weed control over the six years was obtained with several different herbicides so that no weed types could build up in population. Over the six-year period this system (plus 1 cultivation) increased net profit of a corn-corn-soybean system by 63 percent over three cultivations without an herbicide.

Danger of Resistant Weeds Developing?

It is reasonable to ask whether continued use of chemicals may produce resistant strains of weeds comparable to the insect strains resistant to insecticides. Theoretically it would be possible but it is unlikely to become a major problem for several reasons:

- Resistance develops only after treatment with the same chemical for many generations. Weeds normally have only one generation per year whereas some insects have many. If the same factors were at work, insects would therefore develop resistance sooner than weeds.
- There are few fields that receive the same chemical herbicide year after year. The herbicide is usually changed regularly because of a different crop being grown or because a new and better herbicide becomes available.
- Any weed that is tolerant to the herbicide may be killed by cultivation or hoeing.
- If resistant plants were developed, they would tend to remain within a field, farm or local community unless the seeds are airborne. Seeds may, of course, be carried by birds and in soil stuck to the wheels of moving vehicles, but those methods of spread do not compare in distance or rate with flying insects.

Should You Cultivate If You Don't Have Weeds?

Killing weeds is the *main* reason for cultivating. Much of the early research indicated that it was the *only reason*. Careful study of early research reveals that cultivated corn was compared with corn in which the weeds were *scraped off* with a hoe. Yields were about the same and the conclusion was reached that cultivation didn't pay. Weed control experts now believe that in many cases, shallow scraping with a hoe accomplished much of the effect of regular cultivation and this was overlooked in interpreting the results. The researchers had no way to control weeds without hoeing because they had no effective chemical herbicides.

Most recent research in which complete chemical control was compared with cultivation shows that cultivated plots yielded more. Whether cultivation is advantageous if you have *ideal tilth* and structure of the surface soil has not been proven by research. Most people believe that the advantage of one cultivation is to break a crust (figure 136, page 197) or at least improve the condition of the surface soil between planting and the time that corn is large enough to protect the soil from beating rains. If the surface is in ideal condition (figure 161) and there are no weeds, it is doubtful that cultivation for any purpose other than weed control will pay. An exception to this, of course, is where you must cultivate to shape the surface for furrow irrigation.

Why Rotary Hoes, Weeders and Spike Tooth Harrows Kill Weeds but Not Corn

These tools (figure 162) selectively kill small weed seedlings in corn because the root systems are small and thus are easily broken or dislodged. When the soil around them is moved even slightly, they lose part or all of their capacity to take in water and nutrients. They die quickly on bright, sunny days. Corn has a deeper, tougher root system. Thus, it escapes the action of the weeding tool. When weeds get 4 to 6 inches (10 to 15 cm) tall or larger, they also survive the rotary hoe, weeder or spike tooth, and thus must be killed by other means.

Minimum Secondary Tillage and Weed Control

Minimum secondary tillage doesn't always result in fewer weeds. It depends on the weather and your weed problem.

Weed seeds germinate mainly in the top inch or two (2.5 to 5 centimeters) of soil. When this layer is loose and uncompacted it dries out quickly. If the weather is quite dry right after planting, any minimum tillage system that leaves a coarse seedbed will greatly reduce weeds that start from seed.

But rain right after planting breaks down some of the small clods and makes enough fine soil particles to produce good contact for the germinating weed seeds. It also keeps the surface moist. Under these conditions, you may have almost as many weeds with minimum tillage as in corn planted with regular seedbed preparation.

Some tough perennial weeds — quackgrass is an example — have rootstocks that are in effect cut into pieces and "transplanted" by a moderate amount of secondary tillage after plowing. But if the furrow slice is left loose and it dries soon after plowing, the rootstocks will die.

In fields that are plowed when there is plenty of moisture in the fall and early spring, the rootstocks do not die. If you use a reduced tillage system in this situation, weeds may be worse with minimum tillage than with regular tillage before planting. Harrowing will help to kill them.

Weed Control in No-Till Corn

Both the existing vegetation and the weeds that are likely to germinate after the corn is planted must be controlled if the no-till system of producing corn is to be successful.

The existing vegetation may be a perennial grass and/or legume, an annual cover crop such as winter rye, or it may be annual weeds which emerge before the corn is planted. Regardless of the type of existing vegetation the best control is with a contact herbicide. Paraquat is one of the most commonly used contact killers. Successful control by a contact herbicide depends on uniform and relatively complete coverage of the vegetation to be killed. Therefore a high volume of spray is desirable. Forty to 80 gallons (374 to 748 liters per hectare) of spray is usually recommended. The amount used will depend on the density of the existing vegetation.

A selective herbicide will be needed to provide preemergence and postemergence control of the weeds that will germinate after the contact herbicide is applied. The selective herbicide or herbicides (more than one may be desirable) must also penetrate the existing vegetation to be effective.

Other Methods of Weed Control

Control by Microwaves

A machined called a "zapper" by the developer is reported to kill weeds, nematodes and soil insects by microwaves. The microwaves are the same type that are used in some ovens. The advantages for this type of weed control includes the fact that there is no residue. Weed seeds and seedlings are killed and the machine may be used in windy weather with no danger of drift. The main disadvantage of the system will probably be the cost which may limit its use to high profit crops.

Control by Changing Seed Dormancy

Weed seeds, almost without exception, have a biological mechanism that prevents them from germinating when environmental conditions are unfavorable for seedling growth. This is known as seed dormancy and is controlled in various ways. One of the most common examples of dormancy is the "hard seed" in many legume species. The seed coat of these seeds are impervious to moisture and remain that way until soil organisms or weathering weaken the seed coat enough to permit the imbibition of water. Cocklebur seeds are another common example of seed dormancy. The cocklebur has two seeds per

Figure 163. Root pruning injures corn. For late cultivating, stay as far from the row as possible and throw soil into the row to bury weeds.

fruit, one germinates the first spring but the other remains dormant until the second spring.

Scientists are exploring ways of manipulating seed dormancy as an aid in weed control. A new method of controlling witchweed which is a semiparasite of corn, several other cereals and grasses involves this principle. The germination of witchweed has two phases. The first phase is triggered by favorable moisture and temperature conditions. The second phase requires the presence of a chemical stimulant produced by a host plant. During the second phase the radical (seedling root) emerges from the witchweed seed, grows to and attaches itself to the roots of the host plant. The witchweed plant spends the first 4 to 6 weeks underground and is entirely dependent on the host plant for food and water. In the absence of the chemical stimulant the second phase of germination does not proceed and the first phase ceases until favorable conditions including the stimulant exist again. Weed scientists have discovered that ethylene gas will stimulate the second phase of witchweed germination. By injecting this gas into the

soil witchweed seed is induced to enter the second phase just as if the host plant stimulant were present. Obviously if no host plants are available to be parasitized the witchweed seedling dies.

Biological Weed Control

Biological weed control involves the use of living organisms to control undesirable weeds. It is based on the fact that man is not the only enemy of weeds. Insects feed on them and, as is true of most other living organisms, diseases of various kinds attack them. Among the enemies of weeds are other plants, including corn, which compete with weeds for water, food and light. The use of narrow rows and high populations is a form of biological weed control.

Insects, diseases and allelopathy (the suppression of one plant by chemicals released by another plant) are forms of biological control that are being studied.

The advantages of biological control of weeds include the possibility of being less expensive; less danger of undesirable residues in our feed and food; a probable savings in energy; and less danger to the opera-

235

tor or producer of the crop.

While scientists have long been interested in and researched different biological approaches to controlling weeds, there are few records of success. Most of the successes to date have involved weeds in noncropped areas. Two examples include the excellent control of the Pricklypear cactus in Australia and some other countries and the partial control of St. Johnswort in California through the introduction of insect pests.

The problems of developing a biological weed control for crop land are obvious. The disease or insect must not pose a threat to commercial crops. The control agent must be available in rather large quantities relatively early in the life of the weed and easily portable. This probably means that the control agent must be capable of being increased by commercial means prior to the planting season for the farmer's crop.

Progress is being made. In late 1974, the University of Arkansas Agricultural Experiment Station obtained a temporary permit from the Environmental Protection Agency to use a fungus disease to control northern jointvetch in rice. This will be one of the first attempts to use biological control in a commercial crop.

Killing Weeds with Flame

"Flame cultivation" was first tried in Alabama about 1936. With careful adjustment of the flame, proper foreward speed, and correct angle of the flame direction, small weeds can be killed in the row without damage to the corn. The base of the corn stalk is so thick that the temperature in it does not go high enough to cause injury, whereas both leaves and stems of small weeds are heated enough to be killed. Usually, flaming has to be repeated several times.

Burning weeds has some advantages over cultivating:

• Weed seeds are not brought to the surface to start a new crop.

• Flaming can be used when the soil is too wet to cultivate. This will, of course, cause compaction but may be preferred to letting the weeds grow.

• Less powerful, lighter-weight tractors can be used, thus reducing compaction and the tractor fuel bill.

• Soil moisture is conserved because moist soil is not turned up to the surface.

The disadvantages of flaming:

• Usually it costs more when the cost of equipment, fuel and labor are considered, although this may not be true in certain areas.

• If cultivation is needed to break a soil crust, flaming won't do it.

• You can't use it satisfactorily if the weeds are as tall as the corn.

• Five or more flamings may be needed for tough perennials.

• Flaming does not work well on a rough or stony surface because clods and stones shield the weeds from the flame.

Herbicide Injury

The tolerance of corn to injury by some herbicides is relatively narrow. Yet this disadvantage may be outweighed by the advantage that the herbicide offers in weed control in general or in the control of a specific weed problem. Care in application is the most important step in holding corn injury to a minimum when using any herbicide. It is equally important in reducing the possibility of serious residue injury to the crops that follow corn in your cropping sequence.

Operator mistakes and equipment deficiencies account for much of the injury reported by corn producers. A few of the common operator mistakes include failure to follow the directions on the label, overlapping, and failure to shut off the applicator at the end of the field. These are simple mistakes that can be easily avoided but somehow happen more often than they should.

Herbicide applicators need to be kept in good repair. Worn nozzles on liquid applicators and sagging tubes on granular applicators contribute to nonuniform application which increases the danger of corn injury.

Differences between hybrids in their tolerance to specific herbicides is real but not well documented. However, you may find a discussion of the herbicide reaction of the hybrids you plan to use with your seed corn dealer worthwhile.

Special compounds which are commonly referred to as "safteners" offer another means of holding the danger of herbicide injury to a minimum. Safteners are compounds that are added to the herbicide or applied to the seed. The presence of the compound reduces the effect of the herbicide on the crop but does not materially reduce weed control.

Special equipment and application techniques such as directed sprays allow the use of herbicides that could not otherwise be used. Contact herbicides may be applied if only the stem or one or two of the lower leaves come in contact with the herbicide. Other herbicides which are not readily taken up through the base of the stalk may be used as directed sprays. The directed spray can be effective only if there is a sufficient difference in the height of the weeds and the corn to allow the herbicide to reach the weeds but none or few of the corn leaves.

The USDA has developed a soil layering machine which may be useful in controlling weeds. The machine was developed for the control of witchweed but may be used for other weed problems. A swath of soil 18 inches (about ½ meter) wide and one or more inches thick is scooped up and held by a conveyor belt long enough to allow the application of herbicide to the newly exposed surface under the conveyor. When the scooped up soil is dropped off the conveyor it covers a band of herbicide. Some of the herbicides not normally used in corn can be used relatively safely with this method of application. The system not only keeps witchweed under control in the treated area but also many of the grass weed hosts of the semiparasite.

Read the Label and Follow Directions

This has been called the chemical age in agriculture, and herbicides are an important part of it. Most herbicides are safe when handled and applied according to directions. But many of them are irritating or dangerous to humans and pets. When carelessly used they kill crops, flowers, shrubs and lawns, and have led to many lawsuits. When applied at excessive rates, they can damage the crop that is treated and their residues may injure the one that follows.

9

Identifying and Combating Corn Troubles

Troubles with the corn crop often come without warning. When they strike, it may already be too late for any remedy, in which case the only thing gained is a lesson for the future. Often, though, if the problem can be diagnosed immediately, there is still time to correct it or to take action which will keep it from getting worse and spreading to other fields. Sometimes really serious crop losses can be avoided by prompt action.

The cause may be obvious — flood, hail, windstorms, your own or the neighbors' livestock. More often, it's obvious that something is wrong, but the cause and cure are not at all apparent. In these cases, whether you are the grower, or the dealer who sold the seed, fertilizer, herbicide, or insecticide, you need a guide to the most usual and important sources of trouble with the corn crop.

Pest Problems of Narrow vs. Broad Based Cropping Systems

Many persons who are not thoroughly familiar with agriculture have the notion that most corn pests could be controlled or greatly reduced if corn were grown more in rotation with other crops and not concentrated so much in the Corn Belt. Ecologists have suggested that more crop diversity and leaving fence rows and woodlots to harbor birds and other predators might reduce the need for insecticides.

The perfect example of controlling an insect through rotation is the corn rootworm. But several insect problems are either caused or aggravated by rotations and unmowed fence rows. Chinch bugs migrated from wheat fields and thin grass stands into corn fields. Grape colaspis was a problem only when corn followed clover. White grubs thrived in pastures and old meadows.

The fact is, of course, that the acreage of corn following corn is not large and has been declining as a result of a great increase in soybean acreage in the Corn Belt. Corn and soybeans are enough alike in tillage practices that some weeds are common to both when control is based upon cultivation. But different herbicides are used on the two crops, so weed species do not readily build up in a corn-soybeans system. Insect and disease problems are completely different on the two crops.

Are Pesticide Needs Greater in High Yield Systems?

The false notion is also widespread that high yielding crops are more fragile and therefore require larger amounts of pesticides and fertilizers. In order for that to be true the high yielding germ plasm would have to produce plants that were less competitive with weeds, more attractive or less resistant to insects, and more susceptible to diseases either because of greater succulence, thinner walls or improved nutritional status for disease organisms.

In fact high yielding systems have none of these characteristics as a general rule. It is true that *some specific new varieties* are hard hit by diseases especially when introduced without adequate testing into new geographic areas. But for every such case there are many instances of far greater tolerance to diseases and to a lesser extent to insects *because plant breeders have bred resistance into the improved strains.* In the case of weeds, high yield crops are always more vigorous and hence more competitive than are low yielding systems.

Why then has the impression become so widespread that high yield systems require more pesticides and fertilizers? It appears to be based upon the simple observation that U.S. farmers now apply more of these chemicals than they did twenty years ago. And in developing countries increasing amounts are applied in connection with the so-called "green-revolution".

This is not because germ plasm with higher yield potential requires more protection but rather because it will give a greater response to treatment. That is quite a different matter than requiring more protection.

Of course there are a few notable exceptions. Very high fertility makes corn more susceptible to stalk rots. Incidentally, this does not lead to any additional application of pesticides.

How This Section Is Organized

The information which follows is designed as a guide to all types of corn troubles; it describes and illustrates nutrient deficiencies, diseases, insects, and unfavorable weather effects. There are several approaches.

• First, a list of corn troubles in about the order they occur through the growing season (pages 241 to 245).

• Second, illustrations and descriptions of corn troubles as they appear from planting time until the crop is harvested and stored (page 246).

• Third, suggestions for trouble shooting when the seed, fertilizer, herbicide or insecticide is blamed for a poor stand or slow growth (page 297).

• Fourth, a description of tissue testing as a tool to help confirm nutrient deficiencies and spot hidden hunger (page 298).

• Finally, a list of important considerations in determining whether to tear up a poor stand and replant (page 300).

Some of the troubles that are described may seem quite obvious or elementary, but they are included here in the interest of supplying a complete reference.

CORN TROUBLES THROUGH THE SEASON

First Stage: Before Emergence

If corn doesn't come up on time, dig and look for trouble. In many cases a few minutes of digging will reveal that the corn has sprouted and will come up later. A little digging has saved many farmers the unnecessary expense and yield loss of disking up a field and replanting. In other cases it identifies the real problem.

- *No seed planted* . . . . Empty planter box
  Delivery system clogged

- *Seed isn't sprouted*
  Skips in the row . . . . No seed delivered

  Anhydrous ammonia injury (page 255)
  Aqua ammonia injury (page 255)

  Kernels normal, not swelled . . . . Too dry

  Kernels swelled, not sprouted . . . . Too cold, 50 F° (10° C) or less
  Too wet
  Fertilizer in contact with seed (page 249)

- *Rotted seed or seedlings*
  Dead Seed
  Pythium, Diplodia, or Gibberella . . . . (page 247)

- *Sprout twisted or leaves expanded underground*
  Crust . . . . (page 247)

  Mechanical injury to embryo . . . . (page 248)

  Seed planted too deep in cold, wet soil . . . . (page 248)

  Cloddy soil allows light to reach seedling too
  soon . . . . (page 248)

  Herbicide damage . . . . (pages 254 - 255)

- *Seed eaten, dug up, or sprout cut off*
  Kernels hollowed out . . . . Seedcorn maggot (page 246)
  Wireworm (page 246)
  Seedcorn beetle (page 246)
  Thief ant

  Plants pulled up, kernel eaten . . . . Crows, pheasants, blackbirds (page 249)

  Plants and kernels dug up and eaten . . . . . . Mice, ground squirrels

Second Stage: Emergence to Knee-High

- *Stand loss, stunted discolored plants grading into normal plants at margin of affected area* . . . . . . Garden symphylan (page 253)

- *Color normal but plants grow slowly.* . . . . Low general fertility
  Too cool, mainly below 55°F (13° C)
  Too dry

- *Plants discolored*
  Lower leaves dead, tips dying on
  upper leaves. . . . . Fertilizer injury (page 255)

  Pale green color overall . . . . Nitrogen shortage (page 260)
  Sulfur deficiency (page 264)
  Water logged (page 251)

  Leaf edges yellow or dead. . . . . Potassium shortage (page 260)

  Purplish or reddish, especially leaf tips. . . . . Phosphorus shortage (pages 256–257)
  Grape colaspis (page 253)
  Injured leaves (page 285)

  Whitish or yellow striping *between*
  leaf veins . . . . Magnesium shortage (page 262)
  Low pH (acid soil) (page 257)
  Iron shortage (page 262)
  Manganese shortage (page 265)
  Boron shortage (page 265)

  Whitish striping *along* leaf veins . . . . Sulfur shortage (page 264)

  Broad white areas, especially in center
  or toward base of leaves. . . . . Zinc shortage (page 258)

- *Leaves rolled, plants wilted* . . . . Drouth (page 259)
  Root or stalk-feeding insects

- *Leaves tightly rolled, not wilted.* . . . . 2, 4-D (page 254)
  Genetic characteristic

- *Leaf margins wilted or dead* . . . . Molybdenum shortage
  (according to Krantz and Melsted)

- *Plants suddenly wilt and die* . . . . Wireworms (page 246)

- *Plants cut off at ground level* . . . . Cutworms (page 252)

- *Leaves eaten*
  Large, gouged holes . . . . Sod webworm (page 252)

  Leaf margins only. Yellow-striped armyworm (page 253)

  Narrow whitish strips, leaf surface only . . . . Flea beetle (tiny black shiny beetle; damage insignificant)

Large areas appear speckled . . . . Thrips (tiny, slender, several colors, quick-moving; damage insignificant)

• *Plants twisted or broken off.* . . . . 2, 4-D injury (page 254)
Other herbicide injury (page 254)

• *Leaves appear watersoaked, then gray,*
then dead. . . . . Frost (page 250)

• *Dull gray areas on upper leaves.* . . . . Near frost and/or intense sunlight (page 250)

Third Stage: Knee-High to Tasseling

Several of the troubles that occur before the corn is knee-high carry over into the knee-high to tassel stage. The appearance of some nutrient deficiency symptoms change as the plants get older (see table 32, page 261).

• *Plants lean or fall over* . . . . Rootworms - western, northern, southern (page 269)
Wind lodging, especially in wet soil

• *Stalks break off* . . . . Corn borer, plants break at *borer holes*
2, 4-D injury, plants break at *lower joints* (page 254)
Cutworms, plants break at ground level (page 252)

• *Leaves eaten.* . . . . Several insects, including fall armyworm, true armyworm, chinch bugs, common stalk borer

• *Leaves shredded* . . . . Hail injury (page 273)

• *Leaves completely white*
Top leaves . . . . Heat (pages 266–267)

Scattered leaves. Amino triazole herbicide damage

• *White stripes and some white leaves on*
scattered plants only . . . . Genetic stripe (page 282)

• *Dead leaves or plants, usually row ends only,*
small areas. . . . . Ammonia burn (page 268)

• *Tassel abnormal, green bunch of finger-*
like branches . . . . Crazy-top (page 282)

• *Grayish colored galls changing to black*
on leaves, ears, stalks or tassels . . . . Smut (page 284)

• *Stunted plants, yellow and/or red leaves,*
multiple ears, extra long shanks, barren
stalks or poor ear formation . . . . Corn stunt (page 266)
Maize dwarf mosaic (page 266)

Fourth Stage: Silking to Maturity

- *Delayed silking or failure to silk* . . . . Population too high for sensitive hybrids
Drouth
Low phosphorus supply
Nitrogen shortage
Severe aphid attack (page 275)

- *Silks eaten off* . . . . Rootworm adults (pages 273 – 274)
Grasshoppers or Katydids (page 275)
Japanese beetle (page 286)
Woolybear caterpillar

- *Large, irregular areas eaten in leaves,*
  especially near edges of fields . . . . Grasshoppers (page 275)

- *Kernels tunneled and eaten* . . . . Corn earworm (page 275)
Corn borer (page 273)
Picnic beetles (page 276)
Corn sap beetles (page 276)

- *Reddish or purple leaves and stalks* . . . . Genetic character for purple color
Barren stalk (page 285)
Injury to leaf or stalk (page 285)
Corn stunt (page 266)
Maize dwarf mosaic (page 266)

- *Premature sudden dying of individual plants* . . . . Stalk rot (pages 288 – 289)
Severe corn borer damage (page 273)

- *Premature dying of plants in limited areas*
  of the field . . . . Pythium stalk rot (page 289
Drouth (page 289)

- *Dead, frosted appearance of leaves (see*
  table 33 for details) . . . . Leaf blights (page 276)

- *Barren stalks, no ears or only stunted nubbins* . . Population too high for hybrid and season
Low fertility
Drouth at critical ear-setting time
Aphid attack (page 275)
Silks eaten off by insects
Ear smut
Corn stunt
Maize dwarf mosaic
Severe early leaf blight

- *Full size cob, only scattered kernels* . . . . Lack of pollen at silking time
Insects ate off silks before pollination
Non-receptive silks due to drouth

244

Fifth Stage: Mature to Harvest

- *Stalks broken mainly below the ear*
  Between *joints*........................ Diplodia stalk rot (page 287)
  Weak stalks especially due to potassium
  shortage (page 260)
  Pythium stalk rot (page 289)
  Charcoal rot (page 288)
  Anthracnose (page 281)

  At *joints*............................ Giberella stalk rot (page 287)
  Brown spot (page 280)

- *Stalks broken mainly above the ear* .... Corn borer

- *Ears dropped off*
  Shank broken, whole ear dropped .... Corn borer

  Ears fallen out of husks................. Hybrid susceptible to ear drop

- *Rot or damage on ears or kernels*
  Whole ear or large section.............. Diplodia (page 290)
  Gibberella (page 290)
  Nigrospora (page 291)
  Physalospora (page 291)

  Small areas on the ear................. Fusarium (page 290)
  Ear worm damage (page 275)
  Penicillium (page 293)

Sixth Stage: In Storage

- *Ear and grain rots*........................(page 292)

- *Rats and mice damage*.....................(page 294)

- *Red stripes on kernels* ....Red streak (page 295)

- *Ears ¾ pound (.34 kilos) or larger* ....Planted too thin

- *Ears less than ½ pound (.23 kilos)* ....Low fertility
  Drouth
  Poor pollination
  Planted too thick
  Disease
  Insect attack on plants

- *Stored grain insects*......................(page 296)

CORN TROUBLES ILLUSTRATED

The following information is arranged according to the growth stages of the corn crop: before emergence; emergence to knee-high; knee-high to tasseling; silking to mature; mature to harvest.

Many troubles are confined to one of these stages. But others start in one stage and continue into the next; if you can't identify the trouble under the proper growth stage, look in the next earlier or later stage.

First Stage: Before Emergence

Seed Eaten By Insects:

• *Seedcorn maggots*

These insects often eat the entire kernel leaving only the seed coat. Partly eaten kernels may germinate but in most cases they soon die. The damage is scattered over the field and is often unnoticed. It becomes worse when any condition delays germination. Maggots can be controlled by seed treatment, band or broadcast insecticides.

• *Wireworms*

This insect eats the germ out of the kernel, attacks young seedlings, and continues until plants are knee-high on mineral soils and all summer on organic soils. Wireworm damage is worst in cool, wet spring weather. The insect is prevalent in poorly-drained areas and corn following meadows or pastures. Because there are several different species, changing rotations is not a suitable way to control them. When replanting an infested field, straddle the old rows: the wireworms will not move to the new rows. Therefore you can cultivate out the old rows. Seed treatment will partially protect the seeds and a broadcast insecticide will guard against later attack.

• *Seedcorn beetles*

These tiny beetles eat the kernel and have about the same effect as seedcorn maggots. They can be controlled in the same way.

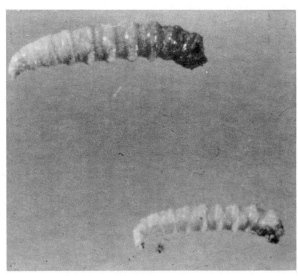
Seedcorn maggots (length: ¼ inch, .6 cm.)

Wireworms (length: 1½ inches, 3.75 cm.)

Seedcorn beetle (length: ¼ to ⅓ inch, .6 to .8 cm.)

246

Seedrots and seedling blights

A hard crust prevents emergence

- *Thief ants*

Small, orange to red in color. Damage is restricted to limited areas of the field because the ants live in colonies. Damage does not warrant control.

Seed Sprouted But Seedlings Have Died:
- *Seed rots and seedling blights*

Roots and mesocotyls have brown, water-soaked areas which, if they are severe, kill the seedling. This is most often due to some species of Pythium which thrives in cold, wet soil (below 50° F, 10° C) where conditions are unfavorable for germination and rapid growth of corn. Seed treatment protects the seed but does not protect the young roots and mesocotyl in a cold, wet soil. Pythium attack is not common but can be severe in individual fields.

Diplodia, Gibberella and Penicillium seedling rots are carried over in the seed endosperm from infection in the previous year. Modern seed growing, handling and treatment have practically eliminated these diseases in seedlings.

- *Too dry*

If there is enough moisture for the seed to germinate, it usually will emerge. Continued lack of rain may cause young seedlings to die, especially in loose, coarse seedbed, because the moist soil zone moves down faster than the young roots can grow.

Crust Prevents Emergence

A corn seedling can normally penetrate rather hard soil but sometimes a beating rain on a fine-textured soil makes such a hard crust that seedlings can't get up.

Unless the crust is broken within 2 or 3 days the leaf will emerge from the protective coleoptile and start to open and thereafter cannot penetrate any but the loosest soil even though the crust is broken mechanically or softened by rain.

Treatment: Use a rotary hoe (pulled backward), weeder, spiketooth harrow or cultipacker at once.

247

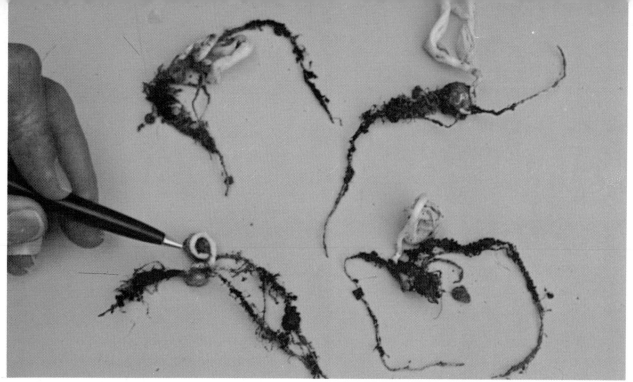

Growth delay (seed planted too deep)

Growth Delay

• *Twisted shoots, leaves expanded underground, roots normal*

Explanation: a) Faulty development of the coleoptile as a result of damage to the embryo from cracks in the seed coat or b) too deep planting. Normally the first internode (the zone between the primary and the secondary roots, figure 5 , page 5) and the coleoptile elongate until the coleoptile reaches light at the soil surface. The coleoptile, which is pointed and capable of being thrust upward through the soil, splits open and the leaf emerges above ground.

When corn is planted too deep, the first internode may not be capable of elongating enough to carry the coleoptile to the soil surface. The coleoptile may rupture and allow the first leaf to expand when light leaks down to it in a cloddy seedbed. Or it may rupture when growth is delayed for several days in a cold soil after germination. The expanded leaf is not stiff and pointed like the coleoptile and cannot push to the soil surface. Some hybrids, especially certain single crosses, appear more susceptible.

Treatment: None.

How to avoid: Plant shallow when planting early in a cool, wet soil. Avoid cloddy seedbeds.

Fertilizer Too Close to the Seed

• *Salt effect (fertilizer burn)*

This occurs mainly from too much soluble N and K fertilizers in contact with the seed (see table 19, page 168).

Treatment: None.

How to avoid: Use side placement; if you have to continue with the same planter, use smaller amounts.

Conditions that favor: Sandy soil, dry weather, fertilizer with a high salt index.

• *Ammonia toxicity (preplant)*

Long and short strips in rows scattered through the field; the corn row happened to be placed directly over the anhydrous band. The rate of NH_3 was too high, the placement was too shallow, or corn was planted too soon after application.

To confirm the diagnosis, take soil samples from two skip areas and two normal stand areas at seed depth and three inches (7.5 cm) directly below the seed. Run a pH test. If

Salt effect (fertilizer burn)

Bird damage

there is excess NH₃, the pH will be much higher in the rows where the stand is missing, especially at the lower depth. *This technique will work only until the ammonium has nitrified,* perhaps a little over a week in a warm soil (60-70° F., 16-21° C.) and up to two weeks when the soil temperature is 50 to 55° F. (10 to 13° C.).

After the ammonium has nitrified, the NH₃ core will become more acid. A nitrate color test such as the tissue test might identify the NH₃ core until rain leaches nitrate out of the zone of application.

Treatment: None.

How to avoid: Place NH₃ deeper, preferably 8 to 9 inches (20 to 22.5 cm) if corn is to be planted within a few days; hold rate at 100 to 125 pounds per acre (112 to 140 kilos per hectare) in sandy soils and 150 to 200 pounds (168 to 224 kilos per hectare) in silt loams and clay loams under ideal moisture conditions; apply 20 inches (½ meter) apart if rate is higher; allow more time (usually 1 to 2 weeks is entirely safe).

Conditions favoring: Sandy soil, dry soil, soil low in organic matter, compact soil, uneven surface.

In addition to anhydrous and aqua ammonia, NH₃ toxicity can be produced by diammonium phosphate (or any liquid fertilizer with free ammonia). Soon after application, one molecule of ammonia is released from diammonium phosphate. This NH₃ moves farther in sands, dry soils, and soils low in organic matter.

- *Biuret injury*

Several years ago some new process urea was heated too much and as a result had enough of the chemical biuret to affect germination when placed too close to the seed. This trouble is rare and is limited to fertilizers that contain urea (either dry or liquid).

- *Micronutrients and chelates*

Corn is very sensitive to boron near the germinating seed. Fertilizers formulated with enough boron to topdress alfalfa may seriously reduce corn stands when applied through the split boot. Probably no more than 1 pound of boron should be applied per acre (1.12 kilos per hectare) with side placement. Check with the supplier about the safety of band application of fertilizers with chelated micronutrients.

Seed Dug Up, Eaten or Sprout Cut Off
- *Bird damage*

Blackbirds, crows, pheasants and other birds sometimes go down the row and dig up shallow-planted corn. These same birds pull young plants after emergence until the plants are 6 to 8 inches (15 to 20 cm) tall. They eat the kernel and leave the seedlings on the soil surface.

- *Rodents*

Mice and gophers sometimes eat scattered seedlings in small areas especially in no-till planting in sod.

Treatment: Chemical repellants mixed with seed.

249

Second Stage: Emergence to Knee-High

Weather Factors

- *Killed by freezing*

Young corn plants are sometimes killed by a hard frost or freeze. Damage is most severe on organic soils (muck and peat) because the specific heat in a given volume of soil is less than in a mineral soil. This danger is most common in low-lying areas because cold air is heavier and accumulates there.

- *Leaves frosted, plants not killed*

A frost that kills the leaves often does not kill the corn plant because the growing point is either still below the soil surface or protected within the thick basal part of the stalk. When only the leaves are killed, the plant usually recovers as in this photograph taken ten days after the frost. Frost injury of this type has surprisingly little effect on yield because the bottom 4 to 5 leaves never get very large even on unfrosted plants. Moreover, they are soon heavily shaded by the larger leaves above them and therefore never manufacture much food for the growth of the corn crop. Don't be in a hurry to disk up a frosted field to replant. Wait a few days. If the growing point isn't killed, it will send up a new leaf within three or four days.

When poor growing weather follows a frost, the seedlings sometimes die. Check for rot by splitting the seedling and looking for dark, water-soaked condition. When this is common the plants usually die.

- *Gray leaf areas*

This condition is quite common when plants are 10 to 18 inches (25 to 45 cm) tall. It seems to occur most often when a very cool, clear night is followed by an extremely clear day. The gray areas tend to be portions of leaves that have a common orientation with respect to the horizontal position. This suggests the possibility of injury from either radiational cooling during the night or high

Frost kill

Frost damage

Gray leaf area

Excessive moisture

temperature due to direct, perpendicular sunlight or a combination of the two. On close inspection the grey areas are dull and appear somewhat wilted. They have never been observed to persist or to die.

• *Lack of moisture*

When young corn plants have enough nitrogen but lack moisture the leaves roll and become dull in appearance but they do not turn yellow. Later in the life of the corn plant a severe drouth may produce nitrogen deficiency even if plenty of nitrogen was applied (page 259).

• *Too wet*

Lower leaves on young corn plants growing in a waterlogged soil turn yellow and die. Plants up to 10 inches (¼ meter) tall have a low tolerance to wet soil because their only roots are even with or below the kernel. As soon as the secondary roots develop nearer the soil surface the plants can stand "wet feet" much better.

• *Wind damage*

Strong winds when plants are 4 to 10 inches tall (10 to 25 cm) can cause several types of damage. Leaf tips and edges turn white and then brown, due to whipping action or beating against the ground. The stalk and/or leaves show the abrasive effect of soil particles. Secondary roots are broken off and not established in the soil. When the plant has been whipped around extensively, a broken ring may form around the stalk just below ground level. The plants show typical phosphorus deficiency symptoms, probably because the secondary roots are not functioning well enough to absorb phosphorus.

Treatment: None. Plants usually recover, though they are temporarily slowed down and may be shorter than normal at the end of the season.

Conditions favoring: Loose soil, especially after rotary hoeing; dry soil, smooth surface.

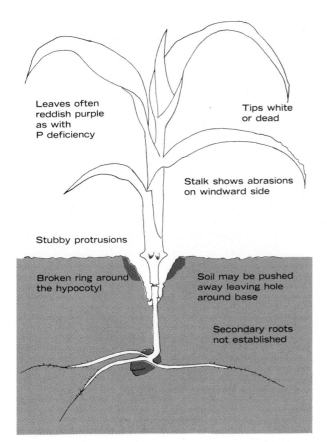

Leaves often reddish purple as with P deficiency

Tips white or dead

Stalk shows abrasions on windward side

Stubby protrusions

Broken ring around the hypocotyl

Soil may be pushed away leaving hole around base

Secondary roots not established

Wind damage

Insects

Several insects attack young corn plants. Brief descriptions of them are given here. Since chemicals for their control are constantly changing, you will want to contact your agricultural extension service or insecticide supplier for the latest information.

• *Wireworms*

This insect feeds on the seed and young seedlings; it continues to work on the base of plants until they are at least knee-high. Wireworms eat out the center of the stalk, causing the center leaves to wilt.

Treatment: None at this late stage.

How to avoid: Disk in a broadcast treatment before planting or band treat in the row at planting time. Check locally for newest insecticide recommendations.

• *Sod webworm*

The sod webworm produces injury similar to wireworms. These insects are a problem only when corn follows sod.

Treatment: Proper insecticide band-sprayed over the row. Seed treatment and soil insecticides do not control them.

• *Cutworms*

Several species attack corn. The most severe damage in the Corn Belt is from the black cutworm. Young worms feed on corn leaves but the larger worms feed below ground level. They completely sever young plants and eat out the center of the stalk base on larger plants. Plants up to 40 inches (1 meter) tall may suddenly wilt and die. During the day the cutworms stay in the soil within 2 to 3 inches (5 to 7.5 cm) from the plant and as deep as 3 inches (7.5 cm). Infestation starts in low spots in fields and may expand to large areas. When plants are cut above the growing point they recover though the yield will be reduced.

Treatment: None at this stage.

How to avoid: Broadcast a recommended insecticide before planting.

Sod webworm

Cutworm at base of severed plant (length: 1¾ inches, 4.4 cm. when fully grown)

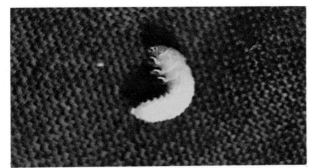

Grape colaspis (length: ⅛ inch, .3 cm.)

Garden symphylan (up to ⅜ inch, 1 cm.)

Yellow-striped armyworms

- *Grape colaspis*

Larvae feed on the roots of young corn plants and cause an apparent phosphorus deficiency with typical reddish-purple color.

Treatment: None after the damage shows. Broadcast or band the proper insecticide before or at planting.

How to avoid: When corn follows a legume sod, fall plowing or early spring plowing will reduce and may adequately control the insect. A liberal application of phosphorus through the planter largely offsets the damage of grape colaspis.

- *Garden symphylan*

A small white centipede-like creature up to ⅜ inch (about 1 cm) which attacks roots and other underground parts. Affected areas first show as poor stands in localized areas. Plant discoloration may be mistaken for nutrient deficiencies. A check will show poor root systems. Plants in affected areas continue to wilt and die. Surviving plants mature late and have no or only small ears. There is often a gradation from no stand to thin stand and poor growth in the center of the affected area to increasingly better stand and vigor toward the periphery of the area. Symphylan damage is often worst in heavy textured soils. But since they cannot make their own tunnels, they use those made by other soil animals or old root channels. A loose surface favors them. Suggested control in corn is to mark the affected areas and treat with an insecticide (parathion has been effective) the following spring.

- *Yellow-striped armyworms*

Armyworms feed on the leaves and in the whorl of young corn. They can be controlled by an insecticide applied to the plants, although it doesn't pay to treat any but the heaviest infestations.

Disease

• *Seeding blight*

Affected seedlings appear unhealthy; they wither and often die. When the kernel is examined it is found to be rotted and the roots and mesocotyls have brown water-soaked areas. Seedling diseases were once common but are now rare because disease-free seed corn is used and nearly all seed is treated with a fungicide.

How to avoid. Use well-matured, undamaged, treated seed.

Conditions favoring: Cool, wet soil. Blight organisms grow at 50° F (10° C) or lower but corn does not. Old seed is more susceptible.

Herbicide Damage

• *2, 4-D*

This is a growth regulator and may cause one or more of the following effects:

Onion leaf, in which the leaves remain wrapped into a tall spike.

Brittleness at the lower joints and thus susceptibility to breakage from high wind or cultivation.

Fasciation (growing together) and upcurling of the brace roots which never make contact with the soil.

Treatment: None.

How to avoid: Use approved rate; keep spray off leaves. To reduce breakage avoid cultivating while the plants are brittle.

Conditions favoring: High rate applications; too much spray on the leaves; very favorable conditions for rapid corn growth.

• *Eradicane, Eptam, Sutan +. Bladex, Lorox, Dalapon, etc.*

Chemicals that are meant for corn but are applied at excessive rates, or chemicals to which corn does not have good tolerance may cause abnormal color, twisted or thickened shoots and roots, and plants that never emerge.

Treatment: None.

How to avoid: Use only recommended herbicides and follow directions carefully on rate and time to apply.

2, 4-D damage (onion leafing)

2,4-D damage (fascination)

Fertilizer "burn"

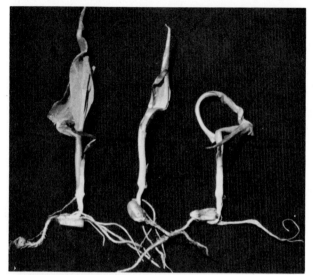
Chemical damage

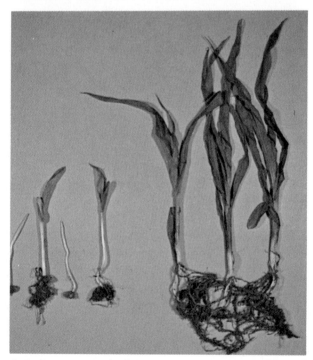
Anhydrous ammonia damage   Normal

Fertilizer Injury

● *Fertilizer "burn"*

Too much soluble fertilizer (especially N and K) placed close to seed may prevent germination; often the seedlings emerge and then die, or they live but are severely stunted. The leaves turn yellow or sometimes die.

Treatment: None.

How to avoid: Use side placement equipment. If you have to continue with a split boot, injury can be minimized by driving slowly, making certain the boot divider isn't worn, and by reducing the rate of fertilizer application.

Conditions favoring: Moist soil at planting followed by a dry period that evaporates moisture and concentrates the fertilizer salt solution; sandy soils; fertilizer with a high salt index.

● *Annydrous or aqua ammonia (preplant)*

Roots appear to be sheared off or dried up at varying depths from the kernel. The first leaf on the plants in the accompanying photograph is stunted, has yellowish areas, and is not fully expanded.

Injury from preplant applications of ammonia is uncommon but may increase if rates go up.

Plants are affected in sections of rows directly above the fertilizer strips and when too much anhydrous is applied too close.

For suggestions on how to confirm the diagnosis, see page 248.

Treatment: None.

How to avoid: see page 249.

Conditions favoring: Dry soil, sandy soil; soils with low exchange capacity; shallow placement of NH_3 combined with deep planting of corn.

Nutrient Deficiency Symptoms

Nutrient deficiency symptoms are most reliable when all other factors are favorable for rapid growth of corn. It is difficult to interpret nutrient deficiency symptoms in extreme drouth and in very cold or wet weather. Under these unfavorble growing conditions, a deficiency symptom tells you that the plant lacks the nutrient, but this may not mean that you should have used more fertilizer or a different fertilizer. For example, phosphorus deficiency symptoms show for a short time on young plants in cold, wet weather even though the most profitable amount of phosphorus was applied to supplement that shown by a soil test. Nitrogen deficiency symptoms have been observed on a dark prairie soil after 30 days without rain where 280 pounds per acre (314 kilos per hectare) of nitrogen were applied before planting. Extra nitrogen would not have prevented the deficiency. The nitrogen was too near the surface and there just wasn't enough moisture to carry it to the roots.

These examples underscore the fact that you must get as much information as possible about each field's history in terms of soil tests, fertilizer applications, and weather in order to interpret deficiency symptoms.

Tissue tests are sometimes helpful to confirm nutrient deficiency symptoms (see the discussion on page 298).

Among the secondary and micronutrients, clear-cut deficiency symptoms are the exception rather than the rule. In the early stages or if the deficiency is moderate, many of the symptoms look somewhat alike. Here are general approaches that you can use to confirm your tentative diagnosis:

1. Compare your conditions (soil and weather) with the conditions that favor de-

Phosphorus deficiency

velopment of a particular deficiency. (These conditions are described under the listing for each deficiency.) If your conditions are not those listed, your tentative diagnosis may be incorrect.

2. Take plant samples and have them tested.

3. Treat several test areas with foliar spray and observe the results; in some cases micronutrient deficiencies can be quickly corrected in this way.

4. Confer with your county extension agent and fertilizer dealer. They are usually eager to keep abreast of micronutrient and secondary nutrient problems and will appreciate being alerted if these troubles are found.

Spotting hidden hunger is a tough job because plants with hidden hunger have no clear-cut symptoms. They don't seem to be quite thrifty enough, or they don't have a deep, dark-green color. Sometimes they look fine until the picker opens the field and only then do you see that the ears aren't filled well and the yield is down.

Tissue testing regularly from the time the corn is knee-high, until the grain is well set, may reveal hidden hunger in time. Another method is to have a trial strip in each field on which you put 50 percent more fertilizer.

Low pH

● *Phosphorus deficiency*

Plants are very dark green with reddish-purple tips and leaf margins. They grow slowly. At this stage — before the plant is knee-high — the root system is quite inefficient in getting phosphorus. Therefore a shortage in the plant can be caused by any of these factors:

1. Not enough P in the soil or the fertilizer band.

2. Soil cold and either too wet or too dry.

3. Soil compacted enought to restrict root growth.

4. Roots pruned by cultivator, fertilizer sidedressing knife, or soil insects.

5. If all soil conditions are favorable, look for root-feeding insects that cut down the number of absorbing roots.

The P deficiency symptoms nearly always disappear even in *low* phosphorus soils when the plants get 24 to 40 inches (60 to 75 cm) tall.

Treatment: If applied P was adequate, wait for warm, dry weather. If inadequate, P can be sidedressed, according to research in Iowa. About 40 pounds of P_2O_5 (17.4 pounds P) per acre (45 kilos P_2O_5, 19.5 kilos P per hectare) is suggested for trial.

How to avoid: Assure enough available phosphorus through broadcast and/or row application. Avoid overworking the seedbed which may cause compaction and a surface crust. Control root-feeding insects.

● *Low pH*

Corn plants growing at very low pH (below 4.5 on mineral soil) often show stunting or beaded streaking of leaves, followed by reddish-purpling and dying of the older leaves. This is similar to magnesium deficiency. In mild to moderate cases, the plants outgrow the symptom when they are 24 to 30 inches (60 to 75 cm) tall.

Treatment: It is not known whether liming is feasible to save the crop.

How to avoid: Use limestone to raise the pH to a *minimum* of 5.5 (preferably 6.0) on mineral soils and 4.8 (preferably 5.5) on organic soils.

257

Zinc deficiency symptoms do not always look the same. The most common symptom is light streaking followed by a broad whitish band starting slightly in from the leaf edge and extending to the midrib. The leaf edges, midrib and tip of the leaf remain green. Internodes are often short and the plant appears squatty. New leaves are sometimes nearly white, hence the descriptive name "white bud." Sometimes the leaf edges and stalks take on a purplish color. The leaf area in the white band may die at any time. Some states report that on acid soils the lower nodes of zinc deficient plants become clogged with iron and are brown or purple when split open.

Unless the deficiency is severe, the plants usually outgrow the symptom as the size of the root system increases. This is much the same seasonal pattern as for a phosphorus deficiency except that zinc deficiency disappears at a later stage of growth. To confirm the diagnosis of zinc deficiency, spray 10 to 20 plants with a solution of one teaspoonful of zinc sulfate in one gallon of water. If zinc is the only nutrient that is deficient, new leaves will have a normal green color as they emerge.

Treatment: Zinc deficiency can be corrected temporarily by spraying with a ½ to 1 percent zinc solution. The Nebraska Experiment Station suggests that this should be supplemented by an immediate sidedressing with a nitrogen fertilizer that contains zinc. They state that zinc in an organic carrier is about five times more effective than the same amount in an inorganic carrier. Some of the organic carriers are: Rayplex Zn, Zinc NTA, Zinc 45, and Sequestrene Na₂Zn (EDTA). Some inorganic carriers are zinc sulfate, Zinc-gro, zinc chloride, zinc MNS, and Zinc-el-izer. Experimental ammonium polyphosphate fertilizers may prove effective carriers for zinc.

Nebraska recommendations are 2 to 5 pounds (1.2 to 5.6 kilos per hectare) of zinc

Zinc deficiency

Zinc deficiency

Drouth

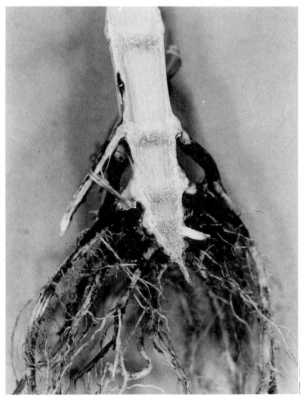

Darkened nodes

in inorganic form for mild deficiencies, 5 to 10 (5.06 to 11.2 kilos per ha.) for moderate, and 10 to 20 pounds (11.2 to 22.4 kilos per ha.) for severe cases. The amounts in organic forms would be 1/5 as much.

How to avoid: Broadcast and plow under needed amounts of zinc after you have learned that you have zinc-deficient soil. Keep the phosphorus at a reasonable level and avoid·phosphorus in row fertilizer on high-phosphorus, zinc-deficient soils. Apply extra zinc when corn follows sugar beets on soils with a marginal zinc supply.

Conditions favoring:

1. Removal of topsoil, exposing a subsoil high in pH and low in organic matter: zinc deficiency is often first observed on fields that have been leveled for irrigation and on cut areas for terraces.

2. High phosphorus in the soil and in row fertilizer applications.

3. High pH.

4. Cool, wet soil.

5. Sugar beets preceding corn.

6. According to some reports, the application of boron nullifies the effect of zinc where zinc is needed.

Third Stage: Knee-High to Tasseling

● *Lack of moisture*

When young corn plants have enough nitrogen but lack moisture the leaves roll and become dull in appearance but they do not turn yellow. Later in the life of the corn plant a severe drouth will produce nitrogen deficiency even if plenty of nitrogen was applied.

● *Darkened nodes*

Some persons have become alarmed at darkened nodal areas at the base of the plants. Attempts have been made to correlate the darkening to certain nutrient deficiencies or toxicities. But in most cases it may be natural darkening with increasing age and the formation of more woody tissues.

Nitrogen deficiency

- *Nitrogen deficiency*

When young corn is short of nitrogen, the *whole plant* is pale yellowish green, small, and has spindly stalks. V-shaped yellowing from the tips of the leaves shows later, beginning with the bottom leaves.

Row fetilizer usually prevents early N shortage except in very wet soils. In low N soils, the symptom gets worse as the season wears on.

Treatment: If the total N in the field from fertilizer, manure, and legumes is believed to be adequate, wait for warmer, drier weather to make nitrates available. If total N is short, sidedress as soon as the soil is dry enough. The various sources of nitrogen are equally effective.

Conditions favoring: Cold or wet soil; drouth, especially after mid-season; large amounts of low-nitrogen residues; sandy soil; heavy leaching rains; ponded areas when temperature is warm.

How to avoid: Be sure that the total nitrogen supplied in all forms (fertilizer, legumes, manure, soil organic matter) is adequate. Supplement strawy residues and cornstalks with extra N. Include nitrogen in the row fertilizer if the soil is cold and wet.

- *Potassium deficiency*

Yellowing and dying of leaf margins beginning at the tips of the lower leaves. This is the most specific and easiest deficiency to recognize. K moves in the plant from the old to the new leaves; therefore the top leaves appear normal unless the deficiency is extreme, then the whole plant becomes yellowish.

Symptoms appearing at an early stage mean that the total soil supply is low or that

260

Table 32. Nitrogen, Phosphorus, and Potassium Deficiency Symptoms Through the Season

These descriptions apply mainly to conditions of moderate to severe deficiency. Slight deficiencies (in the hidden hunger range) reduce the yield but produce no recognizable symptoms.

Emergence to 15 inches (37.5 cm)	15 inches to Silking	Silking to Mature	At Maturity		
			Stalks	Ears	Kernels
NITROGEN Pale yellow, stunted plants. Slender stalks.	V-shaped yellow-orange color becomes more pronounced and leaves begin to die at the tips. The symptom shows most on the lower leaves but progresses up the plant as plants become older. Stalks remain thin and spindly.	In severe shortages the symptom continues to advance to younger leaves up the plant. With moderate to slight shortage the symptom may show for the first time at this stage of growth. Even when large amounts of N were applied the symptom may show at this stage during severe drought.	Slender. Usually little lodging because ears are small and plants are not predisposed to stalk rots.	Small, pinched at the tip. When aggravated by drought, filled kernels stop abruptly short of the ear's tip.	Shiny, glossy, hard, flinty. Often pointed and shrunken near the tip on the side opposite the germ since that is the last part of the kernel to fill and N deficiency is often most severe late in the season.
PHOSPHORUS Leaves dark bluish-green; more narrow than normal leaves; turning reddish-purple starting at tips of upper leaves. This is the period during which the symptom is most often seen.	Usually the symptom disappears during the early part of this period unless the deficiency is severe. Reddish-purple color at this stage is more often due to other causes.	The symptom rarely continues to this stage.	No special characteristics other than small size.	Small, misshapen, often appear twisted because rows or parts of rows are missing on one side.	No characteristic appearance other than small size.
POTASSIUM The symptom does not show this early except in extreme cases. Leaf margins on the lower leaves turn yellow then start to die from the tip back.	Margins of lower leaves turn yellow and die, starting from the tip. When the deficiency is moderate to severe, leaves may be affected nearly to the top of the plant. Leaf margins shatter and break as the deficiency continues. Plants are shortened but stalk isn't spindly as with nitrogen shortage.	The symptoms described in the preceding stage continue. Leaf blight and stalk rot are more severe when K is deficient. Leaf blight increases stalk rot and this contributes to more stalk breakage and lodging.	Potassium deficient plants have weak stalks and this combined with more susceptibility to stalk rot greatly increases lodging.	Small, chaffy, dull in appearance because kernels are poorly filled.	Kernels thinner than normal; deeper dent; dull, lightweight, soft starch compared to flinty condition with N shortage.

261

Potassium deficiency

Magnesium deficiency

the root system is severely restricted, perhaps by a compacted soil layer.

Treatment: Plan to correct the deficiency before next year! Sidedressing is suggested for trial on a small area as soon as the trouble is identified if plants are 18 inches (½ meter) or less.

How to avoid: Broadcast potassium according to needs indicated by soil tests. Include potassium in the row fertilizer for insurance in cool, wet springs.

Conditions favoring: Sandy soil; strongly weathered soils (soils that are old geologically speaking); organic soils; heavy removal in preceding crop (alfalfa, corn silage); wet or compacted soil.

● *Magnesium deficiency*

Yellow streaking of the lower leaves between the veins, sometimes followed by dead round spots which give the impression of beaded streaking. The older leaves become reddish-purple and the tips and edges may die in extreme cases.

Treatment: The most economical long-term treatment is with broadcast applications of dolomitic limestone. On soils that are already high in pH, 25 pounds per acre (28 kilos per hectare) of magnesium in soluble form can be applied in the row. A foliar spray of 20 pounds of magnesium sulfate (Epsom salts) in 100 gallons of water (about 10 hectoliters per hectare) will supply enough magnesium without burning the corn leaves.

How to avoid: Maintaining a suitable pH (at least 5.5 and preferably 6.0 on mineral soils and 5.5 on organic soils) usually prevents the deficiency. Use dolomitic limestone.

Conditions favoring: Strongly acid, sandy soils in regions of moderate to heavy rainfall where magnesium has been extensively leached from the soil profile; high potassium.

● *Iron deficiency*

Upper leaves become pale green to almost white between the veins; the entire length of the leaf is affected. This deficiency is rare because corn does not have a high iron requirement.

Treatment: Spray with a 1% solution of iron, preferably early in the morning or late in the day. If the deficiency is severe, several, sprayings may be needed to maintain good green color. Ferrous sulfate and several brand-name products may be used. Soil applications are not feasible because the iron is soon converted to an unavailable form.

Iron deficiency   Normal

Nebraska extension specialists suggest that since they are not iron-sensitive, corn, alfalfa and small grains are the most economical crops for iron-deficient soils. Beans, milo and millet can then be grown on soils that are not deficient in iron.

Conditions favoring: Alkaline (high pH) soils; wet, poorly-aerated soils; compacted soils; cool weather.

• *Calcium deficiency*

Rare. Leaf tips are stuck to the next lower leaf, giving a ladder-like appearance. The side effects of low calcium (low pH, too much manganese, iron and aluminum) will usually have an adverse effect on corn growth before the level of calcium is low enough for the ladder-like deficiency sympton to show.

How to avoid: Maintain a suitable pH level, at least 5.5 on mineral soils (preferably 6.0) and at least 4.8 (preferably 5.5) on organic soils.

Conditions favoring: Very low pH, high magnesium and potassium.

Calcium deficiency

263

- *Copper deficiency*

This is a rare deficiency. The young leaves are yellow as they come out of the whorl. Leaves become streaked — much as they do with an iron deficiency. The stalk is soft and limp. In severe cases, the leaf edges die in a pattern similar to potassium shortage.

Treatment: Where needed, copper is usually applied in a mixture with N-P-K fertilizers in the form of copper oxide (70 to 80% copper) or copper sulfate (25% copper) in the band at planting time. Suggested rates are 2 to 4 pounds per acre (2.2 to 4.5 kilos per hectare) of copper for organic soils and ¼ as much for mineral soils. It can be sprayed on at the rate of 1 to 3 pounds of copper per acre (1.1 to 3.4 kilos per ha.) in the form of basic copper sulfate in solution. Since it is not fixed in unavailable forms in the soil, a 20-pound per acre (22.4 kilos per hectare) application of copper will last for many years on organic soils.

Copper deficiency

- *Sulfur deficiency*

Reported in many fields in California since 1968. The yellowing and stunting are usually most severe in the seedling stage, but stunting and interveinal chlorosis persisted to the pre-tassel stage in some fields. California agronomists suggested that a small amount of sulfur in the row fertilizer or some sulfur in the preplant application of nitrogen should correct the problem.

There is little research on which to base treatments for corn. Continued use of ammonium or potassium sulfate, ordinary superphosphate, or sulfate of potash magnesia would likely avert a deficiency. If a shortage is found, powdered sulfur, sulfur in anhydrous ammonia, ammonium thiosulfate, and ferous sulfate are sources.

Smoke returns enough sulfur to avoid shortages near industrial areas but this will be reduced when smoke emissions are controlled.

Conditions favoring: Acid soil; low organic matter; and cold, wet soil which delays the

Sulfur deficiency

release of sulfur from decaying organic matter.

- *Boron deficiency*

Plant symptoms are rarely seen. Deficient plants have a bushy appearance because the upper internodes do not elongate. Leaves are brittle and have small dead spots. Tassels and ear shoots are reduced or fail to emerge. Wisconsin researchers believe that barren stalks in drouth periods are sometimes due to boron deficiency.

Normal   Boron deficiency

Treatment: None for the current crop.

How to avoid: Boron can be mixed with N-P-K fertilizers and broadcast or banded to the side: contact with the seed must be avoided since it is easily damaged by boron. About ½ pound of boron per acre (.56 kilos per ha.) is suggested for acid, sandy soils and 1 (1.1 kilos per ha.) pound for finer-textured soils with high pH.

Conditions favoring: Drouth; high pH, sandy soils.

- *Manganese deficiency*

Corn has a low manganese requirement and therefore deficiencies are rare and symptoms are not clear cut. Leaves become olive green and may be somewhat streaked. Streaking of only the younger leaves, and also of all leaves has been reported by researchers. Michigan research indicates that in advanced cases deficient corn leaves have elongated whitish streaks which turn brown

Manganese deficiency

in the center, after which the dead tissue falls out. Severely deficient plants often have thin, limber stalks.

Treatment when the trouble is diagnosed: Michigan researchers suggest foliar applications of manganese sulfate or other water-soluble forms at the rate of 1 pound per acre (1.1 kilos per hectare) when the symptoms first show and again when the plants are 24 inches (⅔ meter) high.

How to avoid: Manganese can be mixed with acid-forming fertilizer and applied in a band near the row to supply 3 to 8 pounds per acre (3.3 to 9 kilos per ha.) of manganese on mineral soils and 5 to 10 pounds per acre (5.6 to 11.2 kilos per ha.) on organic soils. Manganese sulfate and manganous oxide are suitable. The oxide is preferred by manufacturers. These compounds are not suited to broadcasting because the soil soon makes the manganese unavailable. Chelated forms may be suited to soil application but research results are meager.

Conditions favoring: Peat, muck; sandy soils high in organic matter; high pH.

• *Corn stunt virus and Maize dwarf mosaic*

Corn stunt was identified in San Joaquin Valley, California, in 1942; near Weslaco, Texas, in 1945; in Mississippi in 1962; and in other southern states in 1963. First symptoms are faint yellowish stripes on the upper leaves of plants about 6 weeks or older. The upper internodes are shortened so the plant appears bunchy. Leaves become more yellow and then often though not always turn reddish-purple. Affected plants sometimes tiller excessively and produce several ears with little or no grain. Others have extra-long ear shanks. Some develop brace roots at several nodes above those on normal plants. Individual plants may have one or several of these characteristics. Note that the first symptoms are similar to several micronutrient deficiency symptoms and probably could not be distinguished from them until the more severe symptoms develop. The stunt virus is transmitted from diseased to healthy plants *only* through feeding activities of two kinds of leafhoppers which serve as an alternate host. These hoppers can transmit the disease beginning about two weeks after feeding on diseased plants.

Maize dwarf mosaic is a new disease first found in Ohio in 1963. In 1964 it was identified in several Corn Belt states. The symptoms appear to be the same as those of corn stunt but it does not require an insect as an alternate host. Aphids can spread the disease by carrying it from plant to plant and it can also be spread mechanically by rubbing the juice of infected plants onto healthy plants. Sorghum and several weed grasses contract the disease. It is believed that the virus overwinters in a live plant. In many areas Johnsongrass is the prime suspect.

Maize dwarf mosaic damage is confined mainly to the bottomlands along the major rivers. Fortunately, sources of genetic resistance have already been found and incorporated into corn germ plasm.

Treatment: There is no treatment for plants that show symptoms of either corn virus.

Experience to date indicates that if a few plants in a field have the disease the first year, there is often a great increase the following year. The safest policy is to grow a resistant hybrid or substitute some other crop rather than run the risk of total infestation.

Fields that have symptoms which you suspect are corn virus should be immediately reported to the county extension office or state college of agriculture but plants should not be sent anywhere for diagnosis because of the danger of spreading the disease.

• *Extreme heat*

Temperatures in the range of 100 to 115° F (38 to 46° C) cause some plants to turn nearly white and later to die at the top. The actual temperature at which this takes place depends somewhat on moisture supply. Also, hybrids differ in their ability to stand high temperatures.

Symptoms of corn stunt virus and maize dwarf mosaic

Effects of extreme heat

Lightning damage

Anhydrous ammonia "burn"

• *Lightning*

Lightning can completely kill plants in small areas in a corn field. This is a rare phenomenon; when it occurs plants in the center of the area are completely dead. The injury is progressively less serious as you move away from the point of discharge but the affected area has very sharp boundaries.

• *Anhydrous ammonia "burn"*

A high concentration of ammonia gas in contact with a plant kills the leaves. The dead areas have a bright straw color in sharp contrast to the rich green of unaffected leaves. The injury nearly always occurs at the end of the field when ammonia is released while the knives are out of the soil.

Rootworm damage

Larva of northern corn rootworm

● *Rootworms—Northern, Southern, Western*

Larvae of northern and western rootworms eat on the surface of the roots, especially the crown roots just below the surface; they gouge out holes, and tunnel lengthwise. The southern variety feeds on the roots but does not tunnel lengthwise. It also feeds on the growing point of the stalk while it is still near the soil line and may cause the plant to wilt and die. Root systems are weakened by all three and lodging is common. The lodged plants later turn up but have a crook at the base. The adults feed on corn silks.

Spread of resistance to insecticides: Beginning in 1959, entomologists noted that the western corn rootworm had developed resistance to chlorinated hydrocarbon insecticides. (Resistance to aldrin was previously noted in 1948.) The western rootworm inter-

breeds with the other types; both the larva and adult of this mating closely resemble the western type.

Outlook: Widespread and repeated use of the same or related insecticides caused the emergence of resistant strains because the susceptible insects were killed, leaving the resistant ones to multiply. Many fields in the Corn Belt now have substantial residues of the chlorinated hydrocarbons or their decomposition products. Alternative insecticides are available. Fortunately fields can be checked each year to assess the population of adult beetles in order to determine whether an insecticide should be applied in the following year. One entomologist estimated that a farmer could make $500 per hour spent in such monitoring. Environmental concern together with the develop-

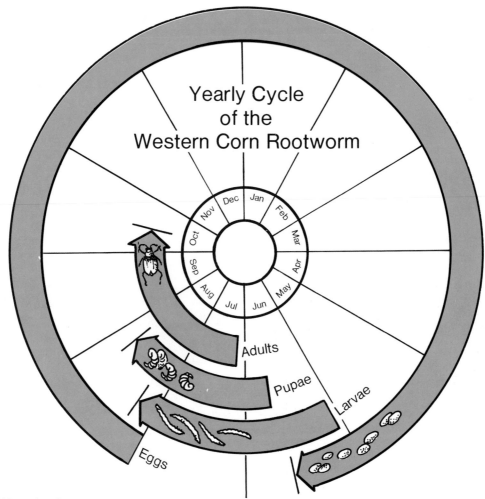

Figure 164. Life cycle of western corn rootworm.

ment of resistance in insects and increased cost of insecticides work against applications of chemicals in the absence of a proven need.

● *Chinch bugs*

These tiny insects move into the edges of corn fields from infested fields of small grain. Chinch bugs are most active in dry seasons and apparently survive best on nitrogen-deficient plants. When they attack a cornfield in large numbers, the lower leaves wilt and eventually the whole plant turns white.

Treatment: Contact sprays and selected sprays applied to the soil surface in the path or migration.

How to avoid: Vigorous growth of any crop reduces chinch bugs because they cannot survive in the shade and high humidity of dense crop growth.

● *True armyworm*

Heaviest attacks of this insect occur when the worms move as an army from small grains or grass meadows into cornfields. In the southern Corn Belt, spring generations are most destructive; in the northern Corn Belt, midsummer broods do the worst damage. The worms begin by stripping leaves. If they eat the growing point, the corn plant will not recover. Damage is also severe if the worms chew off the silks before pollination. The armyworm feeds its tremendous appetite mainly at night; during the day it hides in the soil or corn whorl.

Cool, wet spring weather favors survival of the armyworm while it retards development of their disease and insect parasite enemies. The armyworm can be controlled

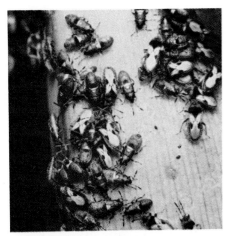
Chinch bugs

True armyworm (length: ½ inch, 1.25 cm. full grown)

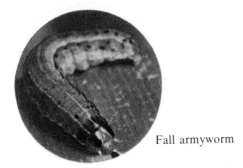
Fall armyworm

by chemicals but expert advice is helpful in deciding whether this will pay. Your decision should be based on the number of worms, their stage of growth, the size of the corn, and the extent to which parasites are already attacking the armyworms.

• *Fall armyworm*

Fall armyworm is usually a pest only in the southern part of the Corn Belt, but occasionally it is serious in spots within late-planted fields farther north. The worms feed on leaves and in the whorl, but more important is the fact that they enter the ear and the upper parts of the stalk. If the number of worms justifies an insecticide, it should be applied early — large worms will already have done their damage and soon stop feeding to pupate.

• *Common stalk borer*

A brown worm up to 1½ to 2 inches (3.75 to 5 cm) long with white longitudinal stripes and a distinct purple area in the middle of the body. The larvae hatch in May from eggs deposited the previous August in weeds and grassy patches along fence rows, ditches and grass waterways. The larvae tunnel into corn, small grains and grasses. By the time the damage is seen, such as holes in unfolding corn leaves eaten in the whorl, it is too late to treat. Generally the insect is of minor importance. Keeping weeds under control in August and September next to fields that will be planted to corn the following year will reduce the pest.

• *Western bean cutworm*

When fully developed the worm closely resembles cutworms and fall armyworms but in earlier stages it is much lighter in color. When first reported it appeared that the Western bean cutworm was spreading eastward at 50 to 60 miles (80.5 to 96.6 kilometers) per year. But after several years it has become a problem only in the region just west of the Corn Belt — central Nebraska, Kansas and eastern Colorado. The worm penetrates

Common stalk borer

the ear husks and eats the grain. Yield losses range from minimal up to a maximum of 60 percent.

- *Cereal leaf beetle*

First recognized in southwestern Michigan and northern Indiana in 1962. It has spread to adjacent areas. The cereal leaf beetle appears to feed only on plants in the grass family — small grains, quackgrass, orchardgrass, timothy, corn. In the first two years after it was found, the insect did not do much damage to corn. The worms, which do the most damage, had passed their peak of feeding before corn was up. The summer adults fed on corn and produced light damage, then they moved on to destroy small grains. The insect may become a threat to corn if it spreads to areas where the crop is planted earlier. In order to slow the spread of this insect, shipment of some commodities from infested regions is regulated by inspection.

Cereal leaf beetle (length: 3/16 inch, .48 cm.)

272

Hail damage

• *Hail damage*

Hail damage is immediately recognizable by shredded leaves hanging in tatters. Small plants and, in extreme cases, even full-sized ones are completely broken off. The real problem is how to assess the damage.

When hail riddles small plants, the net effect on yield is probably about the same or slightly less than from frost. If the growing point is not damaged, the plants will recover. Shredded leaves on young or old plants are not a total loss because the breaks are between the veins that run lengthwise in the leaves. As long as they remain green and turgid, the shredded leaves continue to manufacture some sugars. When all leaves were shredded at tasseling time in an Iowa test, the grain yield was reduced 63 percent. Shredding earlier or later had less effect. Breaking all of the midribs at tasseling reduced yield 20 percent. Bruising the stalks decreased yield 10 percent beyond the decrease from leaf shredding alone.

In summary, up to silking time, hail injury can be estimated by the percent of final leaf area destroyed or a two-third reduction if *all* leaf area is shredded. After silking time, the injury is scaled down, based on the number of days between grain formation and damage.

In deciding whether to replant hail-damaged young corn, the key factor is the condition of the growing point rather than the appearance of the leaves.

Fourth Stage: Silking to Maturity

• *Corn rootworms (adult stage)*

Western, northern and southern rootworms feed on the silks. The southern variety is greenish yellow with twelve black dots. The northern rootworm adult is pale yellow as it emerges from the ground but later turns a uniform green. The western type is yellowish with a dark brown stripe on each wing cover. For information on the larvae of these three rootworms see page 269.

• *European corn borer*

This insect attacks all parts of the corn plant. The young worms feed on leaves in the whorl. Later they burrow into the stalk, tassel, cob, shank and kernels. There are two generations a year in the Corn Belt and three in southern areas. Entomologists estimate that yield is reduced 3 to 4 percent for each first generation borer that matures in a corn plant and 1½ to 2 percent for each second generation borer. The first generation causes stunted and broken plants whereas the second causes dropped or shrunken ears and broken stalks.

Modern corn hybrids have considerable tolerance to the corn borer. Researchers have learned that in resistant hybrids, the first nibble by the young boreres causes the plant to produce sizeable amounts of a chemical DIMBOA (2,4-dihydroxy-7-methoxy-1,4-benzoazin-3-one) which is distasteful to them.

The earliest planted fields in an area are most attractive to the moths that produce the first generation, whereas late-planted fields get the heaviest second generation infestation.

Shredding stalks in the fall, combined with a thorough job of plowing under refuse, greatly reduces the corn borer population. Since this insect overwinters in cornstalks and cobs, fall and spring plowing are equally effective. Good preventive practices, plus natural predators and diseases, have kept the European corn borer from causing the dev-

Western corn rootworm
(length: ½ inch, 1.25 cm.)

Southern corn rootworm
(length: ¾ inch, 1.6 cm.)

Northern corn rootworm
(length: ½ inch, 1.25 cm.)

astation feared when it first struck the Corn Belt. Chemical control is effective — many farmers believe spraying for the second brood reduces adult damage to silks — however, methods vary from one area to another and should be checked locally each year.

A spore-forming bacterium called Bacterium Thuringiensis (BT) is a promising non-chemical means for control. It can be formulated in powders, liquids or granules. Cost will need to be reduced by larger scale production and more potent strains before it is economically attractive for corn.

• *Southwestern corn borer*

This is an important corn pest in the area immediately southwest of the Corn Belt. The insect overwinters in a tunnel in the base of the corn stalk and apparently cannot survive in normal winters as far north as St. Louis. Eggs of the first generation are laid in June and July and larvae feed on corn leaves similar to the European corn borer sometimes cutting off the stalk terminal and causing a condition called deadheart. Most of the damage is done by the second or third generation when the worms hollow out the stalk base for hibernating and the stalk breaks.

Treatment: Spraying in late June to July to control the first generation before larvae enter the stalk.

Control: Early planting is the most practical control because the plants escape major

European corn borer

Southwestern corn borer

274

Corn leaf aphids

Grasshoppers

Corn earworm

attack. Fall disking of corn stubble exposes larva to weather and natural enemies. Clean plowing by May 1 buries the pupae and prevents moth emergence.

• *Corn leaf aphids*

Tiny bluish-green or gray insects that appear in great numbers in the leaf whorl, upper leaves and tassel of scattered corn plants. The plants are weakened; frequently the tassels abort and the silks are not polinated. Barren plants result. Aphids probably migrate from the south into the Corn Belt each year and first appear in late June or early July.

The aphid is preyed on by several other insects: aphid infestations are seldom severe. Insecticides will control aphids but also destroy their predators, so chemical control is rarely justified.

• *Grasshoppers*

Several species of grasshopper attack corn, eating the leaves from the edge inward. They also eat the silks, causing reduced kernel set or completely bare cobs. Damage is worst around the edges of a field. However, it is rare for a field to be completely destroyed, because the grasshopper population usually builds up late in the season.

Grasshoppers usually do not present a serious problem: they have many natural enemies to fend off. Tillage buries some eggs so deeply that the young hoppers can't reach the surface; it exposes the eggs so that many are destroyed by weather and birds. Beating rains at the time the hoppers are hatching account for further destruction.

Insecticides are effective for grasshopper control and should be used if a field is badly infested.

• *Corn earworm*

Earworms enter through the ear tip and tunnel in the developing kernels. In the Corn Belt, earworms mainly attack sweet corn; in southern states, they are more often a serious pest on field corn. Earworms feed in the whorl, on the tassel, and on the ear beginning at the tip. The worms may be green, yellow or brown. Only a few adults survive the winter in the Midwest but a new group flies in from southern states every year.

Treatment for control of earworms has not been generally recommended for field corn in the Corn Belt but it may pay on special seed fields. Control measures are complicated and, therefore, you should check with local sources for the best advice.

Picnic beetles

- *Picnic beetles, sap beetles*

Picnic beetles are scavengers, about ⅜ inch (1 cm.) and black with four orange spots. They attack corn almost exclusively where the plant is already injured. The sap beetle (not shown) is a small brown insect. Both adult beetles and larvae of picnic beetles and sap beetles feed on corn ears. They are not serious pests in field corn but are objectionable on sweet corn and especially abundant on ears that have been damaged by earworms, corn borer and other insects.

- *Leaf blights*

All of the leaf blights tend to increase stalk rot! In fact anything that redues effective leaf surface, for example cutting off ¼ of each leaf, increases sysceptibility to stalk rot. The damage from leaf blights may therefore be greater than would be expected because of increased lodging and greater harvesting losses in years when harvesting is delayed by wet weather.

Northern leaf blight

- *Northern leaf blight (Helminthosporium turcicum)*

Seldom seen before tasseling time. Boat-shaped, grayish lesions develop in a few days at each infected spot. Lower leaves are infected first. The disease spreads to other leaves in cool, damp weather; heavily infected leaves may die.

Northern leaf blight is found nearly every year in southern and eastern corn-growing areas. It is less common in the central Corn Belt, but has been serious as far west as Nebraska and as far north as Minnesota and South Dakota.

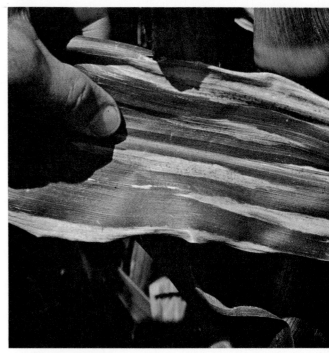

Northern leaf blight

276

Southern leaf blight

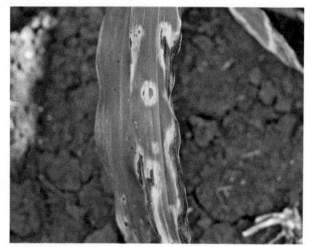

Yellow leaf blight

Fogs, heavy morning dew, and cool, humid weather after the plant reaches full growth especially favor its spread. Northern leaf blight can be controlled by Manzate or Parzote dust or spray (at 5 to 7-day intervals from knee-high to roasting ear stage), but this is too expensive to be practical except in high-value breeding nurseries. Most southern hybrids have a degree of genetic resistance.

A new single-gene source of resistance identified in 1960 by Dr. A. L. Hooker of the University of Illinois promises to wipe out the major damage from this disease. It can easily be put into the parental lines used to make up hybrids; the commercial hybrids sold in areas where leaf blight has been a problem are now quite resistant.

• *Southern leaf blight (Helminthosporium maydis)*

Until the severe outbreak of Race T on susceptible cytoplasm hybrids throughout the southern states and the midwest in 1970, southern leaf blight had been less serious than northern leaf blight. The lesions of the older Race O did not spread. The story of Race T is discussed in detail on page 39. As shown in the accompanying figure, Race T attacks nearly all parts of the plant. Furthermore, it produces a toxin which greatly weakens the plant. Race O of leaf blight is found nearly every year in southern corn-growing areas. It needs warm, moist weather, and therefore except for Race T it is not serious in the main Corn Belt. When compared with its northern cousin, this disease shows up as small, straight-sided spots on the leaves. It usually causes less serious damage than northern blight because lesions do not spread. Severe cases may kill leaves, but this is rare.

Many hybrids are resistant — probably more than are susceptible. Only a few types are severely damaged by ordinary infestations. No control other than genetic resistance has been developed.

• *Yellow leaf blight (Plyllosticta)*

This is a relative newcomer to the Corn Belt being observed first in 1967 in Wisconsin and in 1968 across the Great Lakes states and in southern Canada. Not surprisingly it is favored by cool, wet weather hence the concentration in the northern rather than central Corn Belt though it has been found as far south as central Illinois. Symptoms closely resemble Southern leaf blight.

The fungus overwinters on corn residues and is spread mainly by splashing raindrops. Young plants growing through infected residues are especially vulnerable. As with Race T of Southern leaf blight, the T-cytoplasm is more susceptible than normal cytoplasm. Because of these factors, severely infected and relatively clean fields may appear side by side. Under good growing conditions,

Table 33. Comparison of Appearance of Leaf Blights

An expert may be needed for positive identification but there are differences which can be learned with careful study and a little field experience.

	Northern *Helminthosporium turcicum*	Southern *Helminthosporium maydis* Race O	Race T	Yellow *Phyllosticta maydis*	Eyespot *Kabatiella Zeae*	Brownspot *Physoderma maydis*
Growth stage when symptoms appear	Silking or later	First cycle may show on plants when about 24 in. (60 cm)	Seedling from infected seed may die within 3-4 weeks. Leaf symptoms same time as Race O.	Before tasselling	On small plants	Young plants infected in leaf whorl.
Part of plant affected	Lower to middle leaves first. May spread to upper leaves.	Usually only leaves.	Leaves, stalks, leaf sheaths, husks, shanks, ears.	Lower leaves, especially outer margins. Also leaf sheaths and husks.	Mainly upper leaves of plants nearing maturity. Some on husks and leaf sheaths.	Leaf, sheath, stalk and sometimes husks and tassels. Bands of infection on leaves is common.
Color of lesions	Gray, frosted, especially lower two thirds of plants.	Premature dying of entire plant. More tan than gray.	Same as Race O. Close inspection reveals infection of all parts except tassel.	Yellow lower leaves resemble nitrogen deficiency. Followed by death. More tan than gray but still resemble frosting.		Brown to reddish brown, much stalk breakage.
Size of lesions						
Width	½-¾ in. (1.25-1.6 cm)	¼-½ in. (.6 to 1.25 cm)	Same as Race O.	⅛ in. (.3 cm)	1/10-6/10 in. (1-4 mm) in diameter surrounded later by a dark ring and outer halo	Very small early but coalesce into large patches.
Length	1-6 in. (2.5-15 cm)	½-¾ in. (1.25-1.6 cm)	1-1.5 in. (2.5-3.75 cm)	½ in. (1.25 cm) plus halo		
Shape of lesions	Elongated, elliptical	Parallel sides	Elliptical with yellow-green or chlorotic halo	Rectangular to oval surrounded by yellow, chlorotic tissue.	Circular to oval with dark ring and outside halo resembling an eye	Oblong to round.
Appearance of field in late stages of severe infection	Tan turning more gray with age.	Tan with buff to brown borders	Tan with yellow-green to chlorotic halo later turning dark, reddish brown	Yellow, cream or tan often surrounded by chlorotic tissue. May coalesce and cause leaf tissue, especially margins to die.		Yellowish early, brown to reddish brown later.
Geographic distribution	Most humid areas of the world.	World wide, especially warm, damp climate.	More northern areas than Race O.	Widespread but most troublesome in northern Corn Belt.	Northern U.S., Canada, Japan and perhaps Brazil, Australia, Argentina.	Mainly localized in S.E. United States but sometimes in Midwest.

278

Eyespot

Bacterial wilt

corn may outgrow the infection which tends to be concentrated on the lower leaves. Control is through planting resistant hybrids, plowing under corn residues, and crop rotation.

● *Eyespot*

Like yellow leaf blight, eyespot disease though reported in Japan since 1959 first showed in Wisconsin in 1968. It has been reported in other adjacent areas of the northern Corn Belt and in Ontario, Canada. It infects some fields early but most severe attacks occurred in late August where heavily infected fields were dead within two weeks. In contrast to yellow leaf blight, eyespot is spread readily by wind from infected to uninfected fields. Eyespot can be identified on close inspection by the oval to round tan colored spots surrounded by a dark brown or purple ring and an outer yellow halo which is translucent when held up to light. Clean plowing, crop rotations and resistant varieties are suggested for control. Spraying with a fungicide may be practicable in seed fields.

● *Bacterial wilt, Stewart's disease (mainly a disease of sweet corn)*

Symptoms on field corn are long, irregular, pale greenish streaks that later become yellow, die and turn straw colored. They usually do not show until after tasselling. They may be confused with leaf blights, but the lesions of bacterial blight are much longer (up to several inches) and more irregular in shape. The infection overwinters in corn flea beetles and is introduced into corn leaves where the beetles feed. The beetle survival can be predicted from the sum of the mean temperatures for December, January and February. When it exceeds 100° F (38° C) many beetles will survive. Control is mainly through resistant hybrids and there may be a correlation between resistance to Stewart's disease and to nothern corn leaf blight. Insecticides that control flea beetles will reduce spread but this is not likely to be economical for field corn.

279

Physoderma brown spot

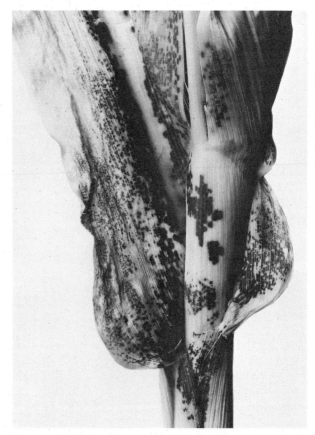

Brown spot lesions start as small spots, later merging to form large blotches.

• *Physoderma brown spot*

This disease has been of minor importance in the U.S., but outbreaks have been important locally, especially in the southeast. It has been found in the midwest. Lesions begin as tiny round yellowish spots on the leaf blade, sheath and stalk. The spots enlarge and often coalesce into brown to reddish-brown blotches. They sometimes occur in bands across the leaf because the infection occurs under a special set of moisture conditions while the leaf is still in the whorl. The only control is resistant varieties.

• *Air pollution injury*

This photograph is believed to show sulfur dioxide (SO_2) damage near East St. Louis, Illinois. Increasing amounts of industries will likely result in more damage from air pollution. Damage symptoms from air pollutants will not likely be characteristic enough to determine the specific cause. Diagnosis will often depend on deducing the cause from weather conditions, wind direction and patterns of injury. Warm, humid weather when smoke seems to hang close to the ground favors injury. Damage will occur downwind of the source and will often be worst in low parts of fields. It will cross field boundaries and roads in contrast to damage due to improper application of fertilizers or pesticides.

Likely SO_2 injury

Anthracnose: on leaves and on outside and inside of stalks.

At first dark green, lesions due to Holcus spot become dry and tan with reddish margin.

- *Anthracnose*

Localized outbreaks occurred in the U.S. in 1971 and 1972. Common in France, Germany, India and the Philippines. Lesions are semitransparent at first and occur anywhere on the leaf. They may enlarge to about .6 inch (1.5 cm), becoming brown at the center with reddish-brown borders. Heavily affected leaves wither and die. The same fungus causes both severe root and stalk rot in some regions.

- *Holcus spot (Pseudomonas syringae)*

Holcus spot is a bacterial disease. The symptoms first appear as small (1/12 to 1/2 inch) (2 to 10 mm) round to elliptical dark green, water soaked spots near the tips of the lower leaves. Later the spots turn creamy white to tan. Then become dry and brown with reddish to brown margins. Control includes crop rotation and resistant hybrids. The disease overwinters in crop residue.

- *Discolored leaf sheath*

An apparently harmless discoloration that develops when saprophytic fungi (fungi that grow on dead plant residues) and bacteria develop on pollen that has lodged between the leaf sheath and the stalk. Note that the stalk underneath the sheath is not discolored.

- *Genetic stripe*

Bright yellowish or white stripes, usually running the whole length of the leaf. All leaves of a plant may be affected, or only a few. Sometimes the stripes show up only on *one side* of the plant.

It is not caused or affected by weather or soil and is not important since only scattered plants are affected. It is shown here so you won't confuse it with diseases. Most cases are genetic accidents that originate from a gene change in a single cell and are passed on to all cells that develop from the changed cell. There is no prevention and no cure.

- *Crazy-top*

The name of this disease describes it well, and you are not likely to confuse it with any other corn trouble. Symptoms vary: in a mild form some tassel branches change to a leaf-like condition, in a severe case the whole top of the plant and the ears are replaced with a mass of leaf-like structures. Often times some affected plants grow very tall and tower over the normal plants.

Crazy-top is a soil-born disease caused by a downy mildew fungus which gets into corn plants only when infected soil or muddy water enters the leaf whorl. Thus, it is only found in fields which have been very wet or flooded. This happens most often when the plants are 4 to 10 inches (10 to 25 cm) tall. About that time the tassel and ears are beginning to differentiate (figure 4 , page 4). The growth regulating mechanism in the differentiating tissues is upset by the fungus and the resulting organs become leaf-like instead of the normal male and female reproductive parts. The effect is so specific and discrete that part of an ear or

Discolored leaf sheath (sometimes called purple sheath)

Genetic stripe

Crazy-top

282

Witchweed *(Striga)* plants parasitizing maize roots.

a tassel may be normal and the part that differentiated only a day or two later is totally misshaped.

Genetic resistance seems to be common, but the disease is so unpredictable that little has been found out about it beyond the cause.

• *Sorghum Downy Mildew (Scherospora sorghi)*

Sorghum downy mildew as the name implies is primarily a disease of sorghum but it also attacks corn. The disease was identified in the U.S. for the first time in 1961 on sorghum in Texas. Since 1961 the disease has moved northward and eastward. It was identified in southern and eastern Illinois in 1974. Symptoms include narrow to wide whitish lesions that often extend the full length of the leaf. The streaks eventually become reddish brown as they fill with dark oospores of the fungus. These spores are released by the splitting of the leaf and overwinter in the soil.

Since the disease attacks sorghum, including shattercane, the most promising method of control is probably the development of resistance hybrids.

• *Witchweed*

Infected corn plants wilt and turn yellow similar to nitrogen shortage. In severe cases they are badly stunted and may die. Witchweeds develop fleshy stems and a tangle of roots mixed with and attached to the corn roots even before the stems appear above ground at the base of the corn plant. In the U.S. witchweed is found in North and South Carolina but could spread unless complete control measures are developed. It is common in Africa, Australia, India and southeast Asia. Control measures include (1) prevention of spread through transport of soil, (2) applying an herbicide directed at the base of the corn plants, and (3) several technics based on the fact that germination of witchweed seeds is triggered by chemical exudates from plant roots. Catch grasses and cereals can be planted to cause germination followed by plowing to destroy seedling and host plants. Non-host leguminous crops cause germination but the seedling cannot parasitize their roots. Recently ethylene gas has been found to trigger germination and when applied in the absence of a host crop, the seedlings die.

283

Corn rust

• *Corn rust*

Small reddish spots on the leaves. These may be clustered very thickly; when scraped, a rusty mass of spores will flake away.

Corn rust seems to be favored by cool humid weather. Infection is rare in most corn-growing areas. Most hybrids are resistant — only a few are highly susceptible.

• *Corn smut*

Smut is first seen as a grayish lump which may grow to considerable size. When the fungus spores are mature, the lump turns black and releases the spores as it bursts open.

Smut attacks all above-ground parts of the corn plant — stalk, leaves, tassel, ear.

Some smut is seen every year. It is rarely serious except in susceptible hybrids.

Smut is not closely related to weather or to soil. It is often more prevalent in drouth years or where there are many barren stalks. It tends to attack plants wherever there is a break in the plant tissue. For example, seedcorn growers often observe smut where tassels have been pulled.

There is no treatment but most hybrids are fairly resistant.

Corn smut

Older corn smut

Barren stalks and red leaf

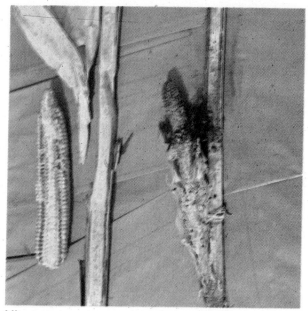

Nitrate test results; eared versus barren stalk

● *Barren stalks and red leaf*

Stalks may be barren (cobs without grain) due to low fertility, drouth, excessive population, aphids, chewed-off silks, or poor timing of silking and pollen shed.

Red leaf is not the result of a specific disease but rather a special combination of effects on the plant. If sugars and other products manufactured by sunlight and chlorophyll remain in the leaf and sheath instead of being transferred to other parts of the plant, the stalks or leaves may turn red. Barren stalks often turn red since there is no ear for the manufactured foods to move into. When a leaf is broken crosswise, the area beyond the break sometimes turns red. Occasionally, the whole plant becomes red above the point where borers have cut into the stalk. The red color is due to anthocyanin pigment which increases when the sugar content of leaves is unusually high.

The fact that barren stalks have a high nitrate content is demonstrated by the strong reddish-pink color that develops on the stalk when a nitrate-indicating powder is applied (see photo). This is probably an important cause of high nitrate that has often been associated with drouth.

Japanese beetle (shiny irridescent; about ½ inch long, 1.25 cm.)

Ear tips damaged by birds

Tassel ears

- *Japanese beetle*

The most obvious damage from these insects results when they feed on leaves or silks. But during about four-fifths of its life the insect is in the larva stage and feeds on the roots of plants, including corn. Japanese beetles are common in only a few places in the Corn Belt.

- *Bird damage to ear tips*

Starlings, blackbirds, crows and even sparrows feed on exposed ear tips in the late milk stage. They shred the husks and continue to attack the ears until the kernels become hard. Damage is naturally worse on hybrids that have exposed tips.

Control: Frightening devices are the only approach on large acreage. Among these are noisemakers and sight frighteners — tinsel and plastic novelties have displaced the traditional scarecrow. Chemical repellants are used around feedlots and mills.

- *Tassel ears*

Most fields have a few scattered plants with combination tassels and ears in the same structure. The photograph is of a field in which each main stalk had a normal ear, but the tillers (suckers) in nearly every case

286

Exposed ear tips

Gibberella infested stalk and its ear (left);
healthy plant (right)

had combination tassels and ears in the terminal position where only a tassel would normally be. No specific cause of this condition is known but it occurs most often on somewhat shorter, spindly plants. It is a reminder that the male and female parts of the corn plant are structurally very closely related.

• *Exposed ear tips*

Most fields have a few ears with exposed tips. In a few extreme cases as high proportion of the ears outgrow the husk cover by ⅓ to ½. This has been observed where extreme drouth prevailed during the time of ear set with abundant rainfall and good growing conditions thereafter.

• *Gibberella and Diplodia stalk rots*

Gibberella stalk rot causes sudden death of plants in late August or early September. The dead plants are usually scattered among healthy ones though very susceptible hybrids may be uniformly infected. Stalks dry up and the lower joints become soft.

Gibberella stalk rot usually causes plants to break *at the joints;* Diplodia infection more often causes breakage *between joints,* low down on the stalk.

Gibberella has small, round, black fruiting bodies that you can scrape off with your fingernail; Diplodia fruiting bodies are embedded and cannot be scraped off.

When the stalk is split open, Gibberella-infected plants show a bright pinkish-red coloration inside the stalk, at the joints and near the crown.

Stalks infected with Diplodia are shredded internally but have no pinkish color.

When they infect the plant early, Diplodia and Gibberella stalk rots cause small ears with shrunken, chaffy kernels. They increase stalk breakage and harvest losses whether they infect the plants early or late.

Both of these stalk rots cause ear rots, page   ; the infection of the ears is a separate one and not the result of the original fungus spreading to the ear.

287

Stalks rotted by Diplodia

Stalks rotted by Charcoal rot

Diplodia is the most common stalk rot in the central Corn Belt, although Gibberella can be equally serious in some years. In the drier western states, charcoal rot is most damaging. North of the latitude of Chicago and east of Ohio through the mid-Atlantic and New England states, Gibberella is the dominant stalk rot disease.

Conditions favoring: Susceptible hybrid; early maturing field; partial loss of leaf surface due to leaf blight, grasshoppers, chinchbugs or hail; and low potassium, especially if combined with very high nitrogen. General high fertility seems to increase susceptibility; it definitely increases breakage because ears are heavier.

How to avoid: Plant resistant, full-season hybrids; keep the level of potassium high; harvest early to avoid losses by lodging.

• *Charcoal rot*

Affected plants sometimes die prematurely. Stalks crumple and collapse after maturity or premature death. The disease is not common in the central and northern Corn Belt but can be serious in the drier western part. Since it is favored by dry, hot weather, it occasionally appears in drouth years in the Corn Belt. There appears to be genetic resistance to the disease.

Premature dying in restricted areas of the field

- *Premature dying in restricted areas of the field*

This is possibly due to disease or lack of moisture. The affected areas are often on slight ridges or on slopes where more water has run off, leaving less for the crop. Often associated with nitrogen deficiency because the surface soil has been eroded, leaving subsoil low in organic matter and nitrogen.

When premature dying occurs in spots of level fields, look for differences in the deep subsoil. Either sandy or clay layers may reduce available water.

Pythium stalk rot is a possible cause. Gibberella and Diplodia tend to kill individual plants or entire fields of susceptible hybrids rather than spots in the field. Sometimes it is hard to tell whether stalk rot is the real cause because stalk rot appears to be worse on the plants that mature first. Premature death for any reason increases the amount of stalk rot damage.

- *Pythium stalk rot*

Soft, dark rotted areas on only one or a few joints near the base of the affected stalk; severely affected plants may die. Moist soil favors the spread of this disease, though damage may show up in any kind of weather.

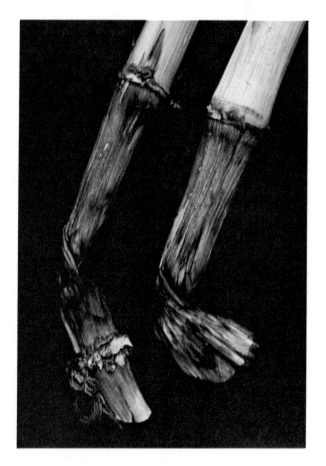

Stalks rotted by Pythium stalk rot

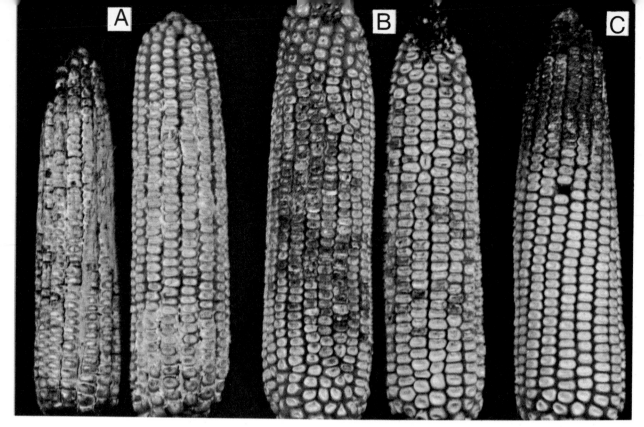

Field ear rots: A. Diplodia, B. Fusarium, C. Gibberella

Fifth Stage: Mature to Harvest

Field Ear Rots

• Diplodia

This is the most common ear rot in the Corn Belt. Husks on ears infected early in the season appear bleached while healthy ear husks are green. The ears are shrunken. They tend to remain upright; the husks stick tightly together because the fungus has grown between them. Ears affected later in the season appear normal until you break them in two or examine the kernels. Then you find a white mold, usually beginning at the base. The ears are most susceptible to infection during the first three weeks after silking. Infection is usually heaviest when wet weather occurs after silking, especially when the preceding period was dry enough for the spores to spread widely before silking time.

Resistant hybrids are the only control.

• Gibberella

This is more common than Diplodia in the cooler, more humid areas of the Corn Belt. Infected ears have a pink to bright red rot that starts at the tip of the ear. Ears that are infected early may be fully covered by the rot with the husks held tightly by fungus threads.

Infected corn is toxic to hogs. When offered as ear corn, hogs refuse to eat it. When it is ground, they will eat it and may vomit, show signs of dizziness, and even die.

There is no control for this ear rot.

• Fusarium

Fusarium attacks individual kernels or groups of kernels scattered over the ear. Kernels that are damaged by earworms or birds are especially susceptible. The infected kernels are pink to brownish with a powdery or cottony mold growth. The disease is favored by dry weather and is worst in the western Corn Belt and in central California. Hybrids that have exposed tips or tend to have seed coats that break are most susceptible to Fusarium. No specific control measure

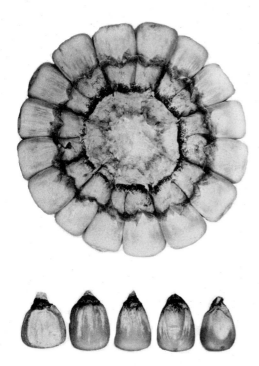

Kernels and cross section of ear infected with Nigrospora. Black dots at kernel tips are spore masses. Whitish streaks are due to air channels in the pericarp.

is known.

University of Illinois researchers have isolated a toxin which they named "vomitoxin" from fusarium molded corn. It caused hogs to vomit.

● *Nigrospora*

This type of cob rot increases when corn is weakened by drouth, stalk rot, severe leaf blight, or severe nutrient deficiency. The cob is discolored, easily shredded, and the pith is gray instead of white. Kernels are poorly filled and easily pushed into the partially rotted cob. The best insurance against this disease is high fertility and full-season hybrids that are resistant to stalk rots and leaf blights — both of which make the ear more susceptible to Nigrospora.

● *Physalospora*

This ear rot causes a dark brown to black felty mold over the entire ear. Less infected ears may have only blackened kernels near the base of the ear.

Physalospora

"Popped kernels"

Molded, sprouted

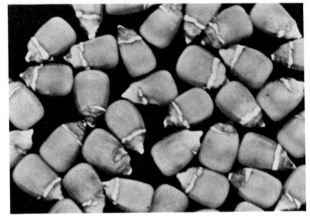

Silk-cut

- *Molded, sprouted*

A combination of erect ear, tight husks and wet, warm weather caused both molding and sprouting in this ear in mid-September.

- *Silk cut and popped kernels*

Some inbreds and the hybrids in which they are used tend to develop kernel disorders that are not related to disease. Two of these are popped kernels and silk cut kernels. An irregular break in the seedcoat over the kernel crown is popped kernels. The kernels look like partially expanded popcorn kernels. A horizontal break or cut in the seed coat appears in the silk cut kernels. Silk cut is not visible until the kernels are shelled from the ear. It is not due to the silk cutting the seed coat. Both disorders may affect only part of the kernels on the ear and both make the kernels susceptible to mold infections.

Sixth Stage: Storage

Kernel rots

The fungi that cause ear rots in the field and those that damage the corn kernels in storage are seldom the same. The more common field ear rots are caused by Diplodia maydis, Gibberella zeae, Nigrospora oryzae and Fusarium moniliforme. These fungi are favored by kernel moisture contents in excess of 20%. The most comon and damaging storage fungi include several species of Aspergillus and Penicillium. These fungi multiply readily at kernel moisture contents as low as 14% if the temperature is relatively high. Both the temperature and moisture content of the stored grain rise rapidly as the storage fungi multiply.

While the fungi that cause ear rots are not the fungi that cause corn to go out of

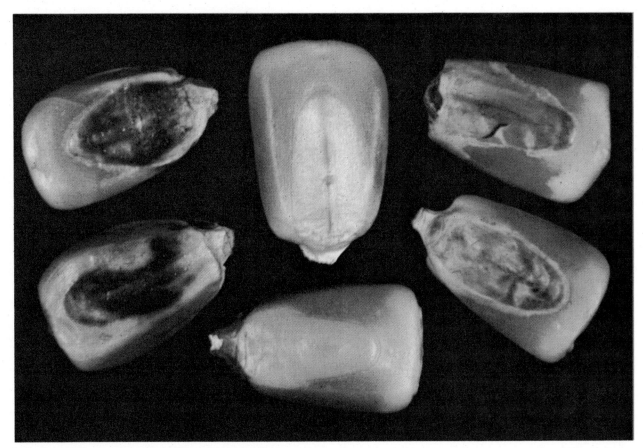

Left, Fusarium rot; right, Penicillium "blue eye"

condition in storage, corn harvested from fields with a relatively high incidence of rotted ears should be stored under proper conditions because the damaged kernels from the rotted ears furnish an ideal environment for the development of storage fungi.

Aspergillus is of special concern because some strains produce an aflatoxin which is highly poisonous (see page 321).

These rots develop on ear corn either after maturity in the field, or in the crib. They often go unnoticed until the grain is shelled because the germ side of the kernel is all that is attacked.

Rats and mice

• *Rats, mice*

Rats and mice took a heavy toll when ear corn was stored in wooden cribs and sometimes even before husking when corn was left in field shocks. Field shelling, artificial drying, and storage in metal bins has nearly eliminated losses on many farms. Specific poison baits have been developed but a few cases of resistance to the poison have been observed in rats. Losses in storage to rodents and insects are still enormous in many places especially the less developed countries.

• *Kernel red streak*

Kernel red streak is caused by the toxin produced when a strain of the wheat curl mite (Eriophyes tulipae) feeds on corn kernels. The toxin causes reddish to pink-purple streaks to develop on the kernels. The kernels near the tips of the ear are most likely to be affected. This is particulary true if the husks are loose. The reddish color develops in the pericarp and as far as is known has no effect on the feeding or nutritional value of the corn.

• *Poorly developed mature ears*

Small, misshapen ears indicate that *something* went wrong but in most cases you can't tell whether the trouble was lack of nutrients, insects, diseases, drouth or excessively thick planting. The ears in this photograph are all from the same crib of corn. Frequently, the small ears are second ears on a single stalk or from tillers. A post mortem doesn't work nearly as well as watching the corn develop every week through the season so you can spot trouble when it occurs.

• *Scattered kernels on full-sized cobs*

This indicates that something went wrong at pollination time. Silking may have been delayed until after most of the pollen was shed. Silks may have been eaten off by insects. Extreme heat and drouth may have reduced the receptiveness of the silks or the amount of viable pollen.

• *Ears too large*

The ears in the photograph average .9 pound (.41 kgs.) each. There is nothing wrong with big ears but they mean that the population was too low for the fertility and growing season. The yield could probably have been 10 to 20 percent higher.

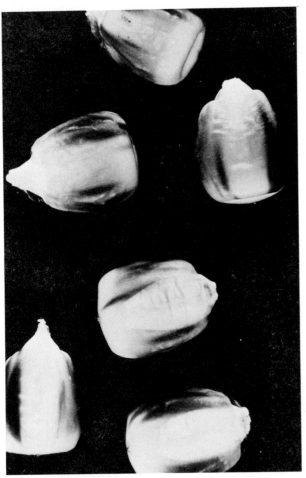

Kernel red streak

Scattered kernels on full-size cobs

Poorly developed ears

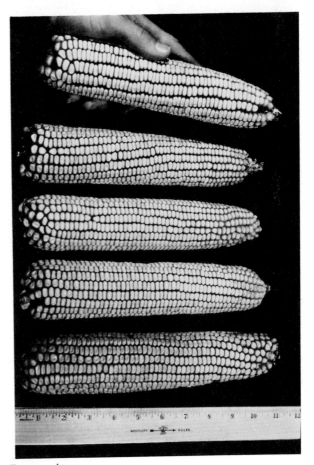

Ears too large

PRINCIPAL STORED GRAIN INSECTS

For safe and effective use of insecticides, always identify the problem correctly.

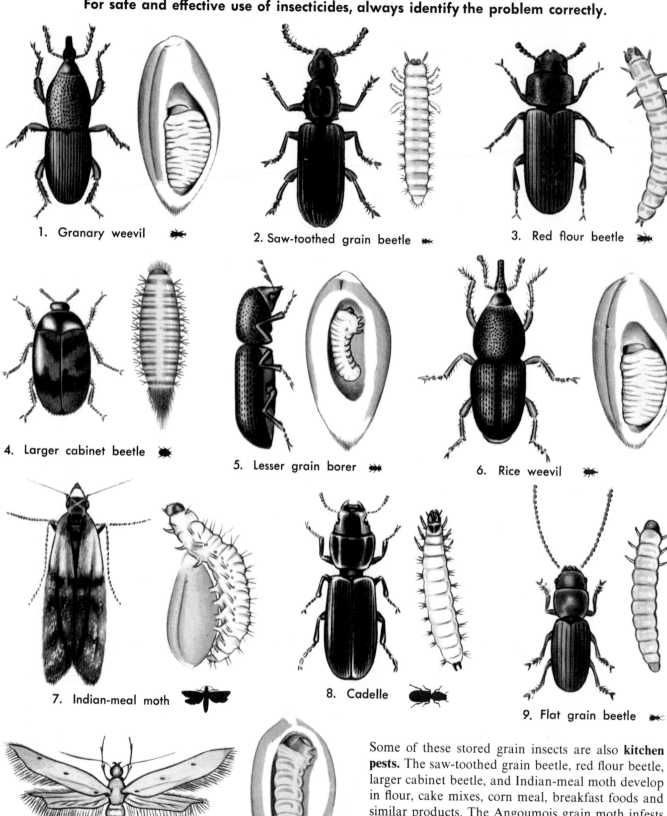

1. Granary weevil

2. Saw-toothed grain beetle

3. Red flour beetle

4. Larger cabinet beetle

5. Lesser grain borer

6. Rice weevil

7. Indian-meal moth

8. Cadelle

9. Flat grain beetle

10. Angoumois grain moth

Some of these stored grain insects are also **kitchen pests.** The saw-toothed grain beetle, red flour beetle, larger cabinet beetle, and Indian-meal moth develop in flour, cake mixes, corn meal, breakfast foods and similar products. The Angoumois grain moth infests popcorn.

Prepared by Extension Entomologists of the North Central States in cooperation with the Federal Extension Service, U. S. Department of Agriculture.

• *Stored grain insects*

A large number of insects attack corn in storage. The pictures show the insects attacking wheat, but many of them also infest corn.

CHECK LIST
FOR TROUBLE SHOOTING

Often there is a marked difference in crop growth from one part of a field to another or from one field to the next. This can be puzzling to the grower and equally baffling to the seed, fertilizer or chemical salesman who is frequently asked to account for the variation.

Here is a check list to serve as a reminder of factors that may provide an answer:

• Is the soil the same in the two areas?

• What crops were grown on the areas last year? The preceding crop affects fertility, tilth and water supply.

• Were the areas plowed or chiseled at the same time? This may affect the available water and the tilth of the seedbed.

• Were the fields worked the same amount after plowing? Over-working can cause crusting of the surface, extra runoff of needed water, and compaction of the plow layer and subsoil.

• Was the same hybrid and same *lot* of seed planted?

• Were the areas planted on the same day?

• Were kernels planted at the same depth? In a cold, wet soil, deep planting can slow emergence and reduce the stand. In a dry soil, shallow planting may result in a poor stand. Kernels may not germinate or may germinate and then die.

• Was the same kind and amount of fertilizer applied through the planter? Not enough fertilizer results in slow early growth. Too much placed too close can reduce the stand.

• Is there a difference in drainage, particularly fields with tile drains.

How to Check on Whether Broadcast Fertilizer Was Actually Applied

Sometimes a farmer believes that the custom spreader failed to apply the fertilizer that he ordered and paid for.

When broadcast on the surface, liquid or dry fertilizers with phosphorus and potassium will stay mainly in the surface inch of soil. A set of samples carefully taken from the surface inch, tested and compared with a duplicate set taken directly beneath them in the 3 to 4-inch (7.5 to 10 cm.) layer will show whether the fertilizer was applied. The sampling technique is not accurate enough to show exactly how much P and K were applied but it does prove that fertilizer was put on.

If the fertilizer was broadcast and harrowed in, it will be mainly in the surface 3 inches (7.5 cm.). The suggested sampling procedure is to compare samples from the top 2 inches (5 cm.) with samples taken at the same spot but between 4 and 6 inches (10 to 15 cm.) below the surface.

Tests on samples taken from recently fertilized fields will be quite variable. Probably *at least* 5 paired samples from the upper and lower layer will be needed. If the fertilizer was broadcast and plowed under, it is not possible to confirm the application by sampling and testing the soil. The fertilized and unfertilized layers will be confounded with fertilizer applied to the plow layer in previous years.

Suggestions on How to Determine Whether a Poor Stand is Due to the Seed

• Check to find whether any other hybrid or different seed lot of the same hybrid was planted in the field. If so, is the trouble common to both areas? If the answer is yes, the trouble is not due to seed.

• If no other seed was used in the field, check other fields on the farm or neighboring farms that used the same lot of seed. If there is no trouble in other fields, the seed is not to blame.

• If some of the questionable seed is still on hand, run a germination test on it either in a laboratory or hand plant a short row in the field and observe the germination and early growth.

Plant Tissue Tests

Tissue tests have been used since the 1940's as one of several tools to diagnose crop troubles.

The tests are useful for a variety of reasons:

• They get the farmer, his fertilizer dealer, or his county extension agent into cornfields often enough to keep track of the crop and *spot any kind of trouble when it first develops.*

• Tissue tests show when nutrients are plentiful in the plant and thus direct attention to other causes of unsatisfactory growth.

• They give warning of nitrogen shortage that will develop during the greatest stress period soon after the ear is set. Sometimes the warning is early enough that nitrogen can be sidedressed. Consider this situation: sufficient nitrogen was applied the previous fall but fall weather was extra warm and rainfall between then and corn planting was heavier than normal. A considerable amount of nitrogen may have been lost by leaching and dentrification. A medium tissue test for nitrates when the corn is waist high tells you that the crop will be very short on nitrogen a few weeks later. You could sidedress nitrogen with special equipment.

• Tissue tests confirm a diagnosis of nutrient deficiency based on visible symptoms.

• They can indicate that a crop has barely enough nutrients or a slight deficiency (hidden hunger) not serious enough to cause symptoms that you can easily recognize. In this case, the tissue test will help in determining next year's fertility plan.

To get the most from tissue tests you must test regularly every 10 to 14 days from the time corn is waist high until early grain development. A test made at only one time does not tell you anything about the trend. Are

Dr. G. N. Hoffer making plant tissue tests

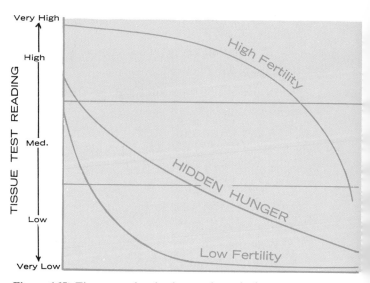

Figure 165. Tissue test levels change through the season. They are highest in young plants and decrease as the plant gets older, even of soils with very high fertility. The effect of nutrient level on yield depends on how early and how fast the test falls.

298

Table 34.

Suggestions for tissue test interpretation. The test is for nitrate nitrogen (NO₃), phosphorus in PO₄ form, and elemental potassium (K). (Courtesy American Potash Institute)

Stage of Growth	Test to be Made	Part to Sample	Minimum Level Needed to Avoid Hidden Hunger
Less than	N	Midrib of basal leaf	High
15 inches (37.5 cm)	P	Midrib of basal leaf	Medium
	K	Midrib of basal leaf	High
15 inches (37.5 cm) to	N	Base of stalk	High
ear showing	P	Midrib of first mature leaf	Medium
	K	Midrib of first mature leaf	High
Ear showing to	N	Base of stalk	High
very early dent	P	Midrib of leaf below ear	Medium
	K	Midrib of leaf below ear	Medium

nutrient levels staying about the same, or are they forecasting trouble? (figure 165)

If you test only once, the best time is right after silking because this is the period of greatest stress.

A book on tissue tests and plant analysis is available from:

American Society of Agronomy
677 South Segoe Road
Madison, Wisconsin 53711

Learn How to Interpret the Test Results

You must understand soils, fertilizers, plant uptake of nutrients, the desirable levels at different growth stages (table 33 and figure 165), and the influence of weather in the days preceding the test.

A *low test* means that the plant is not getting the nutrient for one or more of the following reasons:

• *There is not enough in the soil.* Results from recent soil tests and a study of records of fertilizer put on this year and last year will indicate whether the amount in the soil is short or whether the supply is adequate but the plant isn't getting it.

• *The weather is unfavorable* for growth and uptake of the nutrient. The nitrogen test for nitrate falls quickly in severe drouth, but

P and K may be even higher than normal. On the other hand, nitrate is often high in cool, cloudy weather but the P test is low.

• *Something is wrong with the root system. Compacted soil* causes low tests for P and K because it restricts root growth. Remember that roots must continuously grow into soil areas where the P and K have not been used up, since these nutrients do not move very far to the roots. Insects feeding on the roots reduce their ability to absorb nutrients. Root pruning from cultivating or sidedressing too deep or too close can cause a temporary shortage until the root system regenerates.

A *high test* for a nutrient:

• Tells you that there is plenty of the nutrient in the plant at the time the test is made.

• Does not assure that there will continue to be enough until the corn is mature (see figure 165). The row fertilizer can keep the tissue test high in the early part of the season but may be completely inadequate when the big surge in nutrient need comes later on. By testing every 10 to 14 days, you can note a trend indicating that your corn will probably run out of a nutrient later in the season.

• Does not indicate whether the nutrient would still be adequate if all other growth factors were favorable. When one nutrient is lacking, the others are temporarily high in tissue tests, but they also may become short when the limiting nutrient is added. In this case, the results of recent soil tests and records of fertilizers added are needed to interpret high tests.

Who Should Run Tissue Tests?

They are mainly a tool for experts rather than for farmers. But anyone with good agronomic training who tests regularly through the season, keeps records of tests and weather preceding the testing, learns how weather (especially rainfall) affects the tests, and then uses the test as one tool in diagnosing troubles, can profit from tissue testing.

Plant Analyses

Research workers have long studied complete chemical analyses as a more refined tool than field tissue tests. Since this work can be done only in specially equipped laboratories, the techniques are not described here. Complete chemical analysis is used mainly in connection with soil fertility research.

In recent years, many laboratories have begun to offer a testing service for major, secondary and micronutrients with an instrument called a spectrograph. The tests are quite costly compared to soil tests.

Before sending samples to a laboratory, you should contact them. They will supply detailed instructions on how to take the samples as well as how to send them.

Agronomists have run tests on thousands of plant specimens from hundreds of different soils on the spectrograph. The results have enabled them to set better standards for desirable nutrient levels; to locate areas where specific micronutrients are already lacking; and to identify soil regions where certain micronutrients are adequate now but likely to become deficient in the future.

Is Replanting Advisable?

It is occasionally necessary to decide whether a poor stand should be torn up and replanted. If the stand is a near-failure, the decision is easy. But if the stand is spotted or about 75 percent, the decision is more complex. Here are some points to think about:

• If the optimum planting date is already past, replanted corn will yield less per plant (figure 166). The lower yield *per plant* must be balanced against the increased yield from *more plants.*

In the northern part of the Corn Belt, replanted corn is more likely to be caught by frost before it is mature.

• In the central and southern Corn Belt, replanted corn will often be reduced in yield by heat and drouth at the silking stage.

• Replanting gives you a chance to aim for the optimum plant population (figure 167), but does not guarantee that you will achieve it.

• Replanting costs money.

• When you tear up a partial stand and replant, the second planting, like the first, is subjected to the hazards of extreme dry and wet soil, of insects and seedling diseases. Usually the risk of the soil being too dry is greater than for the original planting whereas the risk of cold soil and seedling diseases are less.

• You can tear up corn and replant the field or part of it with another crop that is less affected by late planting. But usually the alternative crops cannot make efficient use of the fertilizer that has already been applied for corn. For example nitrogen will not give a profitable response on soybeans. The increase may help pay for nitrogen that would otherwise be lost if no crop was grown, but will not return the profit corn does. Phosphorus and potassium will help raise the general level of soil fertility and, though somewhat less efficient, will still be there for future years.

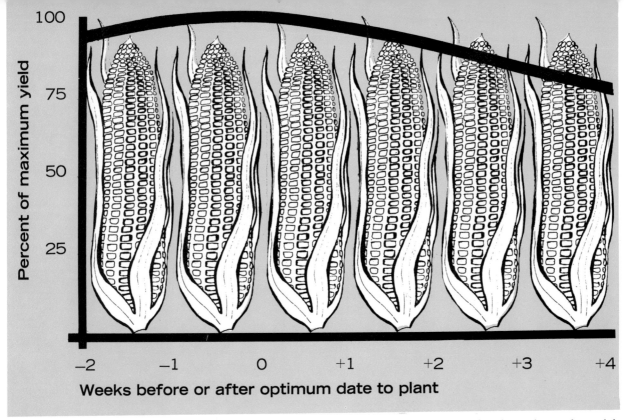

Figure 166. Planting dates and the decision to replant: replanting a 75% stand four weeks after the optimum date might result in a negligible yield increase or none at all.

• Corn plants compensate to a considerable extent for missing hills or skips in the row if there is a full stand adjacent to barren areas. Irregular stands yield well if the total population is high enough.

After you have noted the points on these pages and studied the two charts, use this procedure to decide whether it will pay to replant a field:

Estimated gain from a better stand
  (from figure 167)   _____

Subtract estimated bushels to pay
  costs to replant   _____

Subtract yield loss due to later
  planting (from figure 166)   _____

Net gain or loss from replanting   _____

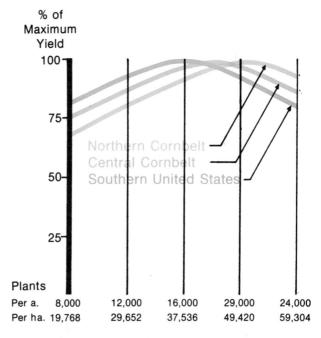

Figure 167. Approximate yield curves of different plant populations.

10

Harvesting and Storing
High Quality Silage

Corn silage is high yielding, easy to ensile and is an excellent energy feed. It is made throughout the corn growing area especially along the northern fringe where grain corn is somewhat uncertain because of a short growing season. Silage is increasing in the Great Plains for feeder cattle.

Harvesting the whole plant as silage gives you about 70 percent more dry weight than harvesting as mature dry grain (table 35). Top quality silage has:

• High energy with plenty of grain, showing that it was cut late enough for near maximum yield.

• Good palatability from cutting at the right time and ensiling properly.

• Good keeping quality, no mold. Mold is prevented by harvesting before the crop is too dry, chopping short enough for good packing, distributing the chopped material well in the silo, and storing in a tight-walled silo.

• Not enough nitrate to be a problem.

Time to Harvest

The total feeding value per acre increases right up to the time the grain is mature. But the digestibility of the leaves and stalks and the keeping quality of the silage decline somewhat earlier.

The ideal time to harvest, then, for safe storage and maximum meat or milk per acre is when the kernels begin to glaze, which is *well past the time when the kernels are just dented!* It is later than you think by looking at the plant and the outside of the ears. You can tell the stage of kernel development best by breaking an ear in two and looking at the base of kernels *opposite* the germ, page 16, figure 19 .

Moisture content of the whole silage is the best guide, figure 168, but it is not easy to

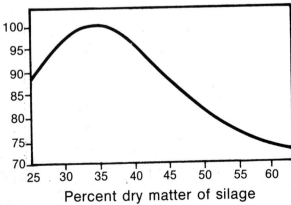

Figure 168. Effect of stage of maturity of corn silage on dry matter harvested.

303

Table 35
Comparative yields and livestock produced per acre from different methods of harvesting and storing the corn crop (based on a yield of 100 bushels per acre, 63 quintals per hectare).

Corn Harvesting System	Acres	Hectares	TDN		Beef Produced	
					Per Acre	Per Hectare
Regular corn silage	100	40.5	712,800 lbs.	323,611 kilos	1,540 lbs.	1,725 kilos
Corn silage (42% of area) and	100		299,376 lbs.	135,917 kilos	1,116 lbs.	1,250 kilos
High moisture shelled corn (58% of area)			249,758 lbs.	113,390 kilos		
			549,134 lbs.	249,307 kilos		
High moisture ground ear corn	100	40.5	491,904 lbs.	223,324 kilos	958 lbs.	1,073 kilos
Corn ear and center-cut silage	100	40.5	607,200 lbs.	275,669 kilos	1,320 lbs.	1,478 kilos

get an accurate test for moisture in chopped silage.

You can afford to let some of the lower leaves die and fall off rather than to rush harvesting of a crop with the grain still filling rapidly. This is different than it was years ago, when silage was cut with a corn binder, dropped on the ground, and loaded on wagons by hand. Dead leaves in those days broke off and were lost. Today, a field chopper saves most of these leaves.

When silo filling took a week to ten days, delayed harvesting was much more risky than it is now with modern field choppers. In the northern corn-growing areas, an early frost often resulted in some corn getting too dry before it was ensiled. This resulted in loss of yield through leaf loss and of feeding value because of molding and excessive heating in the silo.

The Silage Process

Silage making is a pickling process. It does two things to preserve silage: it develops a strong acid, preferably about pH 4.0 to 4.5, which prevents the growth of rotting organisms, and it uses up all the air so that molds cannot grow. Under ideal conditions, the silage-making process uses up only 3 to 5 percent of the feeding value but losses may be as high as 30 percent in corn that is too dry.

Very green, immature corn is low in yield of dry weight and very high in water. When you ensile it, the silo leaks and makes a mess around the farmstead. The silage often has a sour smell, though this doesn't always reduce its palatability for livestock.

Corn that is ensiled too late molds and gets hot; since heat is a form of energy, overheated silage shows that feeding value has been lost. The heat that develops during the first two days after corn is ensiled is caused by respiration of the still-living cells of the corn plant. About the third day, the growth of molds begins to contribute to heating whereas the respiration of corn cells stops. If the silage is well packed, the air supply is soon exhausted, the molds stop growing and heating ceases.

If the silage is not packed tightly, or if the silo walls aren't air tight, molds continue to grow and use up more of the most digestible part of the corn. Continued heating means continuing loss of feed value. Molds can easily destroy 10 to 20 percent of the feed value in improperly stored silage. Even silage that has been well preserved will heat up if the surface is exposed to air during warm weather.

Table 36

Moisture in the crop	Water to be added per ton of silage to bring silage to 65 percent moisture			
Percent	*Pounds*	*Kilos*	*Gallons*	*Liters*
60	167	76	20	76
55	364	165	44	166
50	600	272	72	272
45	889	403	111	420

Adding Water to Corn That Was Frosted or Is Too Nearly Ripe

When the corn crop is too dry for ideal silage because it was frosted or is too nearly ripe, it does not pack well and the air is not forced out. Mold, which must have air, begins to grow. Two things can be done to reduce the amount of air in the silage. First, chop finer to facilitate packing. Second, add water to soften the corn leaves and stalks so they will pack better. This also adds weight, thus forcing out the air.

There is no easy, quick test for moisture in silage. It is hard to get a good sample of the whole plant, including ears. Even if you had the sample, it would be too wet for a grain moisture tester. But you can get a good estimate by carefully weighing about 5 pounds of chopped material to the nearest 1/10 pound and placing it in an oven at 200°F. for 2 to 3 hours, and then reweighing. If you start with exactly 5 pounds, you have the *percentage of dry matter* when you subtract the dry weight from 5 and multiply the remainder by 20. For example: if the dry weight is 1.5 pounds, the weight of moisture is 3.5 (5.00−1.5). The percentage of moisture is 3.5 x 20 = 70 percent.

With the metric system, if 3 kilos fresh weight dry to 1 kilo, the dry matter is ⅓ and moisture is ⅔ or 67%.

The ideal moisture is 60 to 65 percent. Silage will keep at lower moisture in airtight silos. In pit or trench silos, the moisture should be a little higher because there is less weight to pack it and force out the air.

When you have calculated the moisture content from the oven-dry sample, you can figure the amount of water to add from table 36. You can calibrate the rate of flow from a hose by running it into a bucket and timing the number of gallons per minute.

If a ton of silage at 55 percent moisture is unloaded in 10 minutes, water must be run in at the rate of 4.4 gallons per minute: about half of a full stream from a one-inch hose.

When green, immature corn has been frosted, the plant can look deceptively dry. The leaves dry within a couple of days in sunny weather, but they make up only about 15 percent of the total weight! The green stalk and ears dry very slowly. Therefore, frosted silage will require less water than unfrosted, which appears to be equally dry.

Additives: Bacteria Cultures, Limestone, Urea, Ammonia

In recent years there has been a flurry of interest in additives to improve keeping and/or feeding quality. None has become very popular as yet. Here is a brief comment on each.

• *Bacteria cultures.* Corn has all of the bacteria needed for good fermentation. No experiment station research indicates that special cultures will improve keeping quality, palatability, or digestibility of corn silage.

• *Limestone or urea.* Nebraska researchers reported that 20 pounds lowered the nitrate content of silage which may or may not be an advantage depending upon the nitrate level without treatment.

Several experiment stations have reported slight improvements in beef cattle gains from adding 10 pounds (4.5 kilos) of feed-grade limestone or urea to each ton of silage. Other reports indicate little value from limestone or urea alone but good gains from adding both for beef cattle. The reason for adding urea is to effectively raise the protein content for ruminants which can utilize the nonprotein nitrogen it contains. The protein balance would be even better if more than 10 pounds of urea were added per ton, but there is some danger that uneven application could result in animals receiving toxic amounts.

• *Ammonia.* Michigan State University researchers began studies on adding ammonia in the late 1960's in order to supplement the protein content of corn silage. Anhydrous ammonia was difficult to handle so, working with a commercial company, they researched a liquid mix of ammonia, a low-cost source of nitrogen, and minerals to supplement those in corn silage. The practice has been popular locally, but is not yet widespread.

Center-Cut, Pick-Chop and Ear-Corn Silage

Some farmers make silage from ears alone, others from the entire center section of the plant. A method which yields material comparable to center-cut silage is to use an attachment which picks one row and chops the entire plant from the next. Center-cut and pick-chop silage contain at least 40 percent grain. The reasons for these harvest-storage plans are:

• You can harvest the crop early and have lower field losses than when the crop is left in the field until the grain dries.

• You need less silo capacity than for regular silage.

• The product is concentrated enough for fattening cattle. It approaches grain as a concentrate feed to supplement hay for dairy cows.

• It is a way to save soft corn when frost hits too early in the fall. Storage and handling costs may be less than for drying, shelling, and storing dry grain.

• The total yield of feed in center-cut silage is greater than grain alone (but less than regular silage).

The ideal time to make center-cut or ear-corn silage is when the ear is nearly mature; that is, between 30 and 35 percent moisture.

A plastic cap to seal out the air is a must for this kind of silage in a conventional silo. The product is too valuable to let the top 6 to 12 inches (15 to 20 centimeters) mold and spoil.

Stalklage

Through the 1960's and early 1970's there was a trend toward earlier grain corn combining leaving a greener stover. Nearly 40 percent of the feed energy of the plant is in the leaves, stalks, cobs and husks. This material can make acceptable silage if chopped fine enough to pack and if moisture content is high enough. As a rough guide moisture in the plant parts is about twice grain moisture. When the grain is 25 percent, the stover is near 50 percent. That is too dry to keep without molding. For best keeping, water should be added to bring moisture to about 65 percent.

An acre will produce enough stalkage for 240 cow-days; a hectare enough for 600 cow-days. Beef cows do not have high nutritional needs during the dry gestation period but even so supplemental protein is required. Urea or biuret is acceptble.

Husklage

This is silage made from salvaged cobs and husks only. Special equipment would be needed to catch the cobs and husks directly from the combine. In University of Illinois research, heifers made about 60 percent as much gain on husklage as on regular corn silage with grain included. Like stalklage, it requires a protein supplement.

Economics would need to be studied carefully before tooling up for either stalklage or husklage.

How to Handle Frosted Silage Corn

In northern corn-growing areas, some silage corn is frosted nearly every year. As a result, farmers often have trouble with spoilage in the silo. What is the best way to save a frosted crop?

If your crop is very immature (ears only in the milk stage) it is too wet to make top-quality silage. A lot of juice will leak out and the livestock won't eat the silage as well as they should. This crop can dry in the field for several days in bright, clear weather and perhaps a week in damp, cloudy weather. In sunny weather, the leaves will dry within a couple of days. But about 90 percent of the weight is in the stalks and ears which *do not dry quickly.* If you aren't sure, it is better to cut a few days too soon than too late. Your losses in silage that is too dry are more serious than the objections to silage that is too wet.

If your crop is just ready to ensile, get it into the silo as quickly as possible after a frost! If nearly ripe corn dries for just a few days in sunny weather it will be difficult to get it packed well enough to force out excess air. In this case, you should set the chopper for a shorter cut, keep the distributor pipe moving around to prevent light, dry parts from piling up in one place, and consider adding water.

Salvaging a Corn Crop in Extreme Drouth

If you have livestock, you can salvage part of your crop in a severe drouth by making silage. The question is: when should it be cut?

If most of the stalks have ears, it's best to delay harvesting even though the leaves are dying. The stalk and ear have enough extra water for good keeping. The kernels will continue to form and the increase will more than offset leaf loss unless the plants are actually dying. If nitrates are high, they will decrease as the plants get older.

In fields with few ears, there is no reason to wait. Harvest the crop at once. Waiting will not increase the total dry weight (figure 168, page 303) but leaves will continue to die and fall off.

Keeping quality and palatability of immature corn with few ears can be improved by adding 100 to 200 pounds of ground shelled corn to each ton of chopped silage (49.6 to 99.2 kilos per metric ton).

High-population Drilled Corn for Green-Chop Feeding, Silage and Green Manure

From 1958 to 1962, a lot of interest developed in planting 1 to 2 bushels of corn per acre in 7-inch (.63 to 1.26 quintals per hectare in 17.5 cm) rows. Claims were made for yields up to 50 or more tons per acre (112 tons per hectare) for silage or 100 tons per acre (225 tons per hectare) of green manure (in 2 crops).

Thick-planted corn produces green feed very rapidly and is an excellent crop to field crop for green feed. Farmers report cutting it 7 to 9 weeks after planting. There are, however, sudangrass-sorghum hybrids that grow about as rapidly and can be cut several times in contrast to only one cutting from corn.

There are several things to think about before shifting away from corn planted in the usual way if you plan to make silage:

• Immature corn is very high in moisture compared with regular corn silage; the yield of dry matter is low.

• Green, high-moisture corn must either

Figure 169. This field of corn with over 100,000 plants per acre in 7-inch rows (247,100 per hectare in 10.5 cm rows) lodged badly and was a tangled mess at silo-filling time. Thick-planted corn is better suited to green chopping before lodging is likely to occur.

Table 37
Amounts of silage per 3-inch (7.5 cm) layer in upright silos with various diameters; the number of 1000-pound (453.6 kilos) animals needed to eat it fast enough to avoid excessive losses in warm weather.

Diameter of silo		Volume per 3-inch (7.5 cm) layer		Weight of silage at 40 pounds per cubic foot		Livestock needed if you feed 25 pounds (11.3 kilos) per animal per day
Feet	*Meters*	*Cubic feet*	*Cubic meters*	*Pounds*	*Kilos*	*Number*
12	3.7	28.3	.80	1131	513	45
13	4.0	33.2	.94	1327	602	53
14	4.3	38.5	1.09	1539	698	62
15	4.6	44.2	1.25	1767	802	71
16	4.9	50.3	1.42	2011	912	80
17	5.2	56.7	1.61	2270	1030	91
18	5.5	63.6	1.80	2545	1154	102
19	5.8	70.9	2.01	2835	1286	113
20	6.1	78.5	2.22	3142	1425	126

be wilted before ensiling or enough ground grain must be added to bring it to the proper moisture content.

• Lodging is common (figure 169) and harvesting is difficult.

• Insects, diseases and weeds can be serious problems.

• The crop needs somewhat more water and is therefore more sensitive to drouth. Trying to grow two crops in one year without irrigation is very risky in nearly all corn-growing areas.

• The nitrate content is likely to be higher because of more shading of the lower leaves.

• The silage is low in feeding value because it has little or no grain.

Several of these problems can be reduced or avoided by green-chopping the crop early.

Feeding Out to Control Spoilage

When you open up a silo and begin to feed it from the top or end you immediately let air into contact with the preserved silage. Molds that have been dormant get a new supply of air and begin to grow again, which destroys acidity. Feeding silage then becomes a race against spoilage. When the temperature is near freezing, molds grow very slowly and you have no problem winning the race. But when you feed silage in warm weather, you must take at least 3 inches (7.5 cm) off the top of an upright silo or an equivalent off the face of a horizontal silo every day (table 37). Mold growth is self-accelerating: once molds start to grow they multiply rapidly; their activity creates more heat, which allows them to grow still faster.

You can adapt the figures to your own situation and arrive at the correct silo size in relation to your livestock numbers.

In an upright silo, the weight of a cubic foot averages about 40 pounds (18.1 kilos) but the weight near the top is less than near the bottom. In horizontal silos, the weight per cubic foot depends a lot on how tightly the silage is packed.

In all silage, the moisture content affects the weight per cubic foot, but it doesn't appreciably affect the amount of dry matter in a cubic foot. Therefore, it doesn't influence the amount of feed value per cubic foot very much. The increased weight in high moisture silage is in water, not dry matter.

Nitrate Poisoning
from Silage and Corn Stalks

A *nitrate content high enough to kill livestock is not a common problem with corn silage.* Nitrates have often been blamed for obscure livestock troubles without reliable evidence that they were the real cause.

In regions east of the Mississippi River, there have been few if any proven cases of nitrate poisoning from corn silage or corn stalks! In the western part of the Corn Belt, drouths are more severe and so a real danger exists. "Corn stalk disease" has been reported for many years in the western Corn Belt. Livestock grazing on corn fields after harvest have died from nitrate poisoning in drouth years.

Grazing animals that died of "corn stalk disease" were eating mainly the lower portion of the stalk which was highest in nitrates. The grain had been harvested or had not formed because of severe drouth. As a result, the animals did not have a high-energy, low-nitrate source to dilute the nitrate content of the corn stalks.

In the central and eastern Corn Belt, fall rains usually wash most of the nitrates out of the stalk and leaves; therefore, the danger is less than in low rainfall areas farther west.

At the onset of drouth in most corn-growing regions, soil nitrates move upward and concentrate near or on the surface. As a result, nitrates become *less* available. The corn plant is, therefore, often short on nitrates and shows nitrogen deficiency symptoms. In other words, available nitrates and water tend to slow down simultaneously when dry weather comes. There is one exception: when corn is grown on an old

Upper Leaves. Very little nitrate because these leaves are not shaded by other leaves. Nitrates are continually converted to proteins.

Upper Stalk. More nitrates than in the upper leaves but still only a small amount under normal conditions.

Grain. Almost no nitrate in mature grain. The nitrogen is in proteins.

Middle Stalk. This section contains an amount of nitrate intermediate between that in the upper and lower sections of the stalk.

Lower Leaves. The actual amount is influenced by the 7 factors, pages 311-312, but the relative amount is higher than in the upper leaves, because the lower leaves are partly shaded. The enzyme that converts nitrate (NO_3^-) to nitrite (NO_2^-), the first step toward protein building, does not function as well in leaves that are shaded. The higher the plant population, the more the nitrates in the bottom leaves.

Lower Stalk. Nitrates are higher than in any other part of the plant. Under normal growing conditions nitrates are only high enough to assure plenty of nitrogen for top yield and the level drops sharply as the plant approaches maturity. Under abnormal growing conditions this is the place where nitrates may be dangerously high.

Figure 170. The relative nitrate content of different parts of the corn plant. The actual amount of nitrate in each plant part is influenced by the factors described on pages 311-312.

Table 38

The nitrogen in manure and legumes raises the nitrate content of corn stalks in the same way as nitrogen from fertilizer does. The following data is for July 30. Five weeks later, on September 4, the nitrate content was less than half as high. (J. J. Hanway, A. J. Englehorn, Iowa State University)

Tons Manure Applied		Nitrate in Stalks Below the Ear on July 30	
		Following Corn	Following an Alfalfa-Clover-Timothy Meadow
Per Acre	Per Hectare	NO₃%	NO₃%
0	0	2.25	2.62
8	19.8	1.88	4.81
16	39.5	3.75	4.94

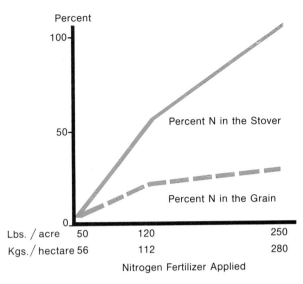

Figure 171. Nitrogen fertilizer (as well as nitrogen from manure or legumes) increases the nitrogen content in the vegetative parts (leaves, stalk) much more than in the grain.

feedlot the deep subsoil is very high in nitrogen accumulated over the years from the manure. During a drouth, nitrogen continues to be available in this situation and may be expected to raise the nitrate content in the corn stalks to a high level.

When and Where Nitrates Build up in Corn Plants

Nitrogen is taken into corn roots mainly in the nitrate form. When conditions are favorable for growth, it moves up the stalk and into the leaves where it is built into proteins. Under normal growing conditions, as the plant nears maturity, the nitrate content gradually declines to near zero. Distribution of nitrates in corn plants is indicated in figure 170.

When conditions are unfavorable for growth, but nitrates are still in good supply in the active feeding root zone, they pile up within the corn plant.

Here are the most important causes for nitrate buildup in corn:

• *A high total nitrogen supply, not just from fertilizer (figure 171), but from any source!* A large growth of legumes (alfalfa, clover, lespedeza, lupines), a heavy application of manure (table 38) and high organic matter content all contribute to the nitrogen supply. Any one or a combination of these factors can cause nitrate buildup in corn when other conditions favor it.

• *Drouth often increases nitrates* because the nitrate reductase enzyme is less able to convert nitrates to nitrates, a necessary step in protein formation. Drouth increases the number of barren stalks and this also leads to a buildup of nitrates because there is no place for proteins to go and less carbohydrates to dilute the nitrates in the plant as a whole.

Levels of nitrates in corn plants high enough to be toxic for livestock are rare except in dry dry western Corn Belt and Great Plains. A drouth by Ohio, Indiana, Wisconsin, Michigan, Missouri or Illinois standards is not so severe as one by Kansas, Colorado or Nebraska standards.

• Very high plant populations increase nitrates because the extra shading causes a drop in nitrate reductase activity in the leaves, the enzyme that converts nitrate (NO_3^-) to nitrite (NO_2^-). Thick planting can

311

cause barren stalks and thus there is no high-energy, low nitrate grain to dilute the nitrate content of the stalk. In an Illinois study, solid-stand corn (100,000 to 200,000 plants per acre, 247,100 to 494,200 per hectare) raised the nitrate content more than did a very heavy application of nitrogen. There are some hybrids that maintain their nitrate reductase activity at high population and therefore are less likely to have a buildup of nitrates.

• *Cloudy weather* increase nitrates because with less sunlight the nitrate reductase enzyme becomes less active in converting nitrate to nitrite.

• *An acute shortage of any nutrient* other than nitrogen increases nitrates in the plant. The roots continue to take in nitrates but, since nutrient deficiency limits growth, the unused nitrates pile up in the stalk and lower leaves.

• *A good rain following a long dry period* will temporarily increase nitrates because the nitrates that were concentrated near the soil surface are swept into the roots along with the water. High nitrate in this case will clear up within a few days when active plant growth begins again.

• Chemical sprays on some weeds and woody plants (not corn) increase nitrates and also improve the palatability of poisonous plants that livestock do not normally eat. This, of course, is a different problem than nitrates in corn.

Dangerous Levels of Nitrate

Different terms are used to describe nitrate content. When you read about nitrate percentages you must know whether they are in terms of nitrogen (N), nitrate (NO_3^-), or potassium (KNO_3). For many years, potassium nitrate equivalent was used, but there is a trend toward using nitrate (NO_3^-). Here is how to change from one form to another:

To change the percent of N to that of NO_3^- multiply by 4.4.

To change the percent of NO_3^- to that of N divide by 4.4.

To change the percent of N to that of KNO_3 multiply by 7.2.

To change the percent of KNO_3 to that of N divide by 7.2.

To change the percent of NO_3^- to that of KNO_3 multiply by 1.6.

To change the percent of KNO_3 to that of NO_3^- divide by 1.6.

There is no single minimum critical level of nitrates in feed and water for ruminant livestock. A healthy herd can tolerate more than a herd that is out of condition. An animal can tolerate more nitrate in feed than in water because nitrate in water is absorbed more rapidly into the blood stream. More nitrate can be handled if the daily dosage is built up gradually because the rumen bacteria adjust to it and detoxify it. A given amount of nitrate has less effect when the intake is spread throughout the day rather than all at one time in feed or water. More nitrate can be safely fed when the rest of the ration is rich in high energy grain.

The most widely used figure for a deadly dosage is 0.93 percent NO_3^- (0.21% N, 1.5% KNO_3) in the *total feed* that is eaten. Silage with 0.3 to 0.6 percent NO_3^- should be fed with caution. If it makes up only part of the total feed and the rest is grain (which is high in energy and low in nitrate) the danger is removed.

Another way to express the maximum tolerable amount of nitrate is on the basis of animal size. About ⅔ ounce per 100 pounds of live weight (625 milligrams per kilogram) fed in a 24-hour period is often fatal to ruminant animals. A thorough literature search by Burden resulted in a range from 330 to 616 mg/kg for cattle and slightly less for sheep.

If you have reason to suspect high nitrate content in your silage, it's advisable to check the nitrate level of your water supply since water supplies may contain nitrates (from seepage or runoff from livestock feeding lots into ground water supplies). Nitrates in water should be added to nitrates in feed to arrive at the *total nitrate intake.*

Non-ruminants (hogs and poultry) can tolerate more nitrates than cattle or sheep. Nitrate toxicity is due to the formation of nitrite (NO_2^-) from nitrate (NO_3^-) by rumen bacteria. The nitrite then gets into the blood stream and reduces the oxygen-carrying capacity of the blood, causing a condition called methemoglobia. The animal actually suffers from lack of oxygen. This conversion does not take place in non-ruminants.

Until recently it was believed that high nitrate intake caused abortions in cattle even though it did not affect the cow. Recent studies cast doubt on that notion. Abortions were not caused in a study when pregnant heifers received enough NO_3^- to convert 40 to 50 percent of the hemoglobin to methemoglobin.

Nitrite (NO_2^-) is about 2.5 times more toxic than nitrate (NO_3^-) to ruminants and 10 times more to non-ruminants. Nitrite is not likely to be high in either feed or water.

The Effect of Nitrate on Vitamin A in Livestock

What is the effect of feeding silage that is above average in nitrates but not high enough to cause death? In the early 1960's, the Illinois, Indiana, and Michigan experiment stations reported that vitamin A content dropped in the livers of feeder catle fed continuously on silage with a slightly higher than normal nitrate content. But even with lowered vitamin A content, these animals made satisfactory gains during the normal feeding period. Cornell University reported no consistent relationship of nitrate to vitamin A in the blood stream. On the basis of information now available, you should apply nitrogen for optimum yield and not worry about the effect on vitamin A.

Until more information is availble, these two practices are suggested:
- Feed vitamins A and E as supplements.
- Feed silage suspected of high nitrate content to fattening cattle rather than to breeding stock.

How Can You Use High-Nitrate Silage?

High-nitrate silage can be safely stored and fed if you take certain precautions. When you know that nitrates are at a dangerous level in your corn crop, there are several things you can do:
- Ensile the crop rather than green feeding it. From 20 to 50 percent of the nitrates will disappear after a few weeks in the silo. This period is, of course, the most dangerous for "silo gas" and proper precautions should be taken to avoid injury to men and livestock.
- Let the crop get a little more mature than usual. Nitrates normally decline as plants get older and the additional grain that develops will reduce the average nitrate content.
- Cut the corn 18 to 24 inches high (½ to ⅔ meter) and leave the stalk butts in the field. The lower stalk section has the highest nitrate content.
- Feed plenty of grain along with the silage to provide a high-energy, low-nitrate source which will dilute the NO_3^- content of the silage.

If you have a choice, feed silage to fattening cattle rather than to dairy cows or beef breeding cattle.
- Check the water supply for nitrates to make certain your water supply is not contributing to the problem.
- Feed small amounts of high-nitrate silage 2 or 3 times per day rather than all at once. Livestock can tolerate nitrates better when spread over a 24-hour period rather than ingested all at once.

The University of Nebraska has reported preliminary results to indicate that adding limestone reduces nitrate in silage.

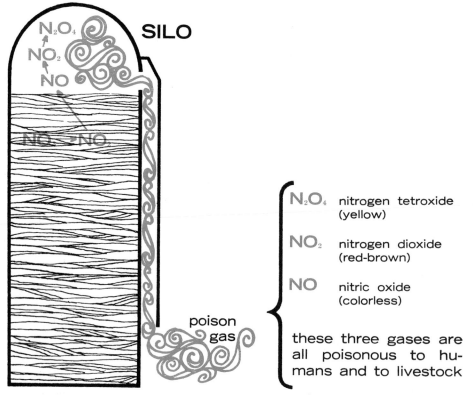

SILO

N_2O_4 nitrogen tetroxide
(yellow)

NO_2 nitrogen dioxide
(red-brown)

NO nitric oxide
(colorless)

poison gas

these three gases are all poisonous to humans and to livestock

Figure 172. When corn silage has an unusually large amount of nitrate (NO_3^-), mainly in the lower part of the stalk and lower leaves, it is coverted to nitrite (NO_2^-) and to nitrous acid in the absence of air within the mass of silage. NO from nitrous acid escapes from the surface of the silage into the air and takes on oxygen to form NO_2 and N_2O_4. All three gases are deadly poisonous to humans and livestock. Before entering a freshly filled silo run the blower for 10 minutes.

Danger: "Silo Gas"

Farmers have been killed and others have become ill from poison gases generated by nitrates in silos (figure 172). Unless farmers are aware of the danger, the instances of sickness and death (to humans and livestock) will increase as plant populations are raised and more nitrogen fertilizer is applied. This problem may eventually be offset by breeding hybrids which will retain their nitrate reductase activity at higher plant population levels than will present hybrids.

Poisonous yellow and brown gases may form in a newly filled silo and below the chute if the nitrate level is high, but farmers don't always notice this warning. Therefore, as a safety measure, the blower should always be run for 10 to 15 minutes before anyone enters a silo for the first 3 weeks after it is filled. Running the blower a few minutes each day will avoid any possible effect on livestock from gases that form and flow down the chute.

Test for Nitrate (NO_3^-)

You can make a simple qualitative tissue test in the middle and lower parts of the stalk (figure 173), to learn whether nitrate is present, but this test does not measure the percent of nitrate. The speed at which the color develops and its intensity are only rough guides to the amount of nitrate. But this is as far as you can go with testing on the farm. If the test shows high nitrate in corn at silo-filling time or in the stalks of mature corn that will be grazed, you should get a laboratory test.

For an accurate test you must freeze the sample immediately (a sample of chopped silage, or of the lower and midsections of stalks) and take it to a chemical testing laboratory. The sample must remain frozen until it reaches the laboratory. However, not all laboratories are prepared to test for NO_3^-. It is not an easy test to make.

White. No nitrate present.

Light blue. Moderate amount of nitrate. There is another nitrate test that develops a pink color to show nitrates.

Dark blue. High nitrate content.

Figure 173. A tissue test on different parts of the corn stalk will show whether nitrates are present. The intensity of the color and speed at which it develops are rough guides to the amount of nitrate. One tissue test shows the presence of nitrate by a blue color, as above, another by a pink color.

11

Harvest, Storage, and Marketing Grain Corn

By the time the crop is mature you have incurred most of the expense in producing corn. But you have no return for your toil and investment until the crop is safely harvested, stored and marketed.

There are many good ways to harvest, dry and store corn. The information presented here will supply you with some of the basic reference data you need to plan a good system for your farm and suggest how best to handle some special problems.

The higher your yield is, the more you have at stake in proper harvesting and storing. You can easily lose 10 to 15 percent by driving a poorly adjusted picker too fast. A harvesting delay of one month can increase losses 3 or 4 percent. It would seem that losing 10 percent in harvesting reduces your profit 10 percent. This is *not* correct. To illustrate, assume that under ideal harvesting conditions and properly adjusted machinery operated at the right speed, you can harvest 125 bushels per acre (78.4 quintals per hectare). A 10 percent loss would equal 12.5 bushels or 7.84 quintals. Suppose it takes 90 bushels per acre (56.5 quintals per hectare) to pay for growing the crop leaving a net of 35 bushels (21.9 quintals) for your labor. A loss of 12.5 bushels (7.8 quintals) is not 10 but rather 35 percent of your return above production costs!

When to Harvest

Corn is mature when the grain has about 30 to 32 percent moisture. The best time to harvest depends on your harvest and storage system, table 39. Early harvesting of grain corn generally is best because:

- You have less lodging from stalk rot and severe storms.
- There is less chance of waterlogged fields which delay or prevent harvesting.
- Ear drop is less.
- Less grain is shelled when the ears hit the snapping rolls.

The effect of delayed harvest is shown in table 40.

In order to harvest your entire crop with the *least field loss* you need to start slightly before the ideal stage, table 39.

The only drawback to early harvesting is that it requires more energy for drying and the price of fuel rose dramatically in 1974. On a typical Corn Belt farm, drying requires about 4 percent of the total energy used in the production of corn. Ways to economize on energy are discussed on page 358. It is not likely that the price of energy will decline in the foreseeable future. But the price of corn may rise enough to maintain about the same ratio of cost of fuel to value of corn. In that case, the main consideration will be fuel supply rather than price.

Table 39

Ideal moisture at which to harvest corn for different storage systems in order to minimize field losses. For lowest losses on your whole crop, you should be half finished by the ideal stage. *The moisture levels shown for dry grain are too high for safe storage without drying.*

| | | Moisture in the Kernels | |
		Ideal	**Preferred Range**
	Picker	25	21 to 28
Dry Grain	Picker-sheller	25	21 to 28
	Combine	25	21 to 28
High moisture grain (stored in a silo)		28	25 to 30
Ground ear corn silage		32	30 to 35
		Moisture in Chopped Material	
Center-cut silage (4 feet (1⅓ meters) centered on ear)		65	60 to 70
Regular silage		65	60 to 70

Table 40

Field losses rise sharply when harvesting is delayed. Averages from tests in Illinois, Indiana, Iowa and Nebraska for several seasons. (V. W. Davis, USDA)

	October % Loss	November % Loss	December % Loss
Machine loss	4.6	7.0	11.8
Total loss	5.0	8.4	18.4

Maximum Moisture for Safe Storage

For long-term storage, shelled corn should be down to 13 percent moisture. If the moisture is even a few percentage points higher, the center of the bin will heat from the natural respiration of the grain. This will cause the humidity of the air to rise enough to start mold growth.

Molding is a self-accelerating process. Each pound of carbohydrate (.45 kilo) that is used up as food for molds produces .6 unit of water. Furthermore, it releases enough heat to raise the temperature of the water 100°F. (55.5°C.). Each pound of fat consumed releases 1.1 pounds of water and enough heat to raise the temperature 1650°F. (917°C.). In a bin of stored corn each ½ percent dry matter that is lost theoretically raises the temperature of the corn

mass 67°F. (37°C.). Actually, of course, some or much of the heat escapes from the storage area. It is easy to see why aeration of molding corn is helpful.

Though ear corn storage has greatly declined in the U.S., here are guidelines for storage. The safe level for ear corn in the crib is higher than for shelled corn because air passes through to remove heat and to dry the corn. In northern corn-growing areas, the upper limit in *narrow cribs* (4½ feet, 1½ meters) is about 25 percent moisture in the grain. If late fall and winter are so damp that the grain does not dry, spoilage will begin with the onset of warm weather in the spring.

In the central Corn Belt where cribs are larger in order to handle more corn, the safe limit is about 20 percent. Research on cribs

Grain temperature

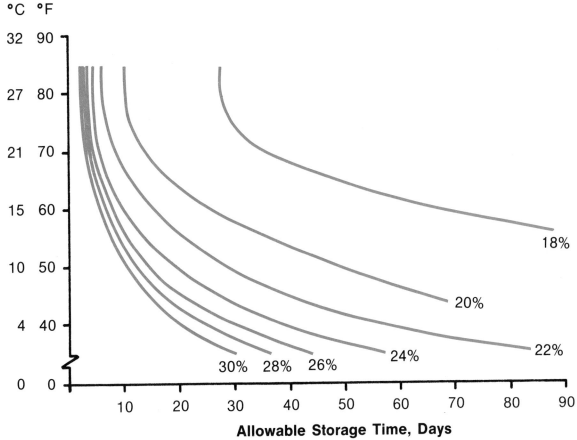

Figure 174. Allowable storage time for shelled corn at various temperatures and moisture contents. During this time the grain will lose ½ percent in dry matter, but will still be acceptable. USDA Grain Storage Research Laboratory, Ames, Iowa.

shows that corn should be down to 18.5 percent moisture by March 1 to avoid spoilage with the onset of warm weather.

One way to handle high-moisture corn if the acreage isn't large is to pick the crop after cold weather hits and feed it out before warm weather comes in the spring.

Safe Storage Time for High Moisture Corn

If you desire to store corn for a short period without drying or if you dry corn in the storage bin, you need to know how long it can be safely held. The time varies with percent moisture and temperature in the grain, figure 174. The grain will lose about 0.5 percent dry weight but will not be downgraded in the market.

To use the chart, begin with the temperature on the left-hand side. Follow horizontally to the right to the intercept with the percent moisture in the grain. Draw a line straight down to the bottom of the chart and read the number of days for safe storage.

Grain Preservatives

Chemical preservation of high moisture grain began in Europe in the early 1960's and in the U.S. a few years later. Commercial test marketing began in the U.S. in 1971. Interestingly a patent was granted to Fannie E. Pierson, Gravity, Iowa in 1918 for a process to preserve high moisture corn with acetic acid.

The two most commonly used preservatives are (1) propionic acid and (2) a mixture of acetic and propionic acids. They are registered with the Environmental Protection Agency. Both are mild organic acids which inhibit growth of a wide range of micro-

319

organisms but are not harmful to animals. They are in fact normal products of fermentation in the rumens of animals and serve as sources of energy for livestock that consume them.

Early feeding trials indicate a 3 to 4 percent advantage for treated high moisture corn over the same grain stored in a silo. An average 3.3 percent advantage over dry grain was found in trials at six experiment stations. Palatability is very good.

The economics of organic acid preservatives will, of course, change with changes in price of acid and of fuel for corn drying. L. D. Hill reported approximate costs taking into consideration overhead costs, operating costs, field losses and shrinkage. He assumed a 4 percent improvement in feed efficiency. Comparable costs for 50,000 bushel volume were:

	Cents per bushel
Bin dryer	11.65
Batch dryer	13.85
Acid (under plastic)	14.10
Glass-lined upright silo	14.25
Acid in bin	19.70
Ear corn in crib	23.10
Commercial elevator	23.30

Preservation with chemicals has the advantages of low capital needs and quick preparation if needed. Chemical preservatives will be especially appealing if fuels for drying become scarce. You could tool up to store high moisture corn under plastic in one season and shift to another method the next year with little or no loss in investment.

Follow the instructions of the chemical supplier for the proper amount to apply to corn at different moisture contents. Treated high moisture corn does not mold even when exposed to air for moderate periods of time. The acid will volatilize in time, more rapidly at high than at low temperature, and the grain will then lose its protection.

Care is needed to avoid dilution of the acid when you store over 1,000 bushels (254 quintals) in a pile. Temperature differences from the top to bottom or interior to the outside of the pile cause moisture to migrate, usually condensing on the surface of the pile. This dilutes the acid and reduces its effectiveness against molds.

Engineers suggest a false floor under the bin and depth of 12 to 15 feet (3.7 to 4.6 meters) or less. Hirning, University of Illinois engineer, recommends that provision be made for aerating acid treated corn when the amount exceeds 1,000 bushels (254 quintals). He suggests turning the fan on whenever the outside temperature for a day averages 10°F. (5.6°C.) colder than when you stored the grain. If you have a small fan capacity of 1 cubic foot per minute, run the fan for 12 hours; if ½ cubic foot per minute run it 24 hours.

Acid preservatives have some disadvantages:

• They corrode unprotected metal or concrete surfaces. Check with suppliers on the way to protect storage surfaces. Wood is not much affected.

• They are a safety hazard. They cause skin blisters. Eyes should be protected when applying acids. Avoid breathing the vapors.

• There is no market for acid treated corn except for animal feed.

Other preservatives are being studied and marketed in a small way in 1974. They include benzoic acid (in combination with acetic and propionic), ammonium-isobutyrate, and an enzyme formula.

High Moisture Grain Stored in a Silo

Instead of drying field-shelled corn, you can put it directly into an air-tight silo. The silo is then used simply as a storage bin. You can put your corn in any time after it is mature, but the ideal time is when it's between 28 and 32 percent moisture. This moisture level has nothing to do with keeping quality since there will be practically no losses in an air-tight silo, but it is suggested because at 28 to 32 percent moisture, you can harvest your crop with the lowest field losses. For some farmers it may cost less to

Figure 175. Highly toxic aflatoxin has been traced in a few cases to Aspergillus flavus mold.

tool up for this kind of storage than to install a drying system. Storing in a silo also requires less handling from field to feed bunker.

One point to keep in mind is that once ensiled, high-moisture grain must be fed, whereas with dry grain you have a choice of feeding or selling.

Moldy Corn Can Be Poisonous

Risk from feeding moldy corn has been debated for many years. The fact is that much has been fed with no apparent effect but occasionally sickness or death has occurred. Moldy corn can cause a variety of problems from poor appetite to death. Moldy corn should not be fed to breeding animals or young calves or pigs below 75 pounds (34 kilos). Young gilts sometimes show false symptoms of pregnancy. Try mixing 3 parts non-moldy corn with 1 part moldy and feeding it to older animals for two weeks. Watch them closely for signs of poor eating

and poor performance. You may have to add something like liquid molasses to improve palatability.

In 1960 death of a large number of turkeys and ducks in England was traced to eating grain contaminated with a strain of mold called Aspergillus flavus. The toxin produced by the mold is called aflatoxin. It is extremely toxic but fortunately seldom occurs in large amounts. It is most prevalent south of the central Corn Belt. Very low tolerances have been established for human foods but no human deaths have been reported.

Aflatoxins must be prevented. Once developed they cannot be removed by ordinary processing methods.

Mold growth is encouraged by high moisture, broken kernels which permit entrance of the mold, and by warm temperatures. Quick drying or chemical preservation after harvest and minimizing broken kernels are ways to reduce the likelihood of aflatoxin development.

Some Special Considerations for Quality of Grain for Feed

• *Protein.* A summary of a large number of trials in several states indicates that if the starting yield is 75 to 100 bushels per acre, and the final yield with extra N fertilizer is 100 to 125 bushels, the first 100 pounds of N will probably raise the protein about 1 percent. The next 100 pounds will raise the protein another ½ percent. These experiments averaged about 8.5 percent protein without extra nitrogen and increased to 10.0 percent with 150 to 200 pounds of N.

Corn protein, or zein, is unbalanced in the amino acids that all livestock require, but which only ruminants (cattle, sheep, goats) can make for themselves. When the protein content is raised by adding nitrogen, it appears that those amino acids which all livestock can make for themselves are increased more than those which only ruminants can make. However, a new high-lysine gene has been found in corn. When it is bred into commercial hybrids even nonruminants can benefit from extra protein produced by high nitrogen fertility.

Applying nitrogen to the soil does not compare in efficiency with adding it directly to feed in the form of urea. Some credit, of course, must be allowed for the nitrogen that is not recovered in the first crop but remains in the soil and contributes to the general level of soil nitrogen and organic matter.

• *Phosphorus.* The phosphorus content of grain from soil with very low available P can be increased about 50 percent with fertilization. However, it is standard practice to supply phosphorus in the feed supplement and, therefore, an increase in phosphorus in corn is not considered very important.

• *Vitamins.* Studies of vitamins in crops prove that climate is the main factor influencing vitamin content within a species of crop. As far as is now known, you do not influence the vitamin content to any measurable extent by your corn growing methods.

Table 41

Examples of apparent and actual penalties paid for selling high-moisture corn when the moisture discount rate is *1½ cents for each ½ percent* of moisture above 15.5. (Adapted from L. F. Stice, University of Illinois)

Moisture	Discount Per Bushel Wet Basis	Actual Penalty for Selling High-Moisture Corn
Percent	*Cents*	*Cents*
15.5	0	—
16.0	1.5	.9
16.5	3.0	1.8
17.0	4.5	2.7
17.5	6.0	3.6
18.0	7.5	4.5
18.5	9.0	5.4
19.0	10.5	6.4
19.5	12.0	7.3
20.0	13.5	8.2
20.5	15.0	9.1
21.0	16.5	10.0
21.5	18.0	10.9
22.0	19.5	11.8
22.5	21.0	12.7
23.0	22.5	13.5
23.5	24.0	14.5
24.0	25.5	15.4
24.5	27.0	16.3
25.0	28.5	17.3

High Moisture Discounts: Why and How Much?

Farmers who sell high-moisture corn usually complain that the discount is too great. Sometimes this is true; but the discount is actually lower than it seems.

High-moisture corn sells for less:
• because it has less dry weight,
• to pay for the cost of drying,
• to discourage farmers from sellin it.

The discount for high-moisture corn is often 1 cent for each ½ percent above 15.5

Figure 176. A combine with a corn head is the most efficient harvester for large acreages of corn. Field losses are lower than by other methods.

percent up to 23 percent and 1½ cents for each ½ percent above 23 percent.

When you sell high-moisture corn, the actual penalty is about 40 percent less than it appears (table 41). The fact is that you are selling extra water and this accounts for 40 percent of the apparent discount.

Some grain buyers discount about 1¼ cents per 1 percent excess moisture and then charge 1 to 1.5¢ drying charge per 1 percent water removed.

Harvesting, Storing and Drying Systems

Harvesting, drying, feeding, selling, or storing dry grain, high-moisture grain, or ear corn silage must be planned like the assembly line in an automobile factory. The parts from the sub-assembly line must arrive on the main assembly line at the proper time and in the right amounts. If you don't plan your harvesting, drying and storing from start to finish as an integrated unit, you'll find that things jam up somewhere along the line.

Your harvesting assembly line must be geared to its slowest component. This usually is the dryer, if you are harvesting at the optimum time for storage as grain.

Here are brief descriptions of harvesting and drying systems, but you will want to get advice from you cooperative extension service or local farm equipment dealer before deciding which is the best system for your farm.

If you have less than 5,000 bushels (1270 quintals) of corn, you may be able to get it harvested most economically by hiring a custom harvester, thus eliminating the need to maintain one complex element of the harvest assembly line.

Combine with a Corn Head

Field losses for a combine with corn head (figures 176 – 177) are about 20 percent less than with an ear-corn picker and 30 percent less than with a picker-sheller. With 8,000 or more bushels (2032 quintals) of corn plus some soybeans or small grains this is your most economical method.

Lowest losses of all are for combine harvest and storage as high-moisture corn. Harvesting can be completed more rapidly with this system than with a combine and drying unit.

323

Field Losses (%)

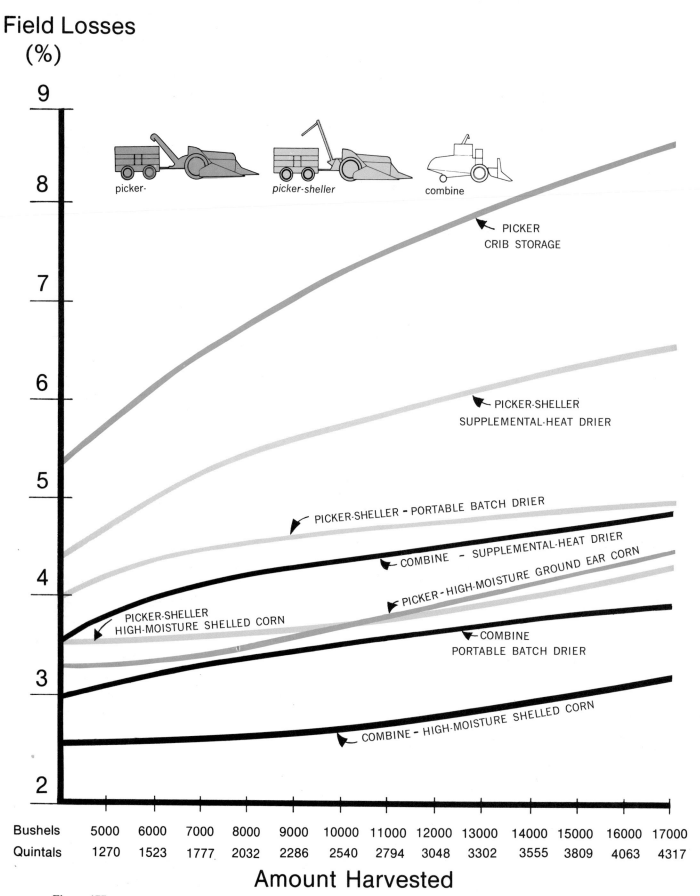

Figure 177.

Ear-corn Picker, Crib Storage, No Drying

Until the early 1960's this was the most widely used system in the central Corn Belt, but has almost disappeared. It was still common in the northern Corn Belt in the mid-1970's. You can't start until the grain is down near 20 percent moisture. If you have a large acreage, the last part harvested is likely to suffer large field losses from lodging, broken plants and ear drop.

Ear-corn Picker, Storage As High Moisture Corn in a Silo

This system reduces field losses to about one half of losses with a picker, crib storage and no drying because you can start and finish earlier than with crib storage.

Picker-Sheller

If the corn goes direct to market or into you own dryer, field losses with a picker-sheller are very slightly more than for picking ear corn of the same moisture content.

Drying Systems for Shelled Corn

Since the dryer is the slowest component in the harvest assembly line, it is essential that you have the best possible drying system for your farm. Here are the alternatives suggested by Davis and Brandt in *Successful Farming:*

• *Dry and store in the same structure*

Unheated forced air can handle corn from 18 to 22 percent moisture. Since this is a slow method, it is not suggested for more than 4,000 bushels (1016 quintals), unless you have several units.

Heated air drying will handle up to 25 percent moisture. Practical for 4,000 to 10,000 bushels (1016 to 2540 quintals).

This system always results in some over-drying on the hot air intake side and under-drying on the air exhaust side of the bin. This is because the air picks up moisture and loses heat as it moves through the grain thus losing drying power. Overdrying results in a weight loss if you sell the grain and may

also cause more seed coat cracking. The underdried part of the bin may mold.

Greatest overdrying results from high air temperature and low relative humidity of the imput air. For example, with a constant 10 cubic feet per minute air flow the amount of overdrying of the bottom layer in order to dry the surface to 15 percent moisture at four temperatures was:

	Overdrying
80°F (27°C)	1.75%
100°F (38°C)	2.50%
120°F (49°C)	3.75%
140°F (60°C)	5.00%

Low air flow also increases the amount of overdrying.

• *Batch-in-bin (18 to 30 percent)*

Each day's harvest (2 to 4 feet, ⅔ to 1 meter) is dried by forcing heated air through a perforated floor; the batch is then moved to a storage structure. The last part of the crop is dried in layers and may be left in the dryer.

For a volume of 8,000 bushels (2032 quintals) or more.

• *Portable batch (18 to 30 percent)*

Each batch is dried in a portable (non-storage) unit and then moved into storage. For 10,000 bushels (2540 quintals) or more.

This system also overdries on the hot air imput side and underdries near the exhaust side. But in batch drying, this unevenness is corrected when the dried batch is mixed while being moved to the storage bin.

At a constant air input temperature of 140°F (60°C) the amount of overdrying of the bottom layer to reach 15 percent in the surface layer was:

5 cfm air	7%
10 cfm air	5%
20 cfm air	4%

• *Continuous-flow (18 to 30 percent)*

The grain travels in a continuous stream through the dryer at a rate calibrated for drying it to the desired moisture content by the time it emerges from the discharge end

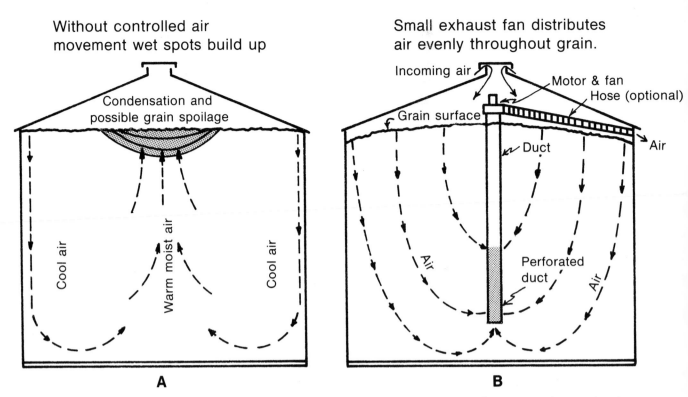

Without controlled air movement wet spots build up

Condensation and possible grain spoilage

Cool air

Warm moist air

Cool air

A

Small exhaust fan distributes air evenly throughout grain.

Incoming air

Motor & fan

Hose (optional)

Grain surface

Duct

Air

Air

Perforated duct

Air

B

Figure 178. Unventilated bin A, and bin with a small fan, B, to equalize temperature and prevent moisture migration, condensation and molding.

of the dryer. For a volume of 13,000 bushels (3302 quintals) or more.

• *Dryeration*

This is a combination of drying and aerating. In the usual drying systems the grain is completely dried before it is removed from the heat source.

In the dryeration process, the corn is dried to 16 to 18 percent and then, while still hot, it is transferred to a temporary storage bin. After a few hours, the fan is turned on to cool the corn. In about 12 hours, the corn is ready to be transferred to the final storage bins. Dryeration results in less stress cracks; it was actually developed to eliminate stress cracks in corn for milling and has proved useful to anyone who needs to speed up dryer capacity.

• *Custom drying.* Many farmers who do not own a dryer have corn custom dried. The problem is to get the service when needed to permit timely harvesting to minimize field losses.

Avoiding Wet Spots in Dry Stored Grain

Even after corn has been dried to a safe moisture content for storage it can develop wet spots that will mold, figure 178. This happens when there are large temperature changes. The air near the outside wall cools, becomes heavier and moves downward when the outside temperature drops sharply. Warmer air is displaced upward in the center of the bin. When it reaches the surface it cools and moisture condenses in the upper layer of grain and mold develops.

Moisture migration can be easily controlled by installing a very low volume fan at the top of a perforated duct, figure 178, which, by pulling air down through the storage bin, will equalize the temperature and prevent migration and condensation. No heat is introduced and no overall drying is accomplished.

Figure 179. Ventilated plastic storage may be used for holding excess shelled corn for several weeks. Suction fan is connected to air collection box in center of grain pile. Continuous operation of fan pulls cool air through grain and holds plastic in place. Not recommended for use before November 1 or with shelled corn wetter than 22 percent moisture.

Temperature
for Drying Corn to Retain Quality

If you are drying *corn for feed* you don't need to worry about high temperatures. Any temperature that is practical in the dryer will not affect the nutritional value.

The drying temperature of grain that is *sold for processing* should not go above 140°F. (60°C.). Higher temperatures cause the gluten to toughen and cling to the starch, which clog filters and sieves, reducing the yield of refined oil.

Distillers obtain low yields of alcohol from corn dried at temperatures above 140°F. (60°C.). Dry millers and manufacturers of breakfast foods report more shattered and broken kernels from high-temperature drying.

Unfortunately for the processing industry, about three-fourths of the market corn is headed for livestock feed and therefore the market does not recognize superior milling quality with a premium price.

A bonus to keep in mind is that drying at moderate temperature makes more efficient use of the heat and therefore costs less.

Low Temperature Drying

This system involves drying with air heated only about 5°F (3°C) above outside air temperature. Preferably the moisture content should be no more than 24 percent. The total amount of fuel used in drying is only slightly less than with rapid drying, but it spreads the peak fuel load.

This system is especially suited to small acreages where the crop is custom-harvested and stored on the farm. The bin can be filled continuously.

Low temperature drying is best suited to average (night time low plus day time high divided by 2) temperatures of 30° to 50°F. (-1° to 10°C.). Drying to safe storage level will be completed in 30 to 40 days if air flow rates are as follows:

Moisture	Air flow per minute
22%	1 cubic foot per bushel
24%	2 cubic feet per bushel
26%	3 cubic feet per bushel

Farmers who have a large amount of corn could use low temperature drying to hold wet corn until the regular dryer is available or to carry through a period of temporary shortage of fuel.

327

Figure 180. A South Dakota farmer with the aid of an Extension Agricultural Engineer and the local Electric Power Cooperative built a solar energy drier in 1974. Offset newspaper printing plates painted black on the outside were mounted on the south side of the storage bin. Clear plastic was mounted a few inches outside to serve as a channel to carry the air from the plates to the fan.

Solar Energy for Drying

South Dakota extension agricultural engineer Bill Peterson worked with local electric cooperatives to design a low cost solar drying system, figure 180. The system collects heat from the sun during clear days and is supplemented by electrical energy at night.

The aluminum plates are painted black on the outside to collect heat and left unpainted on the inside. They are mounted on the south side of the bin on thin wooden strips. The clear plastic envelope mounted a few inches from the metal plates held the heat and served as a channel to the crop-drying fan. This arrangement heated the air 5 to 7 degrees F (3 to 4°C) on sunny days. That was enough to dry the grain from 20 percent down to 13 percent. The bin was designed to accept 24 percent moisture corn but the corn field dried to 20 percent before harvest.

Engineer Peterson intended solar heat to provide only part of the energy – the rest to be supplied by fossil fuel – but farmer Pederson satisfactorily dried the 20 percent corn by operating the fan continuously and added no heat.

Several other engineers began in 1975 to experiment with ways to capture the sun's energy to meet drying and heating needs.

Should You Own a Moisture Tester?

Having your own moisture tester can save you time and money:

• You don't have to run to the elevator with samples to decide when you should start harvesting or how long to continue drying.

• Overdrying costs money in extra fuel and lost time.

• Overdrying loses you money because you get no premium for corn that is below 15½ percent moisture. If you overdry to 13 percent, you lose 3 bushels out of every 100. On 10,000 bushels this amounts to $750 with corn at $2.50 per bushel.

Corn Topping

Since the mid-1950s, topping corn has been promoted as a means to speed drying of the ears and reduce field losses. Topping needs to be examined from three standpoints:

· What is the effect on yield?
· Does it speed drying?

Table 42

Estimated percent of FIELD LOSSES with a corn combine for the entire corn crop on the farm. For a corn picker, multiply the loss figures by 1.25; for a picker-sheller by 1.31. The best time to START harvesting for the LOWEST FIELD LOSS is indicated in color. To choose the best time to start, each farmer needs to also consider drying costs or market discounts for high moisture corn. (V. W. Davis, USDA)

Estimated number of days it will take to harvest the entire acreage	Field losses (%) for the entire acreage when harvest begins at these moisture levels					
	30%	**28%**	**26%**	**24%**	**22%**	**20%**
8	3.0	2.7	2.5	2.6	3.1	4.4
14	2.8	2.6	2.6	3.0	3.5	4.9
20	2.8	2.8	3.0	3.4	4.0	5.4
26	3.0	3.0	3.3	3.8	4.5	6.1
32	3.3	3.4	3.7	4.2	5.0	6.7
38	3.7	3.8	4.2	4.8	5.6	7.5
44	4.1	4.2	4.7	5.4	6.3	8.3
48	4.4	4.6	5.1	5.8	6.8	8.9

Figure 181. Having your own moisture tester is a great convenience and may make money for you.

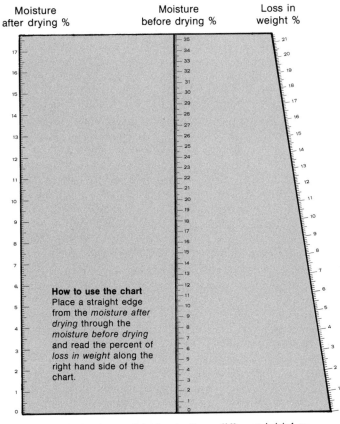

How to use the chart
Place a straight edge from the *moisture after drying* through the *moisture before drying* and read the percent of *loss in weight* along the right hand side of the chart.

Figure 182. Drying weight losses from different initial to different final moisture contents.

329

Table 43

The effect on yield of topping corn at different stages. Average of 2 years. (J. L. Schmidt and W. G. Lovely, ARS, USDA)

Stage at which corn was topped	Per Cent of Maximum Yield
Not topped	100
Ten days after pollination	90
Kernel moisture about 70%	91
Kernel moisture about 50%	97
Kernel moisture about 38%	94

• Are harvesting losses reduced?

The effect on yield depends on when you top the corn. When the tops are cut off before the grain is fully mature, the earlier the topping, the greater the yield reduction (table 43). The reduction is, however, much less than expected because when the upper leaves are removed, the lower leaves receive more sunlight. The increased efficiency of these lower leaves largely compensates for the loss of the upper leaves. The researchers did not offer an explanation for the greater loss when topped at 38 percent than at higher moisture. It may have been sampling variability.

Rate of drying was not affected by topping in Iowa trials in 1958 or in a late planting in 1959, but topped corn was 1 to 4 percent drier in an earlier trial in 1959.

Topping did not reduce harvesting losses in these trials.

Temperature at Which Frost Occurs

Central Corn Belt farmers seldom experience corn severely frosted well in advance of maturity. But in 1974 corn was planted late and the stage was set for trouble unless frost occurred later than usual. Unfortunately the first killing frost came 3 to 4 weeks earlier than normal.

Several interesting observations were made.

• Frost occurs at temperatures well above the freezing point of water when the air is very clear and very still because of heat loss through radiational cooling. Heat is radiated from leaves into the outer atmosphere. The amount of radiation is related to the difference in temperature between the radiating and receiving bodies. On very clear nights the extremely cold outer atmosphere is the receiving body. On hazy or cloudy nights, the receiving body is the haze or clouds which are far warmer than the outer atmosphere. Furthermore the haze and clouds reflect radiation back to the earth. On clear, still nights frost often occurs at 35 to 36°F. (2°C.).

• When the temperature is very close to the freezing point, slight differences in the lay of the land result in frost kill in depressions with no effect on areas only a few feet higher. Persons who live in hilly or rolling regions are familiar with this pattern due to air drainage, colder air being slightly more dense thus flowing into low areas.

• Plants in thin stands and along field margins are more affected because of greater radiational cooling and less heat trapped within the crop canopy.

Handling Soft Corn

When corn is killed by frost before it matures, the stalk and cob are wetter than they are when corn matures normally. For a short time after frost, the movement of nutrients and water into the kernels is slowed down. Then it picks up again. As a result of transfer of water from the stalk and cob, the grain may stay at the same moisture content or even become wetter until the kernel is finally sealed off from the cob and stalk.

Corn killed at a very immature stage, the "soft corn" problem of agricultural writings, field dries much more slowly than expected. There are several possible reasons.

1) The amount of moisture in the grain is greater than most persons realize.

2) The moisture content of the stalk is far higher than in mature corn.

3) The husks on immature corn remain tight thus reducing moisture loss out the end of the ear.

Canadian researchers found that the weight of grain increased after premature simulated freezing (plants killed with a chemical defoliant) showing that material was translocated from the stalk into the grain.

The livestock man has several choices in handling soft corn, since it has the same feeding value per pound of dry matter as sound corn. Properly preserved soft corn can be fed to all livestock in cool weather; therefore the livestock farmer has the following choices:

• *Hog it down.*
• *Make silage out of the whole plant or only the ears.*
• *Dry it as a grain farmer has to do.* Heated forced air is the best approach to save soft corn, either shelled or ear.
• *Dry it on the stalk.* Field drying is simple and economical if the frost is followed by dry weather. However, this method has drawbacks. If wet weather follows the frost, the corn may not dry down to 20 percent until spring. There will be extra loss due to stalk lodging if the crop has stalk rot. Frosted immature corn has more stalk breakage than mature corn.
• *Store it in a crib.* If the corn contains 20 to 30 percent moisture, it may be husked and cribbed. Few farmers in the central Corn Belt have cribs but temporary ones can be made with snow fence. Special precautions must be taken in storing the crop. Air circulation is essential to prevent spoilage. Clean husking is important because any debris that fills spaces between the ears will slow air movement. Distribute the corn evenly in the crib to avoid forming a mass of shelled corn and husks below the spout. Use crib ventilators to increase movement of air through the crib. Make periodic checks of the stored corn, especially in warm weather.
• *Sell it if possible.* Corn that contains over 30 percent moisture cannot be cribbed safely as ear corn. This corn should be partly dried on the stalk (if stalk rot is not serious), shelled when frozen, and sold to an elevator. To avoid a large moisture discount, it may be possible to sell the soft corn to a livestock feeder in the area.

Recent Changes in the Corn Market

The corn market in the United States now differs in important respects from that between the 1930's and the early 1970's.

First, the U.S. crop is now part of the world market for feed grains. The size of crops in other parts of the world influences the U.S. price.

U.S. corn is an important item in the balance of trade with other countries. Corn shipments overseas help the U.S. to import needed materials *especially fuel oil.*

The federal government is much less involved in support prices and is out of the business of providing grain storage bins. The price of corn is likely to have higher peaks and valleys than when the government purchased large amounts to raise the price in years of surplus and to dampen the price rise by releasing feed grains from storage in years of short supply.

The federal government imposed a temporary embargo on corn exports at one time when domestic prices were rising rapidly. This adds an element of uncertainty to the market which cannot be predicted from supply and demand information.

About 1973 interest increased in establishing world grain reserves. It is not yet clear where major storage capacity will be developed. There will be some at all levels: on-farm, local elevators and grain terminals.

Since 1963, there has been a great increase in the movement of corn directly from the field to local elevators in cash grain areas. This has put a heavy strain on storage and transportation facilities. Railroad boxcars have often been inadequate to move all of the corn during the rush period. The situa-

Two types of permanent cribs

Figure 183. Types of storage for ear corn, pages 332 and 333. *Reproduced by permission of Information Canada.*

Temporary crib made of snow fence

tion is aggravated by ideal weather for continuous rapid harvest.

On-Farm Storage

In the 1950's and early 1960's the U.S. government was in the grain storage business in a big way. The long rows of storage bins have been dismantled. Farmers and commercial elevators have taken up the slack. Enlarged storage capacity somewhere is absolutely essential because the volume of corn is increasing steadily.

On-farm storage has expanded. This has several advantages:

• It avoids long waits in line at receiving elevators during the height of the harvest season.

• It provides for more orderly marketing in place of a great surge in the fall.

• It gives you more options at harvest time. You can sell direct if you wish or dry, store, and hold the crop if you feel the price will be higher later. You can store high moisture grain in a silo.

• You may find it to your tax advantage to sell corn in other than the year it was grown.

Selling Direct from the Field Versus Storing on the Farm

If you grow corn for the market, you have to decide whether you can make more profit by selling direct from the field or by storing the crop for a while. The important factors are the cost of farm storage and your prediction on trends in corn prices after harvest.

Table 44 gives information on storage and drying costs. Hinton calculated that if you were to have corn commercially dried and stored you would need to receive at least 20 cents more in March or 34 cents more in July to gain over selling wet at harvest time. Likewise you would need to receive

Table 44

Estimated costs to *dry and store shelled corn* that has 25 percent moisture, assuming that the corn is dried to 13 percent moisture, which is necessary for extended storage, but drier than it need be for No. 2 corn. (Adapted from T. A. Hieronymus, Cir. 833, University of Ill.) Starting moisture increased from 22 to 25 percent. Costs increased 25 percent to adjust for inflation, interest increased 50 percent.

	Months in Storage			
	1	3	6	9
	Cents per Bushel			
Drying, fixed costs	3.50	3.50	3.50	3.50
Storage, fixed costs	4.00	4.00	4.00	4.00
Drying, operating costs	4.42	4.42	4.42	4.42
Interest at 6 percent	.83	2.47	4.95	7.42
Insurance	.19	.34	.58	.78
Extra handling and dry matter loss	1.94	1.94	1.94	1.94
Taxes	00	00	1.88	1.88
Deduct for market discount minus weight loss	−2.56	−2.56	−2.56	−2.56
Total without fixed costs	4.8	6.6	11.2	13.9
Total including fixed costs	12.3	14.1	18.7	21.4

28 cents in March or 36 in July to give you equal return for storing on your farm rather than selling direct from the field.

Prior to the development of a major world market for corn, T. A. Hieronymus of the University of Illinois arrived at these general conclusions about the price trends *through the season* after harvesting begins:

Influence of the national crop:

When there is a short corn crop the price peaks early in the season.

When there is a large crop following a short crop, there is relatively little price change in the months following harvest.

A second successive large crop results in a larger-than-average price increase between harvest time and the following harvest. (In other words, the price at harvest time takes a sharp plunge; then, later in the season, a higher-than-average increase results.)

Influence of noncrop factors:

The price increases during periods of improving general business conditions and declines as unemployment increases.

The price decreases when livestock numbers are declining and increases when they are increasing.

In summary based mainly upon the U.S. situation:

(1) The odds favor regularly storing corn for a short time after harvest, (2) storing until the next fall is risky, and (3) success with corn storage over a period of years depends upon selecting the right time to sell in individual years.

Except for the period right after harvest, the average rise in price is little more than the costs of storing.

Having storage capacity on your farm increases your flexibility in deciding when to sell your crop. Some large local or regional elevators will accept delivery of your crop and than let you decide when you want to declare it sold even though they may already have moved it into the grain marketing channel.

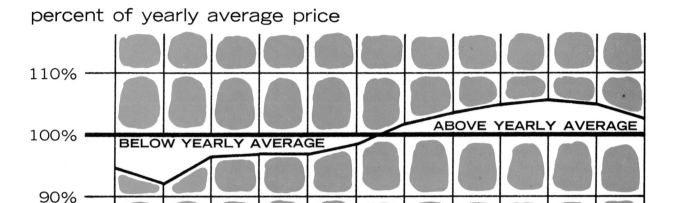

percent of yearly average price

110%

100%

BELOW YEARLY AVERAGE

ABOVE YEARLY AVERAGE

90%

OCT NOV DEC JAN FEB MAR APR MAY JUN JUL AUG SEP

Figure 184. Variation from the yearly average price of corn, throughout the year, by months.

The Cash and Futures Corn Market

The cash price and the futures prices work together to provide orderly marketing of the corn crop. The two prices integrate the supply of the crop with the anticipated demand for livestock feed, human food, the corn processing industry and for export. The prices represent the combined judgement of many persons, both buyers and sellers. The market prices change in response to new information on the size of the crop, numbers of livestock, amount of corn in storage, amounts of other feed grains both domestic and world wide, announcements of intentions to buy large amounts for foreign countries, and on general economic conditions.

The U.S. government got out of the grain storage business in the 1960's so it does not influence the market by buying for or releasing corn from its storage bins. The loan rate was a factor when it was near the market price but in 1974 the cash price was more than three times the loan rate. It is not yet clear whether export limitations will be a regular policy in times of rapidly rising prices.

The following paragraphs explaining the cash and futures pricing of corn are adapted from a grain marketing newsletter by a marketing specialist, L. F. Stice, University of Illinois.

During the growing and harvest seasons, you have a four-way choice:
1. Sell your corn at the local elevator.
2. Hold your corn in storage.
3. Hold your corn in storage and sell July futures.
4. Sell your corn and buy futures.

What you do depends on what you think is going to happen to corn prices and to the relationship between cash and future prices. Your action will depend on your forecast.

It is desirable to use futures in some years and not in others. By using futures, you can (1) set the price for your crop before delivery or (2) delay setting a price until after your

.crop is delivered. When selling futures, you are setting your price before delivering or perhaps harvesting. When buying futures, you are delaying pricing.

Using futures is not a way to avoid risks. When to sell is a judgement decision associated with operating a farm business, one that cannot be avoided. However, the use of futures can provide greater flexibility in implementing your decision. Deciding when to sell might be thought of as simply a guessing game. But it is much more like a game of forecasting, because farmers do have considerable information on expected yield and use of the crop on which to base their decisions.

Deciding when to sell a crop is quite different from speculating in futures. Yet, it is easy to turn futures trading from its use as a management tool in the farm business into outright speculation. *Positions in futures must offset cash positions, in size and direction.* A futures position larger than the amount of grain produced is an outright speculation; a long futures position when cash grain is held in storage also represents outright speculation; similarly, with a short futures position after cash grain is sold. The rule is: *equal amounts and opposite in direction.*

One well-established pattern is the way the cash price approaches the futures price during the delivery period, figure 185. This happens because there is a cost involved in storing cash grain, but little in holding futures. The gain of cash price versus futures price varies from year to year, depending on the size of the crop and the space available for storage.

If a farmer stores grain, he will get paid — sometimes more than the cost of commercial storage space. If he sells cash and buys futures, he will pay someone else to store his grain. *An extra large spread between the cash and futures price is a signal that on-farm storage is being encouraged.*

What a farmer does in respect to the cash and futures market depends on his expectations.

• If he expects a general price decline and expects the cash price to gain less than the cost of storage, he sells corn not later than harvest.

• If he expects the cash price to go up more than the cost of storage and expects the cash price the following summer to be higher than the current futures price, he holds his grain in storage.

• If he expects the cash price to go up more than the cost of storage but also thinks the current futures price reflects a higher cash price than the one that will prevail the following summer, he holds cash and sells an equal amount of futures.

• If he expects the cash price to gain less than the cost of storage (or if storage is completely unavailable) and thinks the current futures price reflects a lower cash price than the one that will prevail the following summer, he sells cash and buys futures.

In deciding whether to enter the futures market and if so whether to buy or sell futures, you must (1) forecast corn prices; (2) forecast the gain of the cash price in relation to the futures prices; and (3) determine whether you think next summer's cash price will be above, below, or the same as that reflected by the current futures price.

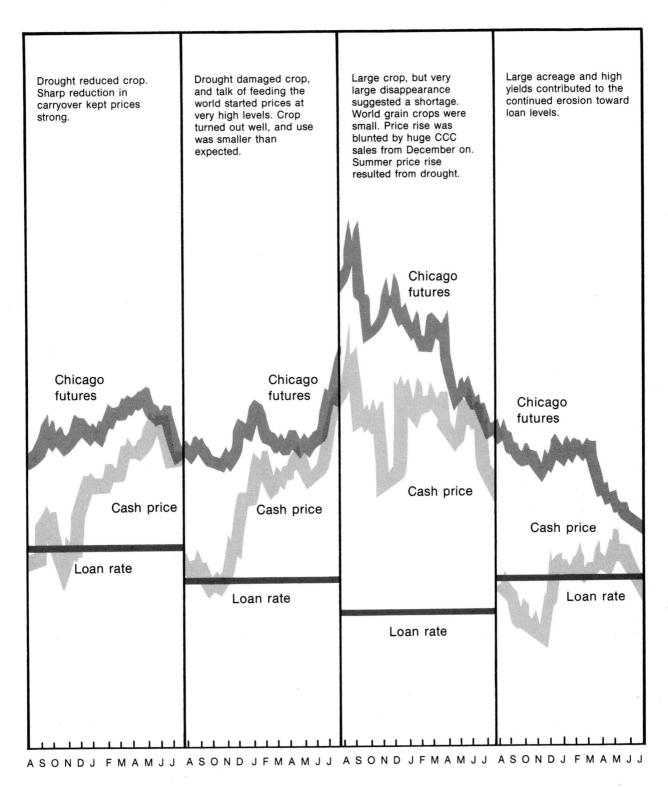

Figure 185. The relationship between cash price (central Illinois elevators), July futures (there are of course other futures) and the loan rate for four consecutive years with different sets of conditions listed in the upper part of the chart.

12

Environmental Protection and Improvement

Agriculture has a tremendous impact on the environment. The basic purpose of agriculture is, in fact, to manage part of the environment in order to meet the food and fiber needs of mankind. Agriculture in the United States has been eminently successful in meeting these needs. To date, decisions have been based mainly upon economic considerations, restrictions being limited to those necessitated by a clear health hazard. Society is now asking all segments of the economy, including agriculture, to reassess their activities in relation to environmental quality.

In the early 1970's three concerns emerged, one directly on the heels of the other:

- A tremendous increase in concern for environmental quality and pollution abatement.
- An awareness that world food supply was in jeopardy.
- Energy needs were outrunning supply especially for gas and oil in the developed industrialized nations. The Arab countries' short-term embargo dramatized a problem which had been building for more than a decade.

The extent to which environmental and food production goals are in conflict, at least locally, is not yet known. When they are in conflict, society will almost certainly opt for adequate food production at the expense of some environmental quality. It should be the goal of all to minimize the conflict.

Farmers and those who advise farmers have a solemn obligation to address themselves not only to production practices, which are the focus for most of this book, but also to environmental protection which is the focal point of this section. It is the right thing to do and it is in their enlightened self-interest. *Unless agriculturists take additional initiatives soon in environmental protection there will be unwise regulations and constraints on production practices imposed by governmental agencies at public insistence.*

This section is intended to give you perspective on the impact of agriculture on the environment and to suggest how to minimize undesirable effects of corn growing.

Before considering what should be done in the future it is worthwhile to look at what has been done up til now.

Cutting the Forests, Plowing the Prairies

The first major intrusion of man into a slowly evolving but relatively stable ecosystem in the United States began with the cutting of forests and plowing of prairies by pioneers. Hunting, fishing, and trapping, of course, began much earlier. In the natural state, soil-building and soil-depleting processes were proceeding at the same time.

Soil-building processes included slow accumulation of organic matter, nitrogen, and phosphorus, and improvement in structure of the surface soil. Soil-depleting processes included leaching of base elements — potassium, calcium, and magnesium — resulting in both a loss of available plant nutrients and an increase in acidity. Leaching of micronutrients was also soil depleting.

Tillage of the soil by early farmers in order to grow crops and to pasture livestock caused great effects on the environment, some desirable, others undesirable. Among these were:

Consumptive use of native soil productivity. The supply of available nutrients and physical condition are two important characteristics of productive soils. Stirring the soil accelerated the oxidation of humus and of fresh plant residues within the plow layer, thus releasing nutrients for utilization by crops but also causing a deterioration in soil structure and tilth. The nitrogen released from humus undoubtedly raised the nitrate levels in surface and underground waters.

Accelerated erosion and sediment pollution. Soils were unprotected for extended periods during the year in many of the early cropping systems.

A reduction in the runoff of soluble organic phosphates. This desirable effect of farming has thus far been overlooked. In the pre-farming period, plant residues remained on the soil surface. Upon decay, soluble organic phosphates were removed in surface runoff, especially during the winter in northern sections when soils were frozen and in early spring when rainfall greatly exceeded infiltration capacity. Lower amounts of soluble phosphate were carried in runoff under agricultural use than under virgin conditions because plant residues were *mixed into* the soil. Total phosphorus from land runoff was likely increased as a result of tillage but much of the increase was in phosphorus adsorbed on soil particles. Phosphorus thus held is less available for the growth of algae in lakes and reservoirs than are soluble or organic forms.

Artificial Drainage

The primary purpose of drainage was to facilitate timely plowing, planting, cultivating and harvesting. From an environmental point of view, the effect, like that of tillage, was to speed up the oxidation of soil organic matter and humus. The consequences of this were described in the preceeding paragraphs.

Shift from Animal to Mechanical Power

Another major change in crop-production technology took place with the shift from oxen, horse and mule power to mechanical power. From 1910 to 1960 more than 1 million horses and mules were displaced in a single state, Illinois. Undesirable effects on the environment of this change were:

- increases in unburned hydrocarbons, carbon monoxide, and nitrogen oxides emitted into the air as a result of burning fossil fuels,
- consumption of resources and the addition of pullutants associated with manufacturing the power units and processing the required fuel,
- problems of disposing of obsolete farm machines.

Conversely, the shift to mechanical power resulted in:

- less animal waste,
- less demand on fertility nutrients to produce feed,
- less erosion and sediment pollution associated with feed production for draft animals.

Furthermore, oxen, horse and mule power required feed and generated pollutants 8760 hours per year, whereas tractors are on the average operated only 500 hours per year. Animals for horepower consumed feed and produced manure for two years before they were old enough to supply power. Much of these wastes was, of course, easily assimilated by the environment.

But it may well be that the shift from animal power to mechanical power on balance *reduced* undesirable effects on the environment.

The "Intrusion" of Plant Nutrients

From reading popular, nontechnical environmental literature one gains the impression that many persons view the application of commercial fertilizers as an intrusion of plant nutrients into a virgin environment, hence likely to upset the balance of nature. But until recently plant nutrient levels and the organic content of soils, far from being maintained at original levels, have been declining since farming began (figure 186). The downward trend in soil supplies of available phosphorus and potassium has only been reversed since about 1940. Many fields have now been replenished and some exceed virgin conditions for these nutrients.

The downward trend in nitrogen and organic matter, however, has at best been arrested in some soils and perhaps reversed in a few. The maintenance of soil organic matter is extremely difficult under cropping (see pages 149 – 150). Rebuilding it to original levels is not economically feasible. A practicable goal is to return to the soil large amounts of readily decomposable residues which will help to compensate for the loss of humus.

Returning the plant nutrients contained in food and human wastes to agricultural land is sometimes suggested as a means of solving the problem of declining organic matter. For the foreseeable future, however, waste return will be limited mainly to disposal programs on a relatively small proportion of the land rather than being a general recycling of nutrients to the fields from which they came. The nitrogen in all human wastes in the Corn Belt states is less than 5 percent of the

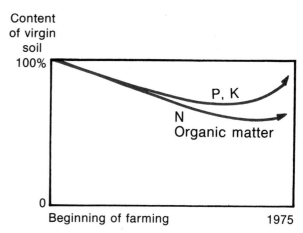

Figure 186. During most of the time since farming began soil fertility declined in the United States. The trend changed about 1950. P and K levels in some soils have now been built to higher than original levels. In nitrogen and organic matter content, the decline has at best been stopped and perhaps built slightly in a few fields.

fertilizer nitrogen in the region. Nor is composting of residues a solution on large areas because the return of crop residues to the soil is already standard farming practice in most places. Composting is at best a return of only part of the nutrients that were removed in harvested crops or in animal products.

If, for the lack of adequate supplies of nitrogen, organic matter is allowed to continue to decline at the rate that it has during the past 100 to 200 years, soil structure will deteriorate, water infiltration capacity will be impaired, and productivity will decrease. As a result, future generations will have increasing difficulty not only in maintaining adequate production of food but also in contending with floods, erosion, and sediment pollution.

The last reported death from high nitrate water in the U.S. was in 1949. None has been reported from consuming water from a public supply.

The Nature of Pollution from Agriculture

There is a fundamental difference between the way that farmers view the environment as a receptacle for waste products as compared to industries and municipalities.

• Farmers have a vested interest in *not polluting* surface waters with nitrogen, phosphorus, organic matter, pesticides, and silt.

These production factors represent financial investments, hence, farmers will not intentionally lose them to surface or ground water. Neither does agriculture intentionally use lakes and streams to dispose its waste products. Livestock manure and crop residues have historically been returned to the land (with a few exceptions) in order to maintain soil productivity. Municipalities and industries, on the other hand, have in the past intentionally utilized streams and lakes to dissipate heat, sewage, and industrial wastes.

• Agricultural runoff also differs from city and industrial wastes in that, except for pesticides, it contains little toxic substances such as cadmium, lead, chromium, zinc, phenols and plasticizers. Agricultural pollution is therefore biodegradable and up to a point can be assimilated by the environment including surface waters.

• Agricultural pollution of waters is associated almost directly with runoff from medium to heavy rains. This means that there is water for dilution. City sewage treatment plant input to streams is about the same during spring floods and in mid-summer when water flow is minimal and water temperatures are favorable for unwanted algal growth.

• Finally, water pollution from cities and industries usually traces directly to easily identified point sources whereas that from agriculture is widely distributed and occurs wherever surface water runs off. This is a very important difference. Environmental protection agencies can easily check point sources to determine whether they are meeting established standards. But there is no feasible way to monitor non-point sources like agriculture. This means that in place of performance standards, regulations that apply to agriculture will be in the form of acceptable and unacceptable practices. This will cause problems because of lack of flexibility to change practices quickly when bad weather, especially at planting time, interferes with normal plans.

Sediment

In sheer bulk, sediment is the greatest pollutant of surface waters. It is objectionable because:

• It "muddies the waters", making them less pleasing to look at or to swim or fish in.

• It fills reservoirs and reduces storage capacity.

• It covers fish spawning beds and otherwise destroys some water organisms.

• It usually carries along some organic matter, plant nutrients and pesticides.

The Soil Conservation Service began a vigorous program to control erosion in the early 1930's. That was the first major effort to control water pollution. The program stressed proper land use, strip cropping and terraces where needed, cropping systems suited to the slope of the land, and fertility to assure good crop growth. Much was accomplished. But improvements along some lines was partly offset by a great increase in acreage of row crops, mainly soybeans in the Corn Belt.

Unfortunately there are few long-term records on erosion per acre or per hectare. Data from four river reservoirs in Central Illinois indicate that the total amount of sediment deposited was only one half as much from 1945 to 1966 as from the 1920's to 1945. From the early to the later period the percentage of cropland in row crops increased from about 50 to 85.

On the other side of the scale, corn plant populations doubled and average yields more than doubled thus returning more residues to help hold the soil in place. The combination of higher yields resulting from more fertilizer, thicker planting and other good practices and some soil conservation measures evidently more than offset the effect of the increase in row crops.

Furthermore, the overall yield in terms of grain equivalent increased 2½ times. Based on that increase in production with only one half as much sediment, it can be said that

342

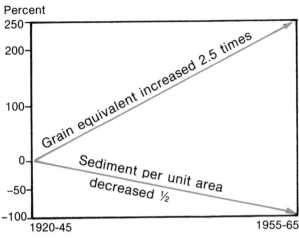

Figure 187. Change in crop produced and in sediment in four reservoirs in central Illinois.

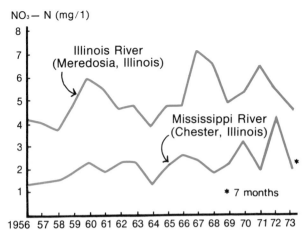

Figure 188. Trends in nitrate content in two major midwest rivers. At Meredosia the Illinois river had received drainage from most of the corn growing area of the state. At Chester the Mississippi carries most of the drainage from the Central and Western Corn Belt. Ill. State Water Survey data.

five times as much grain was produced per unit of sediment in the latter period as in the earlier period, figure 187.

The concept of amount of undesirable environmental effect per unit of food produced should always be applied to compare alternative agricultural practices.

Iowa was the first state to enact legislation to control erosion from agricultural land. It set permissible limits on soil loss for each soil. Acceptable practices were to be determined by using the Universal Soil Loss Equation (see page 219). But the provisions of the law were not to be enforced until the state legislature budgeted funds to cover three fourths of the cost to individual farmers. This said in effect that if the public desired to reduce sediment pollution it should share the cost with farmers. The law was implemented in 1974.

What is likely in the future? The U.S. government has asked each state to set up standards for land use.

- Before 1980, the issue of property rights in land use and management will likely be faced and at least partly decided.
- The amount of sediment control for which society is willing to pay will be more clearly defined.
- The effect on food supply and price will be one important factor in the decision.

- There will be more stress on reduced tillage and planting in sod on strongly sloping fields.
- Winter cover crops will be encourged on early fall plowed land.
- Narrow, unplowed buffer strips will be tested on level land that is fall plowed.
- The amount of sediment per unit of food produced will continue to decline.
- Sediment lost per unit of land area will tend to level off.

Energy Balance within a Stream

A fact only recently uncovered is that when the amount of sediment from land runoff is reduced, a stream tends to at least partially replace it by scouring its banks or streambed. This is because each stream has an energy balance determined by rate of fall and number of curves in its course. When the sediment input is reduced, the stream flows faster and this causes it to pick up more from its bed and banks. Because of this behavior, land management practices which reduce erosion may make less improvement than expected in water quality.

Nitrates in Surface and Ground Water

The nitrate concentration in many rivers in the Corn Belt is tending irregularly upward, figure 188.

343

Figure 189. Severe wind erosion sometimes occurs on fall plowed fields. Avoiding fall plowing seems logical but in many fields this results in delayed planting in wet years. Leaving unplowed strips, trash on the surface or fall seeding spring oats are alternates to consider.

Nitrate concentration of water is of concern mainly because of a possible health hazard to infants under six months especially if suffering a digestive upset.

The U.S. Public Health Service standard is 10 parts per million of nitrate nitrogen (45 parts nitrate) in drinking water. That standard appears to have a sizeable safety factor built in with respect to causing the blue-baby effect technically known as methemoglobinemia. Some researchers speculate that nitrates may have hidden undesirable effects but nothing has been proven. Many infants have been raised in farm homes and whole cities where the nitrate content of drinking water is two to five times the USPHS standard.

The last reported death from high nitrate water in the U.S. was in 1949. None has been reported from consuming water from a public supply.

No one could question the 10 parts per million standard if it were easily attainable. But many midwestern streams already exceed it for a few weeks in most years. And several cities in the midwest and in Califor-

nia with deep wells as yet unaffected by modern farming practices have water supplies at least double the standard. California has set the standard at 20 instead of 10 parts per million of nitrate nitrogen.

Possible effects on aquatic life from raising the nitrate content of surface waters have been studied very little.

Causes of High Nitrates in Water

- High organic matter in the soil.
- Application of nitrogen fertilizer.
- Large applications of animal manure or sludge.
- Nitrogen released after legumes are plowed under.
- Nitrogen applications to sandy soils which have a low water holding capacity.
- Heavy rains which move nitrates down to tile drains or groundwater.
- A high proportion of row crops resulting in tillage which speeds up the release of nitrogen from soil organic matter.
- Poor crop growth resulting in low uptake of nitrates from the soil water.
- A high proportion of the land area arti-

Figure 190. Daily spreading of manure from dairy barns was recommended for many years. Application near streams and lakes, especially on frozen sloping fields, is no longer acceptable because of the risk of runoff of plant nutrients and organic matter.

ficially drained.

- Workers in Nebraska found that surface water near large feedlots absorbed large amounts of ammonia from the air.

Though the factors are well known, it is not yet possible to put all of the information together and predict the nitrate content that will appear in water under a given set of conditions. Several researchers are working on models aimed at such predictions.

The Illinois Pollution Control Board held public hearings in 1971 to determine whether restrictions should be placed upon the application of nitrogen fertilizer and animal manure. In a landmark decision in 1972 the Board said:

"We conclude that the water quality standards for nitrate nitrogen are presently being violated in certain streams of the state and that the potential nitrate problem will grow as the demand for food increases. The record has not demonstrated that health effects have resulted. Deficiencies in available knowledge on the credibility of the nitrate standard, on the contributions of various nitrogen sources to nitrates in water, on the effectiveness of possible control measures and on undesirable side effects on the environment from alternative practices convince us that at this time we should make provision for more information on which to decide the issue rather than to promulgate regulations of upredictable effectiveness and side effects."

The nitrate issue will not go away. A growing demand for food will require increasing amounts of nitrogen for crop production. There are, fortunately, possible alternatives to explore besides restricting nitrogen fertilizer applications.

Sensitive elements in the human population — infants and perhaps others — could be protected by supplying them with water that is low in nitrates.

Some doctors suggest that adequate intake of vitamin C offers considerable protection.

At some future date, public water supplies and even whole rivers may be treated to remove nitrates.

Fertilizer Nitrogen vs. Other Sources

There is a common false impression that fertilizer nitrogen affects the environment differently than nitrogen from other sources. But nitrate ions derived from fertilizer are neither more nor less subject to leaching than nitrate ions from other sources. Nitrates (except for a small amount in some fertilizers) result from the nitrification of ammonium (NH_4^+) whether the nitrogen source is plant residues, animal waste, soil humus, or fertilizer. The total amount of available nitrogen that must be in the soil during the growing season is approximately the same regardless of source.

There is little reason to believe that the amount of nitrate that moves into surface or ground water *per unit of crop produced* would be less if the nitrogen were supplied by sources other than nitrogen fertilizer.

Some persons reason that since the rate of nitrogen release upon decay of plant residues and part of the nitrogen from manure corresponds roughly to the time of need of corn, supplying more nitrogen from legumes and manure would result in less nitrate in waters. The concept may be worth further study but it has one important flaw. *It results in more nitrate in the soil in the fall after corn is harvested.* That nitrate is most subject to leaching because there is plenty of rainfall to move it downward and no growing crop to absorb it in the fall, winter and early spring (figure 130, page 191).

Slow-release nitrogen fertilizers have the same drawback as organic matter. Readily available nitrogen that is applied shortly before the time that corn roots absorb it will be used most efficiently and will leave the least amount in the soil at the end of the growing season.

The practical question to be answered is whether there are alternative strategies for meeting food production needs that would result in fewer nitrates. Possibilities worthy of further exploration include:

1. Increased planting of small grain or grass cover crops to absorb nitrates that form in the fall after row crops are harvested.
2. Chemical compounds that inhibit nitrification, thus preserving nitrogen in the ammonium form in which it is essentially nonleachable.
3. Reduction in rates on some of the most heavily fertilized fields.
4. Applications nearer to the time of maximum uptake by crops and no early application on sandy soils. These are discussed on pages 113 to 115

Major changes in cropping patterns and a shift in eating habits away from meat, milk and eggs have been suggested as ways to reduce the need for nitrogen. Humans would eat more grain crops directly rather than feeding them to livestock. This is not a viable alternative for the short-term future.

Phosphorus

Concern for phosphorus is because of its role in excessive algal growth and accelerated aging of lakes and reservoirs. There is difference of opinion among scientists as to whether phosphorus is always the controlling factor in these undesirable effects. But there is little doubt that it often is a major factor and that reducing phosphorus inputs would be beneficial.

Until recently many persons believed that excess phosphorus would cause algal blooms in rivers. It is now known that the problem does not occur in streams and rivers — only in lakes and reservoirs. The natural background level of phosphorus is high enough in streams in intensively farmed regions to support excessive algal growth if the water were not flowing.

Phosphorus in streams and lakes is in three general forms: in solution, in organic matter, and attached to soil particles. Phosphorus in solution is immediately available for the growth of algae and higher plants. Phosphorus in living or dead plant and animal tissues readily becomes available when the tissues decay. Much of the phosphorus in bottom sediments is in this category. Phosphorus that is adsorbed on soil particles is in balance with the surrounding solution. When soil particles are washed into streams

Figure 191. A rainfall simulator is an important tool for studying the effects of seedbed preparation and residue management on runoff of nutrients and sediment.

and lakes they may:

    a) withdraw phosphorus from solution if the soil particles are relatively low in phosphorus,

    b) add phosphorus to the solution if they are rich in phosphorus.

Under typical surface water conditions a given amount of phosphorus attached to sediment will likely support less algae than the same amount in solution or in plant residues. This is because of the slow rate of release of sediment-associated phosphorus.

It has been generally assumed that converting virgin land to agriculture contributed to excessive algal growth and accelerated aging of lakes. This is open to some question. Minnesota researchers learned that though total phosphorus runoff was greater under corn, the soluble phosphorus runoff was greater from an alfalfa field. This leads to the tentative conclusion that agricultural systems which turn under the residues may result in less runoff of soluble phosphate compounds than a virgin prairie or forest.

Sources of Phosphorus Inputs to Water

In contrast to nitrogen, which mainly reaches waters by moving *through* the soil, nearly all of the phosphorus from agricultural land runs *off* the surface. The phosphorus holding capacity is so great that even on well-fertilized soils very little moves as deep as tile lines in a farmer's lifetime except on organic soils (muck and peat). The holding capacity can of course be exceeded if repeated heavy applications of manure or sludge are made, especially on sands which are prime targets for disposal because of

347

their ability to absorb water rapidly.

Major sources of phosphorus in streams and lakes are:

- Sediment from cropland. Fields that test high contribute sediment that is richer in phosphorus.
- Soluble organic compounds from the decay of plant residues especially when heavy rains occur on frozen soils.
- Soluble phosphates from animal manure especially on frozen, sloping fields.
- Phosphorus from fertilizer. Purdue University researchers found that only 1 percent washed off a steep slope after 5 inches of simulated rainfall.
- City sewage treatment plants. This is an important source because much of the phosphorus is in soluble form. Besides the impact from this source continues through the summer when the amount of water for dilution is small and the temperature is favorable for algae growth.
- Phosphorus in rainfall. This has recently been identified as a significant source but data are preliminary.

How to Reduce Phosphorus Runoff

Where the receiving water is a lake or reservoir or a stream that leads to such bodies of water, phosphorus runoff should be controlled if possible.

Points to consider are:
1. Control soil erosion.
2. Avoid spreading animal manure or fertilizer on frozen, sloping fields.
3. Avoid building unnecessarily high soil tests for phosphorus.
4. If feasible, work heavy broadcast applications of phosphorus fertilizers into the soil rather than leaving them on the surface.

Some persons have suggested that systems which eliminate plowing and leave residues on the surface to control erosion would be desirable to reduce phosphorus runoff. This may be counter productive for two reasons:

- Though total phosphorus runoff will be reduced, the amount of soluble phosphorus may increase.
- No-plow systems leave phosphorus fertilizer concentrated in the surface one to two inches. Hence the sediment, though low in amount, will be rich in phosphorus.

Furthermore, no-plow systems may require larger amounts of herbicides which are also undesirable in runoff.

Pesticides

A great amount of pesticides is applied for corn. Fortunately the undesirable environmental effects are, with few exceptions, small. Herbicides make up about 97 percent of the total pesticides applied on corn. Most are worked into the soil and many are not very soluble hence are not easily carried off the soil except when erosion occurs. Since plants are not closely related to insects, animals or humans, the chemicals that are toxic to weeds generally are not inherently hazardous to members of the animal kingdom. There are exceptions, of course (paraquat for example), and the carriers of the herbicide are sometimes irritating.

The most obvious undesirable effects from herbicides are from drift or accidental application to sensitive crops, gardens or shrubbery adjacent to sprayed fields or roadsides. The logical remedy is greater care in application.

Farmers themselves frequently pay a price for using herbicides in the form of damage to sensitive crops the following year from carryover herbicide. The solution is to avoid overapplication, band apply where possible to reduce the amount, and to use a non-persistent herbicide the preceeding year.

The major use of insecticides on corn is for rootworm control. Chlorinated hydrocarbons (aldrin, dieldrin, chlordane, heptachlor) have caused two significant problems. First, rootworm strains developed that were resistant to this class of chemicals. To offset

Figure 192. Producing very high yields per acre with the use of modern technology on the best suited land avoids the need to crop additional less-suited land and thus minimizes several unwanted environmental effects.

this resistance farmers increased rates of application and when that was ineffective they shifted to other chemicals. Second, these persistent chemicals were absorbed by soybeans that followed corn and showed up in some soybean products. Unacceptable levels of dieldrin and related breakdown products were found in poultry which had to be destroyed. The Environmental Protection Agency banned the further use of aldrin and dieldrin in 1974 and chlordane and heptachlor were being challenged in 1975. This problem should be enough to convince all skeptics that pesticides must be thoroughly tested and used with caution.

The concept of *integrated pest management* began to receive increased attention in the early 1970's. It refers to using a variety of control measures wherever feasible — rotations, burying residues that harbor insects and diseases, applying small amounts of chemicals at key times in the life of the pest, using biological control where possible and learning to tolerate small populations of some pests — rather than to depend entirely upon chemicals or to aim for complete eradication of insects.

An emerging problem in the pesticide area is that at the very time when many environmental groups are clamoring for less persistent and less broad spectrum chemicals, the cost to research and develop a new chemical and obtain information for clearance has risen sharply. Several companies have discontinued research on new chemicals. Government regulations have been one factor that discourages the development of new chemicals. It is a price that society is paying in order to have greater safety in the chemicals that are used.

Because corn represents a large potential market, both public and private researchers will continue to search for new and better pest control methods. Some minor crops will fare less well.

Impact of Agricultural Technology on Balance

Possible undesirable effects of modern agriculture have been widely publicized: increased nitrates and phosphates in water, injury to non-target species by certain insecticides, spillover and drift of pesticides on land adjacent to treated areas, sediment from an increase in row crops. The environmental *benefits* from producing needed food through the use of available technology have received little attention.

The great increase since 1945 in plant nutrients supplied by commercial fertilizers is representative of the growth in the application of science and technology in agriculture and illustrates some of the positive effects of technology generally.

• The decline in soil fertility which had proceeded inexorably from the first farming attempts of the settlers until about 1940, can now be arrested and in some cases reversed (figure 186, page 342).

• Higher yields reduce the area required for food production, hence agriculture can be concentrated on soils that are least erosive. This reduces floods and sediment pollution with its associated burden of phosphorus, nitrogen, organic matter, and adsorbed pesticides. If additional land were brought under cultivation in order to offset production lost by unnecessary restrictions on the use of available technology, the land would not only be more subject to erosion but also have lower yield capability because it would be more likely to be droughty, stoney, wet, or shallow.

• Nitrogen fertilizer allows farmers to concentrate corn and other row crops on level to slightly rolling soils in midwestern states which are subject to relatively little erosion. More sloping fields can be kept in cropping systems that include extensive acreages of sod crops. If legumes were the sole source of nitrogen, cropping with both row crops and sod crops would be required on all soils, irrespective of slope, thus resulting in greater erosion.

• Higher yields per unit of land make possible the preservation of large areas for recreation and wildlife habitat. Barrons calculated that more than 290 million acres (117 million hectares) of cropland were released for alternative uses in the 30-year period between 1938-1940 and 1968-1970 as a result of improved technology in the production of seventeen major crops in the United States.

The main cause of agriculture's increasing impact on the environment is the need to produce more food rather than the unwise choice of practices in how it is produced. Persons who propose to return to more primitive methods with less use of science and technology are generally unfamiliar with agriculture and with land-use capabilities. *Intensive utilization of available crop production technology on the best land, with some important exceptions, will likely meet the needs of society with the least undesirable impact on the environment.*

Agriculture: A Victim of Pollution

The incidents of damage to agricultural crops from toxic emission from industries increased sharply in the early 1970's. The most common causes were sulfur dioxide, fluoride, ozone and nitrogen oxides. The sensitivity of corn has not been determined for most of these air pollutants. Symptoms of damage are not specific enough to be very helpful in diagnosing cause.

Emission control measures began to be effective in many industries by the mid-1970's and it is doubtful that in the future agriculture will suffer more than isolated cases of local injury from air pollution.

Concern for Soil Preservation Is Not New

Many persons feel that the concept of stewardship of the soil originated with the environmental movement in the late 1960's. Contemplate the following quotation:

"I always contemplate the earth with reverence. I like the phrase 'Mother Earth' — the source of all our sustenance, the storehouse of all our supplies, our raiment, our shelter, the pathway of our feet, the final resting place of our worn bodies.

"And of all its elements and attributes, the soil seems to be most appealing and vital, and I cannot but regard its depletion as vandalism and sacrilege.

"If we despoil it, if we fail to maintain it, if we leave it less fruitful than we received it, we are unfaithful trustees, and I feel that in the sight of God we are as culpable as if we robbed the estate of orphan children of whom we were made guardians by decree of court."
(Clarence Gusley, Assistant Secretary of Agriculture, in BETTER CROPS, 1930).

13

Efficient Use of Energy

The 1973-74 oil shortages alerted farmers and the industries that supply crop production items that the direct and indirect effects of energy supplies and costs will greatly influence future corn production. In the short term, the shortage of oil was soon corrected but the price remained high. The United States can become more nearly self-sufficient by exploring and developing new supplies of oil, increasing coal production and substituting it for oil and gas in some industrial uses, and adoption of energy conservation measures. The fuel supply in other major corn growing areas of the world is less predictable. The long term outlook everywhere is for continuing sharply higher prices over the pre-1974 period. This requires a new look at corn growing practices and may influence the geographic areas where corn will be grown.

Though broad issues are discussed in this section, main emphasis is on how individual farmers can adjust to the new energy situation. Higher energy costs affect farmers directly in higher fuel costs to operate their tractors and driers and indirectly because energy is used to make all of the tools of production — fertilizer, herbicides, tractors, tillage tools, combines, trucks.

Nations throughout the world must be concerned about total energy needed for food production. This includes not only fuel to drive internal combustion engines but also energy required to produce farm equipment, process, store, refrigerate and prepare food ready to eat. Individual farmers, on the other hand, are more concerned with supplies and costs of fuel. Furthermore, each farmer can choose between practices that affect fuel usage and efficiency.

Agriculture Both Uses and Captures Energy

Agriculture and forestry are unique in relation to energy — like others they consume energy but unlike others they *capture* energy. Most industrial production uses fossil or nuclear fuels to produce goods and services. It is only a consumer. But energy used to produce fertilizers, pesticides, agricultural machinery and to grow seeds for planting is in fact building a solar energy factory — green plants. In the case of corn, the amount of energy in the grain at harvest time is about 5.7 times the total amount of energy needed to grow the crop (table 45). In other words, grain corn in the Central Corn Belt supplies 5.7 calories for each calorie of energy used.

Table 45

Energy used to grow corn and the energy yield in the central Corn Belt in 1974. Estimates of Illinois agricultural engineers.

	Million Calories	
	Per acre	*Per hectare*
A. To produce equipment and supplies		
Machinery	.40	.99
Fertilizers and chemicals	.68	1.68
Fuel	.27	.67
B. Used in specific operations		
Tillage and planting	.15	.37
Harvesting	.04	.10
Drying	.22	.54
TOTAL	1.76	4.35
Amount in corn grain (102 bushel per acre)	10.00	
(64 quintals per hectare)		24.72
Return per calorie input	5.7	

No doubt there will be increased attention to improving the efficiency of food and feed crops to capture energy.

No crop is really efficient in capturing solar energy and converting it into dry matter. A 125-bushel per acre (78 quintals per hectare) corn crop captures in the entire growing season only the amount of solar energy received in one clear summer day. Even so corn is one of the most efficient crops. It is in fact about as efficient as an algae mass growing in water.

Dr. John Strauss points out that corn cobs can be a very important source of energy. Cobs make up 15 to 20 percent of the weight of ear corn. Based upon a 15 percent figure, a 100-bushel per acre (63 quintals per hectare) crop has over 1000 pounds (453.5 kilos) of cobs. Since each pound of cobs has a theoretical heat value of 1,860 kilocalories, the heat value per acre is 1,860,000 million kilocalories. An average of 120,000 kilocalories are used to dry an acre of corn. Hence,

the cobs from an acre or hectare contain 15.5 times the heat energy needed for drying. Collecting 1/10 of the cobs would provide adequate heat.

Corn cobs are available at the time and place needed for drying. Burning cobs is nothing new to midwest farmers but they are not currently being used for drying. They burn cleanly. The small amount of ashes can be returned to the land thus recycling mineral nutrients. In order to utilize them, modifications would be needed to collect the cobs in the harvesting operation, and in combustion chambers.

Burning cobs to dry corn is not anticipated in the near future but should not be ruled out. Cobs could also be converted to liquid fuels.

Utilizing cobs for energy would have little adverse effect on the soil because there are plenty of organic wastes in the stalks, leaves and roots.

Land not suited to cropland will also be

Table 46

Where energy is used to produce food ready to be eaten in the United States. (Council for Agricultural Science and Technology, 1973)

	% of total
Crop and livestock production	18
Food processing	33
Transportation	3
Wholesale and retail trade	16
Household preparation	30
	100

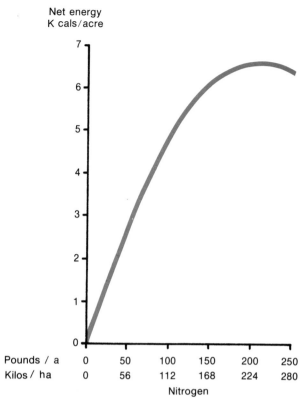

Figure 193. Net energy return per acre from applying anhydrous ammonia nitrogen fertilizer to corn.

examined as a possible place to grow trees and non-food plants in order to capture solar energy which can be converted into useful fuels.

Energy Used in Food Production

Crop and livestock production uses no more than 3 to 4 percent of the total energy from fossil fuels used in the United States and has remained nearly constant for many years — 3 percent in 1939, 4 in 1950 and 3 in 1970. But by the time crops have been processed, transported, stored, merchandised, and prepared for eating, the total has risen to 12 to 15 percent. This is because crop and livestock production represent only 18 percent of the total energy used in putting food on the table ready to eat in the U.S. (table 46).

Manufacturing nitrogen fertilizer requires a lot of energy. About 33,000 BTU's are needed to produce one ton (2000 pounds) of nitrogen in anhydrous ammonia. The fertilizer industry uses 3 percent of the natural gas supply in the U.S. to make nitrogen fertilizer and natural gas is in relatively shorter supply than other fuels. On the other hand, nitrogen fertilizer when properly used in good corn growing systems at optimum rates will return 4 to 6 units for each unit of energy input (figure 193).

In comparison to most other conversions, that is indeed a bargain!

It is sound policy to make efficient use of animal manures and municipal sewage as sources of nitrogen. But these sources will not go far toward meeting the total nitrogen needs for corn. In the Corn Belt the nitrogen in municipal wastes is no more than 5 percent of that applied in fertilizer. Besides much of the human and animal waste in the world is produced outside the main corn growing areas and transporting it for any substantial distance is not energy efficient. At 1975 prices the energy value of manure was greater than the plant nutrient value.

Table 47
Estimated diesel fuel required for alternative tillage systems. For gasoline, multiply figures by 1.4; for LP-Gas, multiply by 1.7. (Illinois Extension Service)

| | Gallons of Diesel Fuel Per Acre Needed for Various Operations | | | |
	Conventional	Chisel Plow	Disk-Plant	No-Till
Disk Stalks	.43	.43	.43	—
Moldboard Plow	1.75	—	—	—
Chisel Plow	—	1.18	—	—
Disk	.51	.51	—	—
Apply NH₃	.36	.36	.36	—
Field Cultivate	.43	.43	.43	—
Plant	.32	.32	.32	.32
Apply Herbicide	—	—	—	.30
Rotary Hoe	.24	.24	.24	—
Cultivate	.32	.32	.32	—
Harvest	1.10	1.10	1.10	1.10
TOTAL	5.46	4.89	3.20	1.72

In the long term, agricultural production systems will be reexamined as to centers of crop production in relation to livestock production and to human population. This is a complex process which can only be worked out by a competitive economic system. For example, farmers in subhumid or arid areas utilize energy in irrigation but unlike farmers in humid areas they use little for drying grain. Individual farmers will contribute to the process of deciding where corn is to be grown by responding to subtle differences in costs and returns in different geographic regions.

Fossil Fuel to Grow Corn

Table 47 gives the amount of fuel needed in various steps in three methods for growing corn in non-irrigated areas of the U.S. Corn Belt. From the data in the table it is clear that the greatest potential for fuel saving is in the preplant tillage operations. This must, of course, be balanced against possible lower yield and additional energy requirements at other points in the corn growing process. For example, zero tillage in sod planting requires no fuel for seedbed preparation but does require $10 to $20 worth of herbicide per acre at 1974 prices to kill the sod. From an overall point of view, herbicides to kill sod may require as much energy as mechanical seedbed preparation and cultivation.

Energy Per Unit of Corn Produced

The energy used per acre or per hectare is not the sole basis for evaluating energy efficiency in corn growing. Practices should be compared on the basis of energy or fuel per bushel or per quintal grown. The energy per unit of product comes into sharp focus when you compare extensive and intensive growing methods.

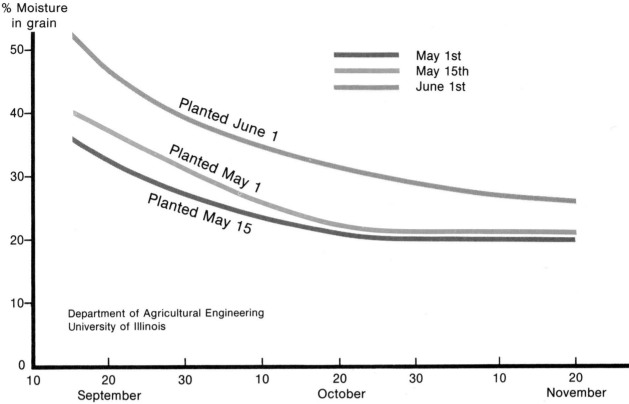

Figure 194. Corn planted May 1 was 3 to 4 percent lower in moisture at the usual harvest date than corn planted May 15 and over 10 percent lower than corn planted June 1. Three-year average data. Urbana, Illinois. H. P. Bateman.

Intensive production methods which produce high acre yields require large amounts of fertilizer and sometimes chemicals for controlling weeds, diseases and insects. Less intensive methods, on the other hand, require more acres or hectares to be plowed, cultivated and harvested. An easily overlooked consequence of farming more land at a lower yield level is that part of the acreage is forced onto less well suited land. This results in less output per unit of energy input. Besides, there are undesirable environmental effects from an increased cropland acreage.

Some persons suggest that modern corn production methods are too energy intensive and that we should revert to methods which require less inputs per unit area and perhaps even to substitute human labor for some machinery and chemical pesticides.

An analysis of their calculations often shows that the energy needs for bullocks or water buffalo in more primitive systems are charged only for the actual time that the draft animals are used in corn production. Unless the draft animals can survive the remainder of the year on crop wastes, the energy charge is too low. Besides animal power must be grown for about two years before it can be used. And it must be fed 365 days per year whether used or not.

It is not at all clear that less intensive farming would conserve energy but it is certain that such an approach generally could not meet world food needs. Furthermore there is little indication that the labor force would readily return to more hand labor that characterized farming fifty years ago. Avoid applying fertilizer beyond the point of efficient return, figure 193. Fortunately optimum profit and efficient use of energy occur at about the same fertilizer rate.

357

Importance of Fuel Supply Timeliness

Within limits, many of man's activities that use energy can take place at any convenient time. But in the temperate zone of the world there is only one period of the year in which to grow corn. The Biblical statement applies that there is a time for sowing and a time for reaping. Prime planting time is less than 30 days each year. Oftentimes a difference of 3 to 4 days in cultivating or spraying for weed control spells success or failure. Delaying harvesting has little effect in years with ideal fall weather, but may result in large field losses in wet falls or when stalk rot disease is prevalent. Field operations in corn growing are always dependent upon suitable weather and cannot afford to be complicated by untimely shortages of fuel.

If government allocates fuel, agriculture will likely receive high priority, but that may not prevent local shortages and will not relieve the burden of higher costs. Higher prices for farm products will be needed to pay rising production costs. Individual farmers will find it increasingly advantageous to conserve fuel in growing and drying corn.

Special Tips Based on Energy, Price, and Supply Considerations

1. *Fertilizer*

Midwest agronomists said during the 1960's that properly timed fall application of nitrogen was acceptable. But higher prices and some actual shortages combined with environmental considerations lead to the conclusion that spring application and side-dressing are now preferable.

2. *Time of Planting*

Early planting requires no more fuel than later planting but usually produces higher yield, hence more corn per unit of fuel.

Early planting means earlier maturity, more chance for field drying and less need for fuel for drying, figure 194.

3. *Eliminate Unnecessary Tillage*

There is still a considerable amount of unnecessary disking and harrowing especially before planting on fall plowed land.

4. *Carburetor Setting*

The idle mixture value should be set where the engine idles *fastest.*

The idle speed should be set at the *slowest* speed where the engine will run smoothly.

Set the fuel flow on the lean side of maximum horsepower.

5. *Tractor Power — Load Balance*

Tractors are most efficient in fuel use when operated near their rated drawbar power. Tractors that are too big for the task waste fuel.

6. *Time of Harvesting*

In an ideal fall, corn in the midwest can be dried to a moisture content safe for storage without artificial drying. But this always results in some additional field loss and risks a large loss in case of wet weather. Extra fuel cost alone is not likely to be reason enough to delay harvesting.

7. *Handling and Storing*

Farmers who have livestock can harvest and store corn in airtight silos.

If airtight storage is not available you may choose between artificial drying and the addition of a chemical preservative such as propionic acid.

Overall energy requirements to produce and apply an organic acid to preserve 25-percent moisture corn are about the same as to dry to 15 percent. Above 25 percent the acid route requires less energy; below 25 percent it requires more than drying.

Before expanding or planning a new drier system, confirm the availability of fuel. You may have difficulty in getting LP-gas or natural gas.

Differences in efficiency among well-designed drying systems are small.

A vigorous field of corn is one of the most efficient crops for capturing solar energy in the temperate zone.

14

A Look into the Future

Looking into the future is always a hazardous undertaking; however, there are several trends already in progress or looming in sight on the horizon that will affect corn producers.

• The pressure on world food supply will increase as a result of more people to feed and a desire for higher quality diets. The future for corn growing is bright in spite of energy problems, higher fertilizer prices and environmental regulations.

• Concern will increase for undesired effects on non-target species and on the environment generally. At some times and in certain places food production and environmental goals will conflict. Environmentalists, agriculturists and environmental protection agencies will increasingly learn the tradeoffs that must be made between the two.

• Cost and availability of energy, especially fuels, will be increasingly important in decisions on amount of tillage and of drying corn.

• Corn residues, both cobs and stalks, will be studied as sources of alcohol or methanol for fuel and cobs as a source of heat for drying corn.

• During the next decade, top farmers will occasionally reach the 200-bushel per acre (126 quintals per hectare) level on their total acreage without irrigation and about 250 bushels (157 quintals per hectare) with irrigation.

• Plant populations will continue to climb into the 22,000 to 28,000 plants per acre (55,000 to 70,000 per hectare) range as more hybrids bred to stand high populations come on the market. Early planting which produces shorter plants and earlier harvesting will help to accelerate the shift.

• Narrow-row planting (mainly about 30 inches, ¾ meter) will predominate as farmers shift to new planters and harvesters. Some farmers will go to 20 inches (½ meter). The change will be encouraged by the yield advantage in narrow-row soybeans, more effective and longer-lasting herbicides, early planting, high population, and high fertility. Solid planting (10-inch, ¼ meter, or broadcasting) does not seem likely in the near-term future. There is little if any yield advantage and there is risk of weed problems unless perfect herbicides are found.

• Nitrogen rates will creep up mainly on fields that have been underfertilized. Rates appeared to have peaked about 1969 to 1970 on the farms that applied the highest rates. Any substantial further increase on these farms will await some breakthrough in corn growing (more population-tolerant hybrids, higher yielding hybrids, irrigation), or a major change in the relative price of fertilizer and corn.

• Fertilizer rates of phosphorus and potassium will tend to level off on the top corn farms. But they will be levels which insure that even in the most favorable seasons lack of fertility will not limit yield potential.

• New areas of response to secondary and micronutrients will be found. Some will be man-made by gross overfertilization with major nutrients. Zinc deficiency accentuated by very heavy phosphorus illustrates the point.

• Some cases of micronutrient toxicity are likely to be produced.

• Coated fertilizers and nitrifying inhibitors to control the rate of nitrogen release are already available; their acceptance hinges on lower cost or conclusive proof that they are significantly better than untreated forms. Widespread use seems unlikely except on sands or for fall application on other soils.

• Herbicides with greater specificity for weeds and wider tolerance by crops will be developed. Additives will be found which increase the toxicity of the herbicide for some weeds or which protect the crop.

• A combination of minimum tillage and longer-lasting herbicides will make cultivation unnecessary in many fields.

• Attitudes toward crop rotation will continue to change, but a two-crop system of corn and soybeans appears to be in the future for the U.S. Corn Belt.

• The amount of tillage used in seedbed preparation will be further reduced on many farms in order to save labor, conserve energy and reduce erosion.

• The feeding value of grain corn will be improved. High-lysine hybrids will raise the feeding value of corn generally and especially that of high-protein corn for hogs and poultry (non-ruminants) and for human consumption. Hybrids which yield high oil of controlled quality are another promising development. Waxy and other special types will increase for specific market use.

• Entomologists will continue to wage a battle against insects that develop resistance to certain chemical insecticides. Sex attractants (pheromones) and juvenile hormones (which interfere with developmental stages) will increase in use. Research on biological control will receive high priority and breakthroughs will be made.

• The big change in insect control which began to emerge in the early 1970's will be in *pest management.* The goal will be less reliance on chemicals as the sole control measure. Smaller dosages applied at key times in the life cycle of the insect will be stressed. Fields will be monitored by trained observers who can advise pesticide application *only when needed* rather than as a form of insurance which often results in unnecessary application.

• Our ability to anticipate insect problems will improve. Entomologists can, for example, make counts in the fall and accurately predict the corn rootworm problem in the following year. An entomologist stated that a trained person could save $500 of unnecessary spraying per hour of work in the fall.

• Diseases will generally become less important as plant breeders find new genetic resistance and transfer it to commercial hybrids.

• Irrigation in humid areas will increase on sandy soils where an adequate water supply can be developed at modest cost. But irrigation will be slow to spread to loams, silts and clays except where hybrid seed is grown.

• Irrigation will increase still further in subhumid areas, for example the regions immediately west and southwest of the Corn Belt.

• There will be continued steady improvement in machinery designed to reduce the time and cost of production.

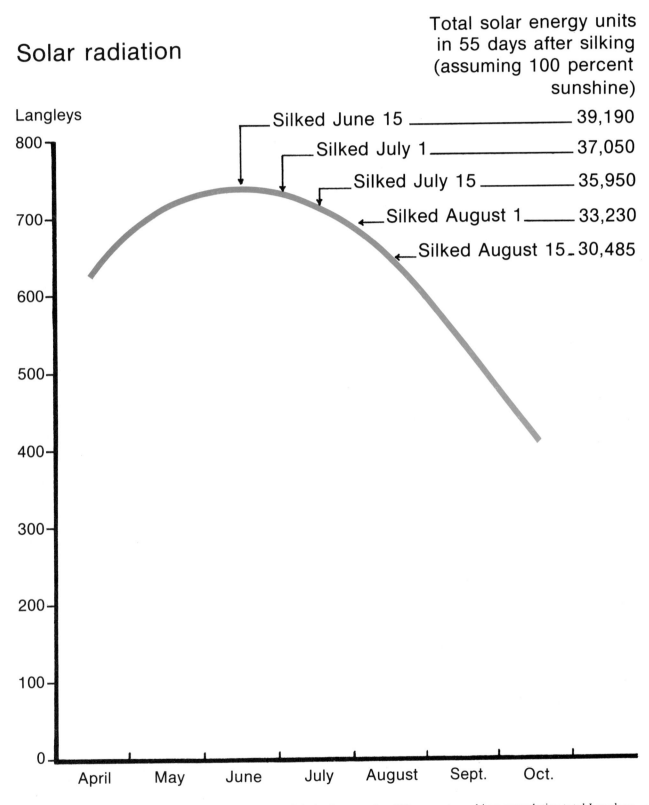

Figure 195. Solar radiation April to October at 40° north latitude assuming 100 percent sunshine; cumulative total Langleys during grain forming for corn that silks from June 15 to August 15.

THE ULTIMATE LIMITING FACTORS

Light-Trapping Efficiency

During the growing season, corn converts into yield only 2 to 3 percent of the light energy that falls on an acre. At some future date, scientists may achieve a breakthrough in techniques to greatly increase this efficiency through genetic improvement in the photosynthesis process or more efficient leaf angle. But for the present, farmers will have to be satisfied with the efficiency they can gain through:

• *Early planting.* Note in figure 195 that during the 55 days after silking, corn that silks July 1 has 3,820 potential more solar energy units (11.5 percent) than a crop that silks August. 1. This is because the days are longer and the sun is more nearly overhead. The steeper angle of incidence of the sun's rays increases the radiant energy received per unit of land area. Unusually early planted corn has shorter internodes hence the leaves, being closer together, shade each other more and this would partially offset the greater solar radiation.

• *High populations* which produce more leaf surface to intercept the sun's energy.

• *Narrow rows* to reduce the amount that plants shade each other.

• *Reflecting light.* Researchers in Illinois laid white plastic between the rows to reflect light back to the leaves when corn plants were 12 inches (30 cm) tall and increased yield 21 bushels per acre (13.2 quintals per hectare).

• *Leaf angle.* Corn plants with upright leaves, figure 196, can theoretically use sunlight more efficiently than those with normal leaf angle. Furthermore, upright-leaf types may tolerate thicker planting. Liguleless hybrids which have a very narrow leaf-stalk angle have been available since the mid-1960's but have not yet proven superior. In one trial aphids attacked the partially protected tassels of liguleless plants more than normal corn.

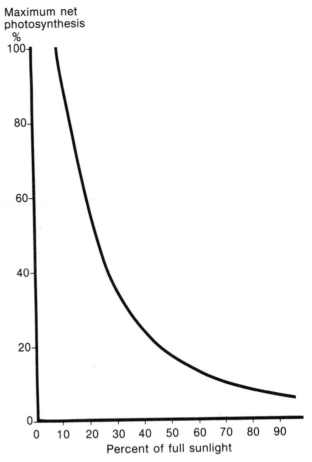

Figure 196. Net photosynthesis per unit of light is greatest at low light intensities.

• *Row direction.* Based upon a computer model of row width and direction and leaf area, angle and distribution, Allen predicted that for eastern Colorado conditions a northeast-southwest row direction might be best because the most light would be absorbed at 10:00 a.m. when moisture stress is not high in the leaf. Least light would be absorbed at 2:00 p.m. when moisture stress limits growth.

Available Water in Non-Irrigated Fields

Water in the soil at planting time, plus normal or even slightly less than normal rainfall during the growing season, would be adequate for maximum yield of corn if it could all be stored in the soil and none lost through evaporation and runoff. Wetting agents to reduce surface tension of water and thus increase penetration of rainfall, combined with chemical or plastic covers to reduce evaporation, may be practical some day for corn. Until they are, farmers will maximize the efficiency of available water by early planting, narrow rows, optimum plant population, high fertility to increase rooting depth and suction power, reduced tillage to improve surface structure, leaving residues on the surface where feasible, and better weed control.

Is Carbon Dioxide a Limiting Factor?

Green leaves need a steady supply of carbon dioxide (CO_2) during the day because it is a basic building block for the products of photosynthesis. Researchers have tried several ways to add CO_2 to the air around corn plants. Since this requires some kind of enclosure to keep the CO_2 from being blown away, it has been difficult to raise CO_2 without also affecting temperature and light. In fact, structures that were designed to keep CO_2 from being swept away from the corn leaves actually reduced air turbulence, by which the CO_2 supply for corn is normally replenished from the inexhaustible supply in the air above the field. Thus the attempt may have been counterproductive.

Research indicates that CO_2 is not usually an important limiting factor. Turbulence in the air as it flows across the rough plant surface in a cornfield normally produces enough interchange between CO_2-rich air above the field and CO_2-depleted air around the corn leaves to prevent more than a slight drop in CO_2.

It is possible, even probable, that there are at least short intervals on extremely calm days (especially in small fields that are protected by surrounding woods or hills) when CO_2 limits the rate of growth. But evidently this situation does not occur often enough to justify steps to correct it in farmers' fields.

How to Grow Contest-Winning Yields

Every year some farmers ask for a prescription that will grow 200 to 300 bushels of corn per acre (126 to 187 quintals per hectare) *without consideration of the cost.*

Here are the suggestions for non-irrigated fields in an Agronomy Fact Sheet prepared by S. R. Aldrich and D. E. Alexander, University of Illinois (up-dated to 1975 conditions):

1. Select a field that has a deep, well-drained soil with a high moisture-holding capacity. Silt loam will supply more available moisture to the crop than will either finer or coarser soils. A field that was in alfalfa or clover last year is best, provided there has been enough rainfall to recharge the subsoil with moisture to replace that used by the legume last fall.

2. Resolve to do everything exactly on time even if it means neglecting some other field. The corn in this field must be pampered.

3. Select a hybrid that will stand thick planting. Maximum yields are most likely to come from thickly planted plots, 22,000 to 28,000 per acre (54,400 to 69,200 per hectare). These high populations place a strain on the plant that many hybrids can't take. Consult the research men of your favorite seed company and follow their directions as to hybrid. You should plant 15 to 20 percent more kernels than the number of plants desired at harvest. Even with the best hybrids, be prepared for a degree of lodging and barrenness, particularly if drouth strikes.

4. Don't overwork the seedbed! Research data shows that you can get top yields with reduced tillage if you have a good stand. Aim for the least seedbed preparation that will assure the stand you want. An overfine seedbed may crust and cause rainfall to run off in midsummer when your corn urgently needs it.

5. Plant in narrow rows (30 inches, ¾ meter, or less) if you have the equipment to handle them.

6. Make sure the plants always have plenty of nutrients. Forget about fertilizer cost. Plow down or knife in 150 to 200 pounds per acre (168 to 224 kilos per hectare) of actual nitrogen. Broadcast and plow under

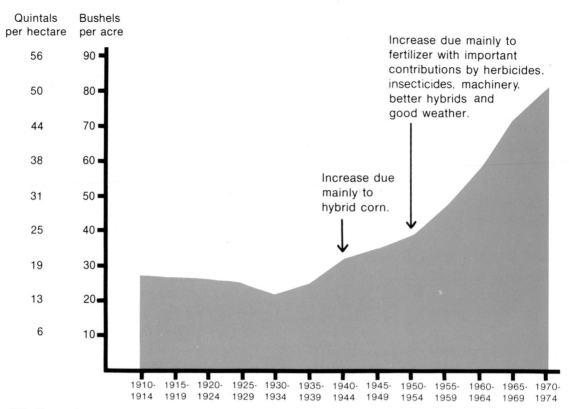

Figure 197. The national average yield of corn in the United States from 1910 to 1974. All of the increase has been made since 1939. From 1940 to 1950 hybrid corn was the main factor in raising yields. Since 1950, in addition to the items listed on the chart, a substantial concentration of corn acreage in the Corn Belt (from 50 percent in 1938 to over 80 percent in 1974) has taken place.

phosphorus and potassium as indicated by soil tests. At planting time, apply about 20 pounds of nitrogen, 30 to 40 pounds of P_2O_5, and 20 to 30 pounds of K_2O per acre (22 kilos N, 34 to 45 kilos P_2O_5, and 22 to 34 kilos K_2O per hectare) through a planter equipped to place the fertilizer 1½ to 2 inches (3.75 to 5 cm) to the side and slightly below the seed. Sidedress 50 to 100 pounds of nitrogen per acre (56 to 112 kilos per hectare) at the time of the last cultivation. To avoid root pruning, place it midway between the rows. If possible, also apply 10 to 20 tons of manure. Apply micronutrients if you farm in an area where they are known to be needed.

7. Treat the soil with an insecticide to control insects and assure a full stand of vigorous young seedlings. Spray or dust to control corn borer or aphids if present.

8. Control weeds completely with a pre-emergence spray in a band over the row or a rotary hoe followed by one or two shallow cultivations. If you control the weeds by spraying and a crust develops, make a shallow cultivation to break the crust so that rain can penetrate.

9. Harvest carefully to save all of the crop. Plan to combine one or two weeks early when the moisture in the grain is about 30 percent, to reduce shelling and avoid lodging, which increases with the age of the plants.

10. At this point, you will have done everything possible to grow a terrific yield. Now order at least an inch (2.5 cm) of gentle rain each week preferable at night so it won't interfere with bright sunshine every day.

11. Finally, prepare to accept either success or failure. When you shoot for 200 to 300 bushels (126 to 187 quintals per hectare) by these techniques, you are gambling. Gamblers don't *always* win. But even if you lose, you may enjoy playing the game.

366

Figure 198.

Reference Tables

Table 1

Pounds of selected plant nutrients contained in crops. Adapted from "Our Land and Its Care," National Plant Food Institute, 1962.

CROP	N	P₂O₅	P	K₂O	K	Ca	Mg	S	Cu	Mn	Zn

NUTRIENT (except as noted lbs. per 100 bushels or kilos per 100 quintals)

CROP	N	P_2O_5	P	K_2O	K	Ca	Mg.	S	Cu	Mn	Zn
Barley[1], 100 bu.											
grain	88	38	17	25	21	2.5	5	8	.08	.08	.15
straw	38	12	5	75	62	20	5	10	.02	.80	.12
Total	126	50	22	100	83	22.5	10	18	.10	.88	.27
Beans[1], dry 100 bu.											
grain	248	83	36	83	69	7	7	17	.07	.10	.20
Corn[1], 100 bu.											
grain	90	36	16	26	22	11	13	10	.04	.06	.10
stover	67	24	11	98	80	18	12	7	.03	1.00	.20
Total	157	60	27	124	102	29	25	17	.07	1.06	.30
Cotton[2]											
Seed & lint, 1500 lbs.	40	20	9	15	12	2	4	2	.06	.11	.32
Stalks, leaves, burs, 2000 lbs.	35	10	4	35	29	28	8	..	..	..	..
Total	75	30	13	50	41	30	12	2	..	..	..
Oats[1], 100 bu.											
grain	62	25	11	20	18	2.5	4	6	.04	.15	.06
straw	30	20	9	100	83	8	10	10	.04	..	.36
Total	92	45	20	120	101	10.5	14	16	.08	.15	.42
Potatoes, 100 bu. tubers	20	8	3	38	32	1	1.5	1.5	.01	.02	.01
Rice[1], 100 bu. (rough)											
grain	62	25	12	12	10	4	5	4	.01	.10	.09
straw	38	12	5	88	73	11	6	..	..	2.0	..
Total	100	37	17	100	83	15	11	4	..	2.10	..
Sorghum[1], 100 bu.											
grain	83	42	18	25	21	7	8	8	.02	.07	.07
stover	108	33	14	158	131	48	30	..	..	..	..
Total	191	75	32	183	152	55	38	8	..	..	..
Soybeans[1], 100 bu. grain	375	88	38	138	115	18	18	10	.12	.10	
Tobacco[2]											
Leaves, 1000 lbs.	38	8	3	60	50	38	9	7	.02	.28	.04
Stalks	18	8	3	25	21	..	..	..	..	..	..
Total	56	16	6	85	71	38	9	7	..	..	..
Wheat[1], 100 bu.											
grain	125	38	17	38	32	2.5	15	8	.08	.22	.35
straw	50	12	5	88	73	15	8	12	.02	.40	.12
Total	175	50	22	126	105	17.5	23	20	.10	.62	.47
Alfalfa hay[3] 1 ton[4]	45	10	4	45	37	28	5	5	.002	.11	.10
Clover hay[3], 1 ton[4]	40	10	4	40	33	28	7	3	.02	.20	.15
Timothy hay[3], 1 ton[4]	24	10	4	38	32	7	3	2	.01	.12	.08

[1] Grain crops cannot be compared on a bushel basis because the weight per bushel varies among crops.
[2] To convert to kilos of nutrients for the indicated yields of cotton and tobacco, divide by 2.2.
[3] Composition, especially nitrogen, varies with maturity of the crop.
[4] To convert to kilos per metric ton divide by 2.

Table 2

GRAIN SHRINKAGE TABLE. Shrinkage when grain is dried to these levels. Figures adjusted for .5% loss in handling. L.F. Stice, University of Illinois.

Initial Moisture	Mositure after drying										
	13.0%	13.5%	14.0%	14.5%	15.0%	15.5%	16.0%	16.5%	17.0%	17.5%	18.0%
Percent	(Percentage of shrinkage)										
15.5	3.37	2.81	2.24	1.67	1.09	—	—	—	—	—	—
16.0	3.95	3.39	2.83	2.25	1.68	1.09	—	—	—	—	—
16.5	4.52	3.97	3.41	2.84	2.26	1.68	1.10	—	—	—	—
17.0	5.10	4.55	3.99	3.42	2.85	2.28	1.70	1.10	—	—	—
17.5	5.67	5.12	4.57	4.01	3.44	2.87	2.29	1.70	1.11	—	—
18.0	6.25	5.70	5.15	4.59	4.03	3.46	2.88	2.30	1.71	1.11	—
18.5	6.82	6.28	5.73	5.18	4.62	4.05	3.48	2.90	2.31	1.72	1.11
19.0	7.40	6.86	6.31	5.76	5.21	4.64	4.08	3.50	2.91	2.32	1.72
19.5	7.97	7.44	6.90	6.35	5.79	5.23	4.67	4.10	3.52	2.93	2.33
20.0	8.55	8.01	7.48	6.93	6.38	5.83	5.27	4.70	4.12	3.54	2.94
20.5	9.12	8.59	8.06	7.52	6.97	6.42	5.86	5.30	4.72	4.14	3.55
21.0	9.70	9.17	8.64	8.10	7.56	7.01	6.46	5.89	5.32	4.75	4.16
21.5	10.27	9.75	9.22	8.69	8.15	7.60	7.05	6.49	5.93	5.35	4.77
22.0	10.84	10.33	9.80	9.27	8.74	8.19	7.65	7.09	6.53	5.96	5.38
22.5	11.42	10.90	10.38	9.86	9.32	8.78	8.24	7.69	7.13	6.57	5.99
23.0	11.99	11.48	10.97	10.44	9.91	9.38	8.84	8.29	7.73	7.17	6.60
23.5	12.57	12.06	11.55	11.03	10.50	9.97	9.43	8.89	8.34	7.78	7.21
24.0	13.14	12.64	12.13	11.61	11.09	10.56	10.03	9.49	8.94	8.38	7.82
24.5	13.72	13.22	12.71	12.20	11.68	11.15	10.62	10.09	9.54	8.99	8.43
25.0	14.29	13.79	13.29	12.78	12.26	11.74	11.22	10.68	10.14	9.60	9.04
25.5	14.87	14.37	13.87	13.37	12.85	12.33	11.81	11.28	10.75	10.20	9.65
26.0	15.44	14.95	14.45	13.95	13.44	12.93	12.41	11.88	11.35	10.81	10.26
26.5	16.02	15.53	15.03	14.54	14.03	13.52	13.00	12.48	11.95	11.41	10.87
27.0	16.60	16.11	15.62	15.12	14.62	14.11	13.60	13.08	12.55	12.02	11.48
27.5	17.17	16.69	16.20	15.71	15.21	14.71	14.20	13.68	13.16	12.63	12.09

Table 3

The amount of shelled corn of different moisture content equivalent to a bushel (56 pounds) or a quintal (220.5 pounds) of No. 2 corn containing 15.5% moisture. (Purdue University, Agricultural Extension Service, Circular 472)

Moisture	Bushel	Quintal	Moisture	Bushel	Quintal	Moisture	Bushel	Quintal
%	lbs.	kilos	%	lbs.	kilos	%	lbs.	kilos
11	53.17	209.3	20	59.15	232.9	29	66.65	262.4
12	53.77	211.7	21	59.90	235.9	30	67.60	266.2
13	54.39	214.2	22	60.67	238.9	31	68.58	270.0
14	55.02	216.6	23	61.45	242.0	32	69.59	274.0
15	55.67	219.2	24	62.26	245.1	33	70.63	278.1
16	56.33	221.8	25	63.09	248.4	34	71.70	282.3
17	57.01	224.5	26	63.95	251.8	35	72.80	286.6
18	57.71	227.2	27	64.82	255.2	36	73.94	291.1
19	58.42	230.0	28	65.72	258.8			

Table 4
How to predict dry test weight from test weight at harvest. Adjustment to be added to wet harvest test weight to obtain expected test weight level after drying to 15.5 percent moisture. Agricultural Economic's Department, University of Illinois.

Kernels Damaged	Percent moisture at harvest							
%	30	28	26	24	22	20	18	16
45	0.3	—	—	—	—	—	—	—
40	0.7	0.2	—	—	—	—	—	—
35	1.3	0.7	—	—	—	—	—	—
30	1.8	1.3	0.8	—	—	—	—	—
25	2.4	1.9	1.4	0.9	0.3	—	—	—
20	3.1	2.6	2.0	1.5	1.0	0.5	—	—
15	3.8	3.2	2.7	2.2	1.7	1.2	0.6	0.2
10	4.5	4.0	3.5	2.9	2.4	1.9	1.4	0.8
5	5.3	4.7	4.2	3.7	3.2	2.7	2.1	1.6
0	6.1	5.6	5.0	4.5	4.0	3.5	2.9	2.4

Table 5
Kernel spacing to obtain various plant populations in different row widths. A 10% stand loss is calculated into each rate.

Plants		40 inch 1 meter		38 inch .97 meter		36 inch .91 meter		32 inch .81 meter		30 inch .76 meter	
		Kernel Spacing									
Per acre	Per hectare	in.	cm.	in.	cm.	in.	cm.	in.	cm.	in.	cm.
12,000	29,652	11.8	30.0	12.4	31.5	13.1	33.3	14.7	37.4	15.7	39.9
14,000	34,594	10.1	25.7	10.6	26.9	11.2	28.4	12.6	32.0	13.4	34.0
16,000	39,536	8.8	22.4	9.3	23.6	9.8	24.9	11.0	27.9	11.8	30.0
17,000	42,007	8.3	21.1	8.7	22.1	9.2	23.4	10.4	26.4	11.1	28.2
18,000	44,478	7.8	19.8	8.3	21.1	8.7	22.1	9.8	24.9	10.5	26.7
19,000	46,949	7.4	18.9	7.8	19.8	8.3	21.1	9.3	23.6	9.9	25.2
20,000	49,420	7.0	18.0	7.4	18.9	7.8	19.8,	8.8	22.4	9.4	23.9
21,000	51,891	6.7	17.0	7.0	18.0	7.5	19.0	8.4	21.3	9.0	22.5
22,000	54,362	6.4	16.3	6.8	17.3	7.1	18.0	8.0	20.0	8.6	21.8
23,000	56,833	6.1	15.5	6.5	16.5	6.8	17.3	7.6	19.3	8.2	20.8
24,000	59,304	5.8	14.7	6.2	15.7	6.5	16.5	7.3	18.5	7.8	19.8
25,000	61,775	5.6	14.2	5.9	15.0	6.3	16.0	7.0	18.0	7.5	19.0
26,000	64,246	5.4	13.7	5.7	14.5	6.0	15.0	6.8	17.3	7.2	18.3
28,000	69,188	5.0	12.5	5.3	13.5	5.5	14.0	6.3	16.0	6.7	17.0
30,000	74,130	4.7	11.9	5.0	12.5	5.2	13.2	5.9	15.0	6.3	16.0
32,000	79,072	4.4	11.2	4.6	11.7	4.9	12.4	5.5	14.0	5.9	15.0

Table 6

Capacity of upright silos in English tons after one month of settling. To convert to metric tons divide by 1.1

SILAGE DEPTH		SILO DIAMETER				
		12 Feet 3.6 Meters	14 Feet 4.3 Meters	16 Feet 4.9 Meters	18 Feet 5.5 Meters	20 Feet 6.1 Meters
Feet	*Meters*	*Tons*	*Tons*	*Tons*	*Tons*	*Tons*
5	1.52	9.4	12.8	16.7	21.2	26.1
6	1.83	11.4	15.5	20.3	25.6	31.7
7	2.13	13.5	18.3	23.9	30.3	37.5
8	2.44	15.5	21.1	27.6	34.9	43.1
9	2.74	17.6	24.0	31.3	39.6	48.9
10	3.05	19.7	26.9	35.1	44.4	54.8
11	3.35	21.9	29.8	39.0	49.3	60.9
12	3.66	24.1	32.8	42.9	54.2	67.0
13	3.96	26.3	35.9	46.9	59.2	73.1
14	4.27	28.6	39.0	50.9	64.3	79.5
15	4.57	30.8	42.0	54.8	69.3	85.6
16	4.88	33.2	45.2	59.0	74.5	92.3
17	5.18	35.4	48.3	63.0	79.6	98.4
18	5.49	37.7	51.4	67.1	84.8	104.8
19	5.79	40.0	54.5	71.2	90.0	111.2
20	6.10	42.4	57.7	75.3	95.2	117.9
21	6.40	44.6	60.7	79.3	100.2	124.0
22	6.71	47.0	64.0	83.5	105.6	130.7
23	7.01	49.4	67.2	87.8	110.5	137.3
24	7.32	51.7	70.4	91.9	116.1	143.7
25	7.62	54.1	73.7	96.2	121.6	150.4
26	7.92	56.4	76.8	100.3	126.8	156.8
27	8.23	58.9	80.2	104.7	132.3	163.7
28	8.53	61.2	83.4	108.9	137.6	170.1
29	8.84	63.7	86.8	113.3	143.2	177.1
30	9.14	66.0	90.0	117.5	148.5	183.5
31	9.45	68.5	93.4	121.9	154.0	190.4
32	9.75	70.9	96.7	126.2	159.5	197.1
33	10.06	73.3	100.0	130.5	165.0	203.8
34	10.36	75.8	103.3	134.8	170.4	210.7
35	10.67	78.2	106.6	139.1	175.9	217.4
36	10.97	80.6	109.9	143.4	181.4	224.1
37	11.28	83.0	113.2	147.7	186.8	230.7
38	11.58	85.5	116.5	152.0	192.3	237.7
39	11.89	87.9	119.8	156.3	197.8	244.4
40	12.19	90.3	123.1	160.6	203.2	251.0
41	12.50	92.8	126.5	165.0	208.7	258.0
42	12.80	95.2	129.8	169.3	214.2	264.7
43	13.11	97.6	133.1	173.6	219.7	271.3
44	13.41	100.1	136.4	177.9	225.1	278.3
45	13.72	102.5	139.7	182.2	230.6	285.0

Table 7

AMINO ACID COMPOSITION (g per 100 g protein) for defatted whole kernels of normal and Opaque-2 Maize, 1967 Crop

Amino Acid	Normal	Opaque-2
Per Cent Protein	*9.0*	*10.5*
Lysine	3.0	5.0
Tryptophan	0.7	1.3
Histidine	2.6	3.5
Arginine	4.9	7.2
Aspartic acid	9.2	8.8
Threonine	4.1	3.8
Serine	5.6	4.7
Glutamic acid	22.6	17.2
Proline	9.6	8.4
Glycine	4.7	5.1
Alanine	9.2	6.7
Cystine	1.7	2.0
Valine	5.7	5.2
Methionine	2.2	2.0
Isoleucine	4.2	3.4
Leucine	14.6	9.3
Tyrosine	5.2	4.2
Phenylalanine	5.8	4.4

(Corn Refiners Association, Inc.)

Index

Acetic acid preservative, 319

Acid soil *see also* **pH** *and* **Soil acidity**
appearance of corn on, 257

Acidity, of soil *see also* **pH** *and* **Soil acidity**
caused by nitrification of ammonium, 113
effect of nitrogen fertilizers on, 108, 113
effect on nutrient availability, Fig. 124, p. 181
effect on phosphorus availability, Table 10, p. 132
most favorable range for crops, Fig. 125, p. 182

Adaptability, of hybrids, 40

Aerial fertilizing, 176

Aerial planting, 92, 220

Aflatoxin, 321

Air pollution injury, 280, 351

Alfalfa
nitrogen from, Table 9, p. 118, Table 17, p. 161
soil improving value of, Fig. 109, p. 160

Alkaline soils, 147, *see also* **pH**
effect on availability of phosphorus, 132
influence on nutrient deficiencies, 124

Amino acids, in corn, 47, 371

Ammonia *see also* **Anhydrous ammonia**
injury to corn from, 248, 249, 250, 255
reactions in soil, 110
retention related to base exchange capacity, 157
toxicity of, 242

Ammoniation of phosphates
effect on water solubility, 127
fertilizers produced by, 125

Ammonium ion
effect on pH of soil, 113
held on clay and organic matter, 110, Fig. 100, p. 144
interaction with potassium, Fig. 94, p. 136

Ammonium nitrate
reactions in soil, 108, 110
salt index of, Table 19, p. 168

Amylomaize, 46

Analysis of fertilizer, 96

Anhydrous ammonia, Discussion of, 99, 110
cause of injury to stand, 241, 243
cause of leaf burn, 243, 268
effect on soil organisms, 100
effect on soil pH, 100
energy to make, 355
in silage, 305
safe handling of, 100
losses of, 99, 100
maximum rate to apply, different soils, 99, 100
reactions in soil, Fig. 73, p. 99, 100, 109, 110
salt index of, Table 19, p. 168

Anthers, 9

Anthracnose, 281

Ants, thief, 241, 247

Aphids, 244, 275

Aqua ammonia
characteristics of, 108, 111
injury to corn, 241, 255

Armyworms, 242, 253, 270

Asphalt barrier, 200

Aspergillus, 321

Atrazine, 29

B *see* **Boron**

Bacteria
cause of disease, 39

Bacterial cultures, for silage, 305

Bacterium Thuringiensis, 274

Barren stalks
cause of red leaves, 285
due to high plant population, 81, 82
increased nitrate content of, 311

Base exchange capacity, Discussion of, 157
of clay, Fig. 100, p. 144

Base saturation, 157

Basic slag, 128

Biological control
of insects, 294
of weeds, 235

Bird damage, 249, 286

Biuret injury, 249

Black layer, 15

Blending, of fertilizer *see* **Bulk blends**

Blends of hybrids, 43

Blight, leaf, 39, 276-279
eyespot, 278, 279
northern, 276, 278
race T, 39, 277, 278
southern, 39, 277, 278
yellow, 277, 278

Blight, seedling, 247

Boron
an essential element, 104
availability related to pH, Fig. 124, p. 181
deficiency of, 141, 265

Brace roots, 6

Broadcast fertilizer, 169-173
how to improve spreading pattern, 171
importance of even spreading, 172

Brown midrib, 50

Brown spot (Physoderma), 280

Bulk blends of fertilizer, Discussion of, 173
dry mixes vs. homogenous pellets, 100, 101

Bulk spreading of fertilizer, 170-173
see also Bulk blends
unevenness of, 170
how to improve, 171

Ca *see* **Calcium**

Calcium
an essential element, 104
availability related to pH, Fig. 124, p. 181
deficiency for corn, 140, 263
gypsum, a source of, 182
removal by crops, Table 21, p. 184; Table 1, p. 368
treatment of deficiency, 263

Calcium carbonate *see* **Limestone**

Calcium cyanamide, 108

Calcium metaphosphate, 125

Calendarization of corn planting, 80

Calibrating of corn planter,
Discussion of, 87-89

Carbon, an essential element, 104

Carbon-nitrogen ratio, 115-118

Carryover of nutrients, 161

Cash grain farming, 32

Center-cut silage, 306

Cereal leaf beetle, 272

Charcoal stalk rot, 288

Check list for corn troubles, 297

Chelates, 141, 143

Chinch bugs, 270, 271

Chisel, for subsoiling, Discussion of, 62
effect on available water, 191
effect on poorly-drained soils, Fig. 46, p. 63

Chisel plow, 59

Chloride, effect on phosphorus uptake, 166

Chlorinated hydrocarbons, 348

Chlorine
an essential element, 104
effect on P uptake, 166
in muriate of potash, 135
rate of leaching, 136

Clay particle
ammonium held by, Fig. 79, p. 110; Fig. 100, p. 144
base exchange capacity related to, Fig. 100, p. 144, 157
diagram and photograph of, 144
in wet vs. dry situation, Fig. 94, p. 136, 137

negative charges on, Fig. 100, p. 144
potassium fixation by, 135

Clay soil
available water in, 191
base exchange capacity of, 157
changing available water supply of, 191
characteristics and management of, 147

Climate, related to corn growing, 20-23
degree days, Fig. 23, p. 22, 36
favorable temperature, 20-23
frost-free period, 24
growing degree days, 20-23, Fig. 23, p. 22, 36
heat units, 20, 23
rainfall, Fig. 24, p. 23, 189, 194-201

Coated fertilizer, 112

Coleoptile, 2, 3, 249

Colloidal phosphate, 126

Common stalk borer, 271

Compaction
caused by tractor wheels, 56, 69
effect of chiseling on, Fig. 46, p. 63

Compost, 105, 341

Continuous corn, 25-29
effect on diseases, 26, 30
effect on insects, 26, 30
effect on yield, 26, 30
indications of excess, 28
on Morrow Plots, Fig. 27, p. 27
related to kind of soil, 28
slope limit for, 28, 29

Contour farming, Fig. 154, p. 221

Copper
an essential element, 104
availability related to pH, Fig. 124, p. 181
deficiency for corn, 141, 264

Corn
conditions for growing, 19-29
drying, 323-328
fertilizing, 95-187
growth, stages of, 1-17
harvesting, as grain, 317
harvesting, silage, 303
marketing, 331-337
meeting water needs of, 189-217
on steep land, 29
planters, 85
planting, methods for, 77-93
preparing seedbed for, 53-75
recognizing and treating troubles of, 238-301
selecting hybrids of, 35-51
trends for the future, 361-365
weed control in, 223-236
world production of, Fig. 20, p. 19

Corn Belt
features of, 20-25

Corn borer
European, 273- 294
Southwestern, 294

Corn picker, 324, 325, Table 42, p. 329

Corn plant
developmental stages of, Section on, 1-17
germination and seedling establishment of, 2
kernel development of, 13
maturity and drying of, 14-16
pollen shed and silking of, 8
tassel and ear initiation of, 7
vegetative stage of, 5

"Corn stalk" disease *see* **Nitrate poisoning**

Corn stunt disease, 266

Corn troubles, Section on, 238-301
before emergence, 241, 246-249
check list for, 297
descriptions of, 246-290
emergence to knee-high, 242, 250-258
in storage, 292
knee-high to tasseling, 243, 259-272
listed in chronological order, 241-245
maturity to harvest, 245, 290-292
silking to maturity, 244, 273-289
tissue tests for diagnosing, 299

Costs
of fertilizer compared to other factors, 178, Fig. 122, p. 180

of fertilizer compared to value of corn, Fig. 123, p. 181
to dry and store grain, Table 44, p. 334
to grow selected crops, 27
to store grain, 334

Cover crops, 74, 220

Crazy-top, 282

Crop diversity, 31, 239

Crust
cultivating to break, Fig. 136, p. 197
preventing emergence of corn, 241, 247

Cu *see* **Copper**

Cultipacker, 66, 67

Cultivation
by flame, 236
root pruning by, Fig. 163, p. 235
to break a crust, Fig. 136, p. 197
when no weeds are present, 233

Cutworms, 242, 252, 271

Cytoplasm
in relation to disease, 39, 277
control of pollen shed by, 42

Date of planting, Discussion of, 77-80
effect on optimum rate of planting, 77, 81
influence on water efficiency, 198
soil temperature for, 79

Deficiences *see* **Plant nutrients**

Deficiency symptoms *see* **Section 9,** 256-266

Degree days, growing, 20, 22, 23, 26
map of, Fig. 23, p. 22

Denitrification, Discussion of, 120

Depth of planting
cause of poor stand, 241, 248
effect on rooting depth, Fig. 6, p. 5
maximum for seedling emergence, 4, 80
optimum for various soil conditions, 80

Detasselling, 41

Diagnosing troubles, Section on, 238-299
techniques for, 183, 298

Diammonium phosphate
cause of NH3 injury, 169
characteristics of, 108, 125
effect on pH of soil, 108, Table 8, p. 113
phosphorus fertilizer, 125
salt index of, Table 19, p. 168

DIMBOA, 273

Diplodia
ear rot, 290, 292
seedling blight, 241
stalk rot, 138, 245, 290

Disease
causes of, 38
in continuous corn, 26
in high yield systems, 239
part of corn troubles, 241-292
resistance of hybrids to, 38

Disk harrow, 64

Disk plow, 59

Diversity of crops, 31, 239

Dormancy, of weed seeds, 234

Double cropping, 31, 73

Double-cross hybrids, 43

Downy mildew, 282, 283

Drainage
effect on denitrification, Fig. 86, p. 120
effect on environment, 340
for irrigated fields, 216
to speed nitrogen release, 120

Drilling vs. hill drop, 83

Drouth, Discussion of, 208
appearance of effect on corn, 244, 259, 289
effect on nitrate poisoning, 311
patterns in U.S., Fig. 146, p. 209
plant population adjustment for, 197
salvaging corn crop affected by, 307

Dryeration, 326

Drying corn
amount of overdrying, 325
shrinkage from, 369
solar energy for, 328

systems for, 323-328
temperature for, 327

Dry weight growth curve, Fig. 16, p. 14

Dwarf corn, Discussion of, 51

Ear-corn silage, 306

Ear, of corn
beginning of, Fig. 4, p. 4, 7
structure of, Figs. 12-13, p. 10
kernel development of, 13
number of kernels on, 10
number of rows on, 10
physiological maturity of, 14
silk, function of, 8-10

Early planting,
discussion of, 77-80
in relation to water efficiency, 198

Ear rots
Diplodia, 290, 292
Gibberella, 290, 292
Fusarium, 290, 292
Nigrospora, 291, 292
Penicillium, 292, 293

Earworms, 275

Elemental basis for P and K, 96

Embryo, 1, Fig. 1, p. 2, 13

Endosperm, 1

Energy, Section on, 353-359
for no-till planting, 91
in agriculture, 353
in corn cobs, 353
in food production, 355
in nitrogen fertilizer manufacturing, 355
fossil fuel for corn, 356
per unit of corn, 356
tips on conserving, 358

Environment, Discussion of, 339-351
effect of cutting forests, 339
effect of plowing prairies, 339
effect of drainage, 340
effect of animal vs. mechanical power, 340
effect of fertilizers, 341, 345
future concern for, 361
historical perspective, 339
nitrates, 343
phosphorus, 346
pesticides, 348
impact of technology on, 350

Environmental effects
of fertilizers, 341
of herbicides, 223

Erosion
effect of, related to soil type, Fig. 151, p. 217
effect of surface residues on, 57
effect on crop yields, 217
influence of rotation on, 26, 28, 219
influence of subsoil on effect of, Table 28, p. 216
influence of tillage on, Table 29, p. 219
regulations on, 343
trends in, 342
universal soil loss equation, 219

Essential elements, Discussion of, 104

European corn borer, 243, 244, 245, 273, 294

Evaporation, 22; Fig. 58, p. 83, Fig. 130, p. 191

Exchange capacity *see* **Base exchange capacity**

Eyespot, 278, 279

Fall application
of nitrogen, 115
environmental concerns of, 115

Fall plowing, Discussion of, 58
of legumes, effect on soil improving value, Fig. 109, p. 160
safe slope limit for, 59
to permit reduced tillage, 74

Fertilizer, Section on, 95-187
acidity of, 108, 113
aerial application of, 176
blends of, 173
bulk spreading of, 103
"burn", 103, Fig. 113, p. 167, 168, 249, 250, 255
costs and returns from, 162, 178

dry solids, 100
effect on corn maturity, 165, 177, Table 20, p. 178
effect on environment, 341
effect on feeding value of corn, 321
effect on nitrate in corn plant, 310, 311
effect on rooting depth, 194, Fig. 134, p. 195
effect on wager efficiency, Fig. 133, p. 194
essential elements, list of, 104
fall application of, 115
gas form of, 99
grade, analysis, 96
injury from, Fig. 113, p. 167, 168, 177, 249, 250, 255
labeling of, 96
leaching of nitrogen, 113
liquids, 102
micronutrients, 140-144
nitrogen, 106-122
phosphorus, 123-134
physical forms of, 99
placement of, 133, 135, 138, 141, 143, 164-166
potassium, 134-140
premium grades of, 96
rates in relation to price, 180, 181 (see also individual nutrients)
ratio, 96
secondary nutrients, 140
slurry, 104
suspension, 104
sidedressing nitrogen, 175
unproven claims for, 184
use compared to other production factors, 178, Fig. 122, p. 180
yield reduction from, explanation of, 166

Fertilizer injury, Discussion of, 168
from anhydrous and aqua ammonia, 248, 249, 250, 255
from liquid vs. dry fertilizer, 103

Fertilizer placement
advantages of selected placements, Fig. 112, p. 165, Fig. 114, p. 169
best for phosphorus, 133
best for potassium, 135, 138
deep, combined with chiseling, 63
"pop-up", 165
to avoid injury, 100, 168, 248, 249

Field losses, 318, 329

Foliar feeding, 177

Fossil fuel, 355

Frost, 330

Futures market, 335

Garden symphylan, 253

Genetic resistance, 26

Genetic stripe, 243, 282

Germination of corn, 2

Gibberella
ear rot, 290, 292
stalk rot, 245, 290

Grain preservatives, 319

Grain storage, Discussion of, 313-337
molds in, 321
silo storage for high moisture, 320
preservatives, 319
safe moisture for, 318
toxic substances in, 321
drying, storage systems, 323
avoiding wet spots in, 325

Grape colaspis, 242, 253

Grasshopper, 244, 275

Gray leaf, 250

Green manure
value of legumes for, Fig. 109, p. 160
value of thick-planted corn for, 150, 307

Growing degree days (GDD), 20, 23, 36

Growing season for corn, 19-23

Growth, Section on, 1-17
regulators, 223

Growth curve of corn, Fig. 16, p.14

Gypsum, 182

H *see* **Hydrogen**

Hail damage, 243, 273

Hardpan, 62; Fig. 46, p. 63
Harrow see **Disk, Spiketooth, Springtooth**
Harvesting Grain, Section on, 317-337
  losses, effect of harvest date on, 317-318
  moisture for safe storage, 318
  optimum time, 275
  overdrying, 325
  systems for grain corn, 323
  to save "soft corn", 330

Harvesting silage, Section on, 303-315
  adding water to preserve, 305
  feeding to avoid spoilage, 309
  nitrate poisoning, 309-315
  nitrate test, 314, Fig. 175, p. 315
  preservatives, 305
  silage process, 304
  "silo gas", 314
  time to harvest, 303

Heat damage
  to plants, 243, 266, 267
  to pollen, 12

Heat units (growing degree days), Discussion of, 20
  map of, in U.S., Fig. 23, p. 22, 36

Herbicides
  applying in irrigation, 214
  environmental effects of, 223, 348
  herbigation, 214
  influence of rainfall on, 227
  injury from, 236, 242, 243, 254, 255
  liquid fertilizer mixtures with, 229
  residues of, 223
  resistance to, 233

Hexadecanol, 200

"Hidden hunger", 298

High oil corn hybrids, 48

High-population corn
  effect on lodging, 307, Fig. 169, p. 308
  feeding value of, 307
  for green manure, 150, 307

High protein corn hybrids, 47

High sugar corn, 50

Hill dropping vs. drilling, 83

Holcus spot, 281

Humus, Fig. 83, p. 117, 149, 150
  see also **Organic matter**

Husklage, 307

Hybrids, Section on, 35-51
  adaptability to conditions, 40
  disease resistance of, 38
  double-cross, 41, 42
  maturity, importance of, 35
  single-cross, 41, 42
  standability of, 37
  three-way cross, 41, 42
  tolerance to high population, 81

Hydrated lime, 182

Hydrogen
  an essential element, 104
  cause of soil acidity, 113

Insects, on corn, Section on, 238-296
  genetic resistance in, 26, 269, 348
  in continuous corn, 26
  in high yield systems, 239
  in stored grain, 296

Integrated pest management, 350, 362

Iron
  an essential element, 104
  availability related to pH, Fig. 124, P. 181
  deficiency, 141, 262, 263

Irrigation, Discussion of, 207-216
  applying nitrogen in, 213
  applying herbicides in, 214
  costs of, 209-213
  methods of, 216
  optimum plant population for, 82
  sources of water, 208
  time of greatest need for, 215, 216
  water rights for, 208
  yield increase from, Table 27, p. 216

    K see **Potassium**

Kernel
  development of, 13
  physiological maturity of, 14; Figs. 17, 18.
    p. 15, Fig. 19, p. 16

Land planing, 203
Land smoothing, 203
Land use planning, 343

Leaching
  of limestone, 182
  of nitrogen, Fig. 79, p. 110, 113, 344
  of phosphorus, 128, 340, 347

Leaf blights, 39, 244, 276-279
  eyespot, 278, 279
  northern, 244, 276, 278
  southern, race O and race T, 277, 278
  yellow, 277, 278

Leaf feeding, 141, 177
Leaf sheath damage, 282
Leaf temperature, 21, 22, 36

Legumes
  effect on nitrate in corn, 311
  soil improving value of, Table 9, p. 118,
    Fig. 109, p. 160, Table 17, p. 161

Light
  amount during ear-forming period, Fig. 195,
    p. 363
  efficiency of, 83, 84, 364
  efficiency related to intensity, 364

Lightning damage, 268
Liguleless corn, 49

Lime need
  influence of nitrogen fertilizers on, 108, 113
  to correct effect of low pH, 183
  to offset removal of calcium and magnesium,
    Table 21, p. 184

Limestone
  adding to silage, 305
  amounts to offset acidity from nitrogen, 108
  amounts to offset crop removal, 183,
    Table 21, p. 184
  fineness, importance of, 182
  kinds of, 182
  leaching of, 182

Liming of acid soils see **Limestone and pH**

Liquid fertilizers, Discussion of, 102
  herbicide mixtures with, 229
  injury from, 104, 168

Lister, 60

Lodging
  differences among hybrids, 37
  due to disease, 287-289
  due to high population, 37, 307; Fig. 169,
    p. 308
  due to insects, 38, 243, 269
  effect of early planting on, 77
  effect of potash on, Fig. 95, p. 137; 177,
    Fig. 121, p. 179
  improved resistance to, 38
  influence of fertility on, 177; Fig. 121, p. 179

Losses, of grain
  from delayed harvest, Table 40, p. 318
  from different harvesting systems, Table 42,
    p. 329
  from topping, 328, 330
  from weed competition, 324, 325

Low pH see **pH of soil**
Low temperature drying, 327
Lysimeters, leaching studies with, 183
Lysine, 47

Magnesium
  an essential element, 104
  availability related to pH, Fig. 124, p. 181
  deficiency, 141, 242, 262
  on clay particle, Fig. 100, p. 144
  potassium-magnesium balance, 138
  removal in crops, Table 1, p. 368

Magnesium carbonate, 182
Maize dwarf mosaic disease, 244, 266
Major nutrients, list of, 104
Male sterility, 40, 42

Manganese
  an essential element, 104
  availability related to pH, Fig. 124, p. 181
  deficiency, 141, 265
  effect of phosphorus on, 134
  removal in harvested crops, Table 1, p. 368
  toxicity of, 180

Manure, 158-160
  effect on nitrate in corn, 311

Marketing, 331-337
Marl, 182

Maturity of corn
  appearance of kernels at, Fig. 19, p. 16, 17
  importance of, 35
  influence of fertilizers on, 165, 177, 178
  physiological, defined, 14
  related to moisture, Fig. 17, p. 15
  relative, of hybrids, 36

Mesocotyl, 3, 5
Methemoglobinemia, 344
Methionine, 48
Mice, 73, 294
Mg see **Magnesium**

Micronutrients, Discussion of, 140-144
  as essential elements, list of, 104
  availability related to pH of soil, 142,
    Fig. 124, p. 181
  deficiencies, soil conditions favoring, 141, 142
  foliar applications of, 144
  formulations of, 143
  in animal manure, 160
  injury to germination from, 169, 249
  in premium grades of fertilizers, 96
  placement to avoid injury, 169
  removal in crops, Table 1, p. 368
  soil applications of, 142
  spectrographic analysis for, 300

Micro-organisms
  effect of anhydrous ammonia on, 100
  effect of fertilizers on, 105
  effect of soil pH on, 181
  in decay of plant residues, 115, 130
  in denitrification process, 120
  in nitrification process, 119
  in phosphorus changes in soil, 130

Minerals in corn grain, Table 1, p. 368

Minimum tillage, Discussion of, 29, 67-75,
    89-92
  effects on weeds, 234
  influence on erosion losses, 219

Mixtures of hybrids, 43
Mn see **Manganese**
Mo see **Molybdenum**

Moisture, in grain
  at physiological maturity, 15
  discounts for, 322
  for safe storage, 318
  for various harvesting systems, Table 39,
    p. 319
  related to percent of maximum yield,
    Fig. 17, p. 15
  shrinkage from, Table 2, p. 369
  testing for, 328

Moisture, soil see **Water**

Moisture testing
  for grain, 328
  for silage, 305

Molds, 290-293, 318, 321

Molybdenum
  an essential element, 104
  for corn, 141

Monoammonium phosphate, 108, 113, 168
Morrow plots, Fig. 27, p. 27
Muck, Fig. 102, p. 142, 250
  see also **Organic soil**

Multieared corn, 50

Muriate of potash, 135
  see also **Potassium fertilizers**

  N see **Nitrogen**

Narrow crop base, 31

Narrow rows, 83, 84

"Natural" fertilizers, 105

Nigrospora ear rot, 291, 292

Nitrate, in corn plants, 309-315
accumulation in plant parts, 310
cause of poisonous "silo gas", 314
conversion factors to N and KNO_3, 312
dangerous levels of, 312
effect of legumes on, 311
effect of manure on, 311
effect of plant population on, 311
effect on vitamin A, 313
feeding high nitrate silage, 313
influence of nitrogen on, Fig. 171, p. 311
tests for, 315

Nitrate in fertilizers, 108, 110, 111, 113

Nitrate in soil
denitrification of, 120
influence of residues on, Fig. 84, p. 117
leaching of, Fig. 79, p. 110, 113
movement to soil surface, 114
product of nitrification process, Fig. 85, p. 119
reactions in soil, 113-121
uptake by corn, 77

Nitrate in water, 343-346

Nitrate of soda
characteristics and use of, 104
salt index of, Table 19, p. 168

Nitrate poisoning, 309

Nitrate reductase, 311

Nitrification
conditions affecting, 115, 119
importance of, 119
increasing the rate of, 121-122

Nitrogen, Section on, 106-122
amount available from preceding crops
Table 9, p. 118, Table 17, p. 161
amount available related to pH. Fig. 124,
p. 181
amount in air, 106
an essential element, 104
application in irrigation, 213
application of, different times compared,
115, 174, 175
application of, in anhydrous ammonia,
Fig. 72, p. 98, 99, 108, 110, 111, 249,
250, 255
aplication of, in nitrogen solutions, Fig. 75,
p. 102, 108, 111, 255
application of, in row fertilizer, 165, 166, 167
application of, maximum in the row, 165, 167
application of, sidedressing, 175
application of, surface losses from, 173
biological changes in, denitrification, 120
biological changes in, nitrification, 115, 119
biological changes, related to
carbon-nitrogen ratio, 115-120
carryover of, 161, 162
deficiency symptoms of, 242, 260, 261
effect on lodging, 177, Fig. 121, p. 179
effect on maturity, 177
effect on nitrate content, Table 38, Fig. 171,
p. 311
effect on pH of soil, 108, 110, 112
effect on phosphorus uptake, 166
effect on stalk rot, 178, 179
energy to manufacture, 355
fall application of, 115, 175
in animal manure, 158-160
increasing available supply from soil, 121
movement in soil, 113
N-Serve, 112
phosphorus-nitrogen ratio in row fertilizer,
166, 167
potassium-nitrogen balance, Fig. 95, p. 137,
138, Fig. 121, p. 179
price related to price of corn, Fig. 123, p. 181
reactions in soil, 109-122
sidedressing with, 175
"slow release" fertilizer, 112
soil tests for, 151, 152
solutions of, kinds, 108, 111
solutions of, losses from surface, 173
solutions of, mixed with herbicides, 229

Nitrogen (cont.)
solutions of, placement, 111, 173
tissue test for, 299, 314, 315
trends in soil, 350
uptake by corn, 106

Northern corn rootworm, 243, 269

Northern leaf blight, 38, 244, 276-279

N-Serve, 112

No-till, 31, 73, 74, 89, 234, 348

Nutrients *see* **Plant nutrients**

Nutrient removal by crops, Table 1, p. 368

Nutrient uptake
from foliar (leaf) applications, 141, 177
of nitrogen, 106
of phosphorus, 123
of potassium, 134

O *see* **Oxygen**

Oil in corn, 47, 48

Opaque 2, 47

Organic farming, 105

Organic food, 105

Organic matter, in soil, 147-151
effect on sands, silts, clays, 148, 149
effect of tillage on, 149, 150, 339, 340
food for micro-organisms, 115-118
general effects of, 148
influence on available water, 191, 192
methods for increasing, 149
source of nitrogen, 115
source of phosphorus, 130
toxic substance from, 149
trends in soil, 341

Organic soil (muck), 147

Organisms in soil *see* **Micro-organisms**

Orienting kernels, in planting, 93

Orthophosphate, 126

Ovules, number per ear, 10

Oxide basis for P and K, 96

Oxygen
an essential element, 104
involved in denitrification, 120
involved in nitrification, 119

P *see* **Phosphorus**

Pan breaker, 62

Paraquat, 29, 73, 234

Peat *see* **Organic soil**

Pelleted fertilizer, 100, 101, 171, 172

Penicillium ear rot, 245, 293

Percent yield, curves for, Fig. 106, p. 155

Pericarp, 1

Pesticides,
in runoff, 91, 348
in diverse cropping systems, 239

Pest management, 350, 362

pH *see also* **Soil acidity**
effect of nitrogen fertilizer on, 108, 110, 112
effect on nutrient availability, Fig. 124, p. 181
influence on phosphorus reactions, 132
most favorable range for corn, 181
of silage, 304

Phosphoric acid, 126

Phosphorus, Discussion of, 123-134
amount in organic form, 130
an essential element, 104
availability related to pH, p. 132, Fig. 124,
p. 181
"available" in fertilizer, definition of, 126
biological reactions of, 130
carryover of, 161
cause of deficiency, 132, 257
chemical reactions of, 128-132
deficiency for young corn plants, 123, 247
deficiency symptoms of, 242, 256, 257
factors affecting available supply of, 132
fertilizers, 124
fixation of, 128, Fig. 90, p. 130, 131
in animal manure, 158-160
in crop residues, 160
influence of chloride on uptake, 166

influence of nitrogen on uptake, 127, 166
influence of pH on, 132, Fig. 124, p. 181
influence on manganese, 134
influence on zinc, 127, 259, 260
in grain of corn, Table 1, p. 368
in relation to water quality, 346
in row fertilizer, 128, 166
in runoff, 346
movement in soil, 128
placement of, 133, 164-169
release from residues, 128-132
removal in crops, Table 1, p. 368
sidedressing with, 133, 175
soil tests for, 132, 152
trends in soil, 341, 350
tissue tests for, 299
uptake by corn, 123
water solubility, 125, 127-132

Physiological maturity, 14

Physalospora, 241

Physoderma (brown spot), 280

Picnic beetles, 244, 276

Placement of fertilizer, Discussion of, 164-173
foliar application, 174
for most efficient use, 164
of anhydrous ammonia, 110
of aqua ammonia, 111
of nitrogen solutions, 111
of phosphorus, 133, 164-169
of potassium, 137
to avoid injury, 167, 168, 248, 255

Plant analyses, Discussion of, 298-300
see also **Spectrographic analysis and Tissue
tests**

Planters, types of, 85

Plant nutrients *see also* **Individual nutrients**
biological changes involving, 115, 130, 137
carryover of, 161
deficiencies of, 141, 242, 256-266
essential for plant growth, 104
factors affecting availability of, 132, Fig. 124,
p. 181
in fertilizers, 108, 124, 135
influence of pH on, Fig. 124, p. 181
in manure, 158, 159
removed in crops, Table 1, p. 368
supplied by soil, 157-162

Plant population, Discussion of, 81-83, 301
effect on nitrate in corn plants, 310, 311
for early planting, 77, 81
for green-chop feeding, 82, 307
for green manure, 82, 307
for irrigated fields, 82, 213
for silage, 82, 307
in dry years, 198
kernel spacing for, 88; Table 5, p. 370
optimum for water efficiency, 198
recommended rates, 77, 78, 81
related to hybrids, 81
related to lodging, 37, 307; Fig. 169, p. 308
related to water supply, 81, 198
trends for the future, 361

Plant residues *see* **Residues, plant and Organic
matter**

Plant spacing, Fig. 58, p. 83, 88, Table 5, p. 370

Plant tissue tests, 298-300

Planter setting *see* **Calibrating of corn planter**

Planting depth, 4, 5, 80, 241, 248

Planting, discussion of, 77-93
applying water in, 93

Plastic mulch, Fig. 113, p. 177; 179

Plow
chisel, disk, moldboard, 58-60

Plowing, Discussion of, 58-60
date for legume sod, 160
date for years of low subsoil moisture, 198

Plow-plant, 67, 71

Plow-sole, 62

Plumule, 2, 3

Pollen
biological control of, 42

chemical control of, 42
control by male sterility, 42
development of, 8
fertilization of ovules by, 12
shedding date related to silking, 12, 295

Pollination, lack of, 295

Polyphosphate, 126

Popcorn, 51

Popped kernel condition, 292

Population *see* **Plant population**
sensitive hybrid, 81

Pop-up fertilizer, 165

Potassium, Discussion of, 134-140
an essential element, 104
availability related to pH, Fig. 124, p. 181
carryover of, 161
deficiency of, conditions causing, 260
deficiency of, symptoms, 242, 260
effect on lodging, Fig. 95, p. 137, 177,
Fig. 121, p. 179
fertilizers, 135
for early growth, 175
forms in soil, Fig. 93, p. 135
in animal manure, 158
in crop residues, 160
influence on maturity, 165, 177, 178
influence on water use by corn, 196
in plant parts, 135
in row fertilizer, 138, 166, 167
interaction with ammonium, 136, 137
magnesium-potassium balance, 138
maintenance applications of, 167
needs in grain vs. silage system, 137
nitrogen-potassium balance, 138
rate to apply, 137-139
reaction in soil, 136
removed in crops, Table 1, p. 368
seasonal changes in, 138, 139
sidedressing with, 175
soil tests for, 138
supplying power of different soils, Fig. 96,
p. 138, Fig. 97, p. 139
tissue tests for, 299
uptake by corn, 134
when to apply, 137, 175
where to apply, 137

Potassium metaphosphate, 125, 136

Potassium nitrate, 108, 168

Potassium sulfate, 136, 168

Pre-emergence weed control, 226

Premium grades, of fertilizer, 96

Price
of corn through the season, 334, 335
of corn vs. nitrogen fertilizer, Fig. 123, p. 181
of fertilizer and other production factors,
178-180
of corn, regional differences, 24

Primary tillage, 57

Profit, related to yield level, 32, 33

Propionic acid, 319

Protein
influence of nitrogen on, Fig. 171, p. 311
in selected hybrids, 47
amino acids of, Table 7, p. 371

Race T leaf blight, 39, 277

Radiational cooling, 22, 330

Radicle
in embryo, 1
in germination of seed, 3

Rainfall
effectiveness of, related to humidity, 22
effectiveness of, related to temperature, 22
increasing efficiency of, 194-200
map of in U.S., 23

Rates of fertilizer
based on crop removal, 159
carryover related to, 161
for row application, 165, 167
maximum for anhydrous ammonia, 100
maximum for nitrogen in the row, 165, 167,
168

related to crop responsiveness, 164
related to fertilizer "burn", 168
related to soil conditions that limit yield, 164

Ratios, of fertilizer, Discussion of, 96
for row application, 166

Red leaf, of corn, 242, 285

Red streak (kernel), 295

Relative humidity in U.S., 190

Replanting, considerations for, 300

Residues, chemical
from herbicides, 230

Residues, plant *see also* **Organic matter**
amount from corn compared with other
crops, 28
effect on soil temperature, 58
food for soil organisms, 116-118
release of nitrogen from, 115-119
release of phosphorus from, 130
speeding decay of, 118, 121
to control erosion, 219

Response curve
from uneven fertilizer spreading, Fig. 116,
p. 171
related to soil test, Fig. 106, p. 155

Resistance
in insects, 26, 348
in weeds, 233
to disease, 38
to insects, 273

Ridge planting, 92

Rock phosphate, 126, 170

Rodent damage, 73, 294

Rooting depth
related to available water, 194
related to soil fertility, 194, 195

Roots
depth of, related to early planting, 77, 199
depth of, related to fertility, Fig. 134, p. 195
depth of, related to planting depth, Fig. 6,
p. 5
pruning of, by cultivation, Fig. 163, p. 235
sequence of development of, 3, 5, 6

Rootworms, 243, 269

Rotary hoe, 233

Rotary tiller, 62

Rotations, Discussion of, 25-31
advantages of, 29
changes for dry years, 199
compared to continuous corn, 25, 27-30
effect on weed problems, 230
influence on available nitrogen, 118, 160
influence on available water, 26, 199
relative nitrogen needs of corn in, 118, 160

Rots
ear, 245, 290-293
seedling, 241, 247
stalk, Fig. 95, p. 137, 178, 179, 245, 281,
287-289

Row fertilizer, Discussion of, 164-169
effect on rooting depth, 194-195
importance of phosphorus water-solubility
in, 124, 133, 167
need for phosphorus in, 124, 133, 167
"pop-up" placement for, 165
potassium need for, 138, 166, 167
preferred nutrient ratios for, 166, 167
rates of, 167

Rust, of corn, 284

S *see* **Sulfur**

Salt index, of fertilizer, 168

Sampling of soils, for testing, 152

Sands
available water in, 191
base exchange capacity of, 157
characteristics of, 145
leaching of nitrates in, 146, 175
special management of, 145

Sap beetles, 244, 276

Scutellum, 1, 2

Secondary nutrients, Discussion of, 140-144
list of, Table 7, p. 104

Secondary tillage, Discussion of, 64-66

Sediment pollution, 91, 341, 343
effect on phosphorus, 346

Seed *see* **Kernel**

Seedbed preparation, Section on, 53-75
adapted to planting equipment, 55
ideal for corn, 53
influence on erosion, 53, 57, 219
overfitting, consequences of, 56
to control weeds, 54
to improve tilth, 55

Seedcorn beetles, 241, 246

Seedcorn maggot, 241, 246

Seedling development, Discussion of, 2-5
causes of troubles of, 241, 246-249
effects of row fertilizer on, 164, 165

Selling *see* **Marketing**

Sewage, 341, 347, 355

Shrinkage
from drying grain, 329, 369

Sidedressing, 175, 198

Silage, Discussion of, 303-315
adding limestone to, 305
adding water to preserve, 305
center-cut, 306
ear-corn, 306
feeding high-nitrate in, 313
feeding to avoid loss of, 309
from frosted corn, 305
husklage, 307
losses in, 304
molding of, 304
nitrate poisoning from, 309
optimum harvest stage, 303
plant population for, 82, 307
poisonous gases in, 314
potassium removed in, 137
preservatives, 305
salvaging crop in drouth, 307
salvaging soft corn in, 331
stalklage, 306

Silks
cause of delayed emergence of, 13, 82, 244
cut condition, 242
eaten by insects, 244
emergence related to pollen shedding, 13, 82,
144
photograph of, Figs. 11, 13, p. 10, p. 11
role in fertilization of ovules, 10

Silo gas, 314

Silt soils
available water in, 191
characteristics of, 147
exchange capacity of, 157
management of, 147

Simazine, 29

Single-cross hybrids, 41, 42

Slag, basic, 128

Slow release fertilizers, 112, 346

Sludge, 341, 355

Slurry fertilizer, 104

Smoothing, of land, 203

Smut, 243, 284

SO₂ injury, 280

Sod planting, 29, 73, 220

Sod waterways, 218

Sod webworm, 242, 252

Soft corn, 330

Soil acidity, *see* **Acidity, of soil**

Soil conservation, 217-221 *see also* Erosion

Soil humus, 150

Soil moisture, Discussion of, 189-221
asphalt barrier, 200
in various soil types, 191
stretching supply of, 194
movement of, 200-207

Soil temperature
for denitrification, Fig. 86, p. 120
for fall application of nitrogen, 115
for nitrification, Fig. 85, p. 119
optimum for planting, 79

Soil tests, Discussion of, 151-157
by commercial laboratories, 156
by county extension agents and vocational agriculture teachers, 156
by fertilizer dealers, 156
for lime need, 257
for micronutrients, 151
for nitrogen, 151, 152
for phosphorus, 132, 151
for potassium, 138, 151
interpretation of, 154
reliability of, Table 13, p. 151
used with tissue tests, 300

Solar energy, for drying corn, 328

Solubility of phosphorus, in fertilizer, 125, 127-132

Solutions *see* **Nitrogen solutions**

Southern corn rootworm, 243, 244, 269

Southern leaf blight, 39, 277, 278

Southwestern corn borer, 294

Soybeans
cost to grow, 27
nitrogen from, Tables 9, p. 118, 161

Spectrographic analyses, 300, *see also* **Plant analyses and Plant tissue tests**

Spike-tooth harrow, 66, 233

Spreading, of fertilizer, 169-173

Spring plowing, 58

Spring-tooth harrow, 65, 66

Stalk borer, 271

Stalklage, 306

Stalk rots
Anthracnose, 281
Charcoal, 245, 288
Diplodia, 245, 247, 290
Gibberella, 245, 247, 290
Pythium, 245, 289

Stalks
adding nitrogen to speed decay of, 118
nitrates in, 309-313
nitrogen content of, 118, 309, 310, 315
rate of decay of, 117

Standability, of hybrids, 37 *see also* **Lodging**

Stand loss, 81-83

Starter fertilizer *see* **Row fertilizer**

Storage, of grain, Section on, 317-335
costs, 333
high-moisture grain in silos, 320
insects of, 296
safe moisture for, 318
systems for, 323
versus selling direct from field, 333

Stripe, genetic, 243, 282

Strip tillage, Fig. 40, p. 55, Fig. 53, p. 72

Stunt, disease of corn, 244, 266

Subsoil
related to degree of erosion damage, 217
source of water, 194

Subsoiling, 62
related to degree of erosion damage, 217
source of water, 194

Subsoiling, 62

Subsurface tiller, 60

Sulfate of potash, 136

Sulfate of potash-magnesia, 136, 168

Sulfur
an essential element, 104
availability related to pH, Fig. 124, p. 181
deficiency of, 128, 141, 242, 264

Superphosphate
ammoniation of, 115
fertilizers, 125-128
reactions in soil, 128-132

Superphosphoric acid, 126

Suspension fertilizer, 104

Sweet clover, nitrogen from, 160, 161

Symphylan, 253

Tassel
beginning of, Fig. 4, p. 4
ears, 286
function of, 8
pollen grain in, number of, 8

T cytoplasm, 42, 277

Temperature
cause of heat damage to corn plant, 266, 267
effect on denitrification, 120
effect on nitrification, 119
for drying corn, 327
for germination of corn, 79, 241
influence on period from planting to silking, 7
of leaf, 22, 36
of soil, 79
optimum for growth, 20
related to fall application of nitrogen, 115
related to growing degree days, 20, 36

Terraces, 219, 221

Three-way cross hybrids, 42

Tile drains, 203

Tillage, Section on, 53-75
minimum, 67-75, 89-92
primary, 57-63
secondary, 64-71
to break a crust, 196

Till planter, Fig. 40, p. 55, Fig. 42, p. 60

Tilth
effect on results of tissue tests, 299
effect on water intake of soil, 57, 196
for success with minimum tillage, 71
improved by organic matter, 148
improving in seedbed preparation, 56
influence on productivity lost by erosion, 217
related to need for cultivation, 196

Tissue tests *see* **Plant tissue tests**

Topping, of corn, 328

Toxins, 321

Toxic substances from organic matter, 149

Transpiration, 189-198

Tricalcium phosphate, 127

Triplesuperphosphate
ammoniation of, 127
manufacture and use of, 125
water solubility of, 125

Trytophane, 47

Universal soil loss equation, 219, 343

Urea
biuret injury, 249
characteristics and use of, 108, 109, 111
foliar application of, 177
in liquid fertilizers, 108, 111
in silage, 305
losses of, 109, 173
reactions in soil, 109, 111
salt index of, Table 19, p. 168

Ureaform fertilizer, 108

Viruses, 38

Vitamin A, effect of nitrates on, 313

Volatilization of nitrogen, 173, *see also* **Denitrification**

Water, Section on, 189-221
amount needed by crops, 189
available, amount in different soils, 191
available, increased by early planting, 77, 198
available, increasing supply of, 194-197
available, influenced by plant population, 83, 84
available, influenced by row width, 83, 84
available, methods to stretch supply of, 194, 198
available, related to rotation, 26, 199
capillary movement of, 200
conserved by fall plowing, 58
daily loss of, by regions, 215

effect of potassium on need for, 196
efficiency of use by crops, 189, 190, 194, 198
efficiency, related to cropping practices, 194, 198
efficiency, related to humidity, 190
efficiency, related to yield, Fig. 133, p. 194
for irrigation, 207-216
increasing efficiency by chemical treatment, 200
increasing efficiency by early planting, 77, 198
increasing efficiency by high fertility, 194, 195, 198
increasing efficiency by optimum population, 198
increasing efficiency in narrow rows, 83, 198
increasing efficiency of, 194-200
increasing efficiency with plastic covers; 200
increasing infiltration of, 196
in subsoil, 194
loss by evaporation, 83, 195, 199, 200, 215
movement to roots, 200
net amount for leaching of nitrogen, 114
practices that conserve, 219
seasonal balance in soil, 190, 191

Water solubility, of phosphorus
change in soil, 130
effect of ammoniation on, 127
importance of, 133, 148, 167
in fertilizers, 125

Waxy maize, 46

Weed chemicals, injury from, 241, 254, 255

Weed control, Section on, 223-237
by biological methods, 235
by crop rotation, 230
by flame, 236
by minimum tillage, 234
by preplant harrowing, 225
herbicide-fertilizer mixtures, 229
pre-emergence, 226
post-emergence, 228
residue problems of, 230

Weeds
early effect of, 224
effect of minimum tillage on, 234
effect on yield, Table 30, p. 224, Fig. 155, p. 225
perennial, in rotated crops, 30, 230-233
shift in species, 230

Western bean cutworm, 271

Western corn rootworm, 226, 243, 269

Wheel-track planting, 68

White corn, 45

Wide rows, of corn, 84, 85

Wind damage, 251

Wireworms, 26, 241, 242, 246, 252

Witchweed, 235, 283

Woolybear caterpillars, 244

Yellow-striped armyworm, 242, 253

Yield curve, Fig. 106, p. 155

Yield guides, for soils, 145

Yield of corn
components of, 37
effect of temperature on, 20
increase in efficiency of various crops, 20
trends in U.S., Fig. 197, p. 366

Zein, 322

Zero-till, 31, 73, 74, 89

Zinc
an essential element, 104
availability related to pH, Fig. 124, p. 181
deficiency of, 133, 141, 242, 258
effect of phosphorus on, 133, 141, 258
removed in crops, Table 1, p. 368

Zn *see* **Zinc**

Credits

Layout and Design
Paula Wheeler
Stephen P. Wheeler

Cover Design: Paula and Stephen P. Wheeler
Cover Photo: Grant Heilman

1. • **0,** Grant Heilman • **1,** W. O. Scott • **2,** O. T. Bonnett, University of Illinois • **3,** S. R. Aldrich; Grant Heilman • **4,** O. T. Bonnett and E. R. Leng • **5,6,** S. R. Aldrich • **9,** E. R. Leng; Grant Heilman • **10,** O. T. Bonnett; W. O. Scott • **11,** John Knoop • **12,** E. B. Earley • **14,** J. Hanway, Iowa State University • **15,** S. R. Aldrich, W. O. Scott • **16, 17,** S. R. Aldrich

2. • **18,** Grant Heilman • **19,** USDA • **20,21,** P. and S. Wheeler • **22,** USDA • **23,** Kansas State Board of Agriculture • **24,25,** USDA • **27,** S. R. Aldrich • **29,** Crops and Soils Magazine, ASA • **30,** P. and S. Wheeler (S. R. Aldrich data) • **31,** Grant Heilman • **32,** Susan Hyde

3. • **34,** S. R. Aldrich • **38,** P. and S. Wheeler (W. A. Russell, Iowa data) • **40,** Susan Hyde (E. R. Leng data) • **41,** W. O. Scott • **47,** W. O. Scott, D. E. Alexander • **48,** P. and S. Wheeler (D. R. Hicks, Minnesota data) • **49,** W. O. Scott • **51,** University of Illinois

4. • **52,** Grant Heilman • **54,** Allis-Chalmers Mfg. Co. • **55,** International Harvester • **56,** D. Dennis • **57,58,** S. R. Aldrich • **59,** Allis-Chalmers Mfg. Co. • **60,** International Harvester Co. • **61,** F. L. Duley, USDA; Kazik Pazovski • **62,** Allis-Chalmers Mfg. Co. • **63,** Cornell University • **65,** Allis-Chalmers Mfg. Co. • **66,** Allis-Chalmers Mfg. Co. • **67,** Brillion Iron Works, Inc. • **68,** Allis-Chalmers Mfg. Co.; S. R. Aldrich • **69,** Ohio Agriculture Experiment Station • **70,** S. R. Aldrich • **72,** S. R. Aldrich, Deere & Co. • **74,** Deere & Co. • **75,** John Knoop

5. • **76,** Grant Heilman • **78,** P. and S. Wheeler (E. C. Rossman Data) • **79,** University of Illinois • **82,83,** P. and S. Wheeler (S. R. Aldrich) • **85,** S. R. Aldrich; University of Illinois • **89,** International Harvester Co. • **90,91,** Grant Heilman • **92,** W. E. Larson; University of Minnesota

6 • **94,** Grant Heilman • **96,** Iowa State University • **97,** P. and S. Wheeler • **98,** Successful Farming • **99,101,** P. and S. Wheeler (S. R. Aldrich) • **102,** G. Heilman • **103,** P. and S. Wheeler • **106,** J. Hanway, Iowa State University • **107,** Mid-America Pipeline Co., Williams Bros., Gulf Central Pipeline Co. • **110,** J. Whittaker • **114,** S. R. Aldrich, L. B. Nelson (adapted from Thornthwaite) • **115,** L. B. Nelson • **116,** M. Meibers • **117,** P. and S. Wheeler • **119,120,** Susan Hyde (S. R. Aldrich) • **121, 122,** S. R. Aldrich; Grant Heilman • **123,** J. Hanway, Iowa State University • **128,** M. Meibers • **129,130,131,** P. and S. Wheeler (S. R. Aldrich) • **134,** J. Hanway, Iowa State University • **135,136,** P. and S. Wheeler (S. R. Aldrich) • **137,** American Potash Institute **138,** Susan Hyde • **139,143,** S. R. Aldrich • **144,** K. M. Towe, University of Illinois; Susan Hyde • **146,** Susan Hyde • **148,149,** S. R. Aldrich • **151,** Iowa State University • **153,155,** University of Illinois • **158,** P. and S. Wheeler • **159,** Floyd Drauden • **160,** M. Meibers • **163,-164,** P. and S. Wheeler (University of Illinois data) • **165,** Janice Gernon • **167,** S. R. Aldrich • **169-171,** Susan Hyde (S. R. Aldrich data) • **172,** TVA • **174,** J. Hanway, Iowa State University • **175** P. and S. Wheeler (University of Illinois data) • **176,** S. R. Aldrich • **179,** Susan Hyde (University of Wisconsin data) • **180,** USDA • **181,** E. R. Swanson, C. R. Taylor, L. F. Welch (University of Illinois); S. R. Aldrich • **182,** Susan Hyde • **183,** S. R. Aldrich • **186,** P. and S. Wheeler (University of Illinois data)

7. • **188,** Grant Heilman • **189,** Susan Hyde • **190,** USDA • **191,** Susan Hyde (M. B. Russell data) • **192,193,** P. and S. Wheeler (S. R. Aldrich) • **194,** M. Meibers (University of Nebraska data) • **195,** J. Fehrenbacher • **196,** University of Illinois • **197,** Allis-Chalmers Mfg. Co. • **198,** M. Meibers (University of Illinois data) • **199,201,** S. R. Aldrich • **204,205,** W. H. Gardner • **206,** W. R. Gardner, P. and S. Wheeler • **207,** P. and S. Wheeler • **209,** J. R. Borchert, University of Minnesota • **211,212,** Grant Heilman • **213,** R. H. Shaw (Iowa State University) • **214,** Michigan State University • **217,218,** S. R. Aldrich • **221,** Grant Heilman

8. • **222,** S. R. Aldrich • **225,** J. Whittaker (Rutgers University data) • **227,** S. R. Aldrich; M. Meibers • **229,** Glenn Klingman • **231,** P. and S. Wheeler (F. W. Slife data) • **232,** Grant Heilman, Jim Shaffer • **235,** S. R. Aldrich

9. • **238,** Grant Heilman • **246,** J. W. Apple, University of Wisconsin; University of Illinois; Illinois Natural History Survey; J. W. Apple • **247,** Arnold Ullstrup; S. R. Aldrich • **248,** University of Illinois • **249,** S. R. Aldrich • **250,** R. E. Lucas, Michigan State University; S. R. Aldrich • **251,** S. R. Aldrich; M. Meibers • **252,-253,** University of Illinois; Illinois Natural History Survey • **254,** University of Illinois • **255,** S. R. Aldrich; University of Illinois • **256,** A. L. Lang • **257,** S. R. Aldrich • **258,** M. D. Weldon; B. A. Krantz • **259,** S. R. Aldrich • **260,** S. R. Aldrich • **262,** North Carolina Agricultural Experiment Station; McKay Publ. Co. • **263,** A. L. Lang; S. M. Melsted • **264,** S. E. Younts • **265,** Univ. of Nebraska; Univ. of North Carolina; W. O. Scott • **267,** Arnold Ullstrup • **268,** B. Koehler, S. R. Aldrich • **269,** Michigan State University; Illinois Natural History Survey • **270,** Janice Gernon (Purdue University data) • **271,** Stirling Kyd; Illinois Natural History Survey; John J. Faringer • **272,** Grant Heilman, Sterling Kyd **273,** S. R. Aldrich • **274,** Harold J. Ball; Grant Heilman; Illinois Natural History Survey • **275,** Grant Heilman; Sterling Kyd; Grant Heilman • **276,** Illinois Natural History Survey; S. R. Aldrich • **277,** W. O. Scott, S. R. Aldrich • **279,** Arnold Ullstrup • **280,** S. R. Aldrich; B. Koehler; S. R. Aldrich • **281,** K. J. Leonard, North Carolina St. Univ.; B. Koehler • **282,** S. R. Aldrich; A. L. Hooker • **283,** R. R. Nelson (Pennsylvania State University) • **284,** B. Koehler; S. R. Aldrich • **285,** S. R. Aldrich; Earl R. Leng • **286,287,** S. R. Aldrich • **288,** B. Koehler; M. P. Britton • **289,** M. P. Britton; S. R. Aldrich • **290,** B. Koehler • **291,** B. Koehler • **292,** S. R. Aldrich, B. Koehler • **293,** B. Koehler • **294,** Grant Heilman • **295,** W. O. Scott; S. R. Aldrich • **296,** Western Lithograph Co., Inc.• **298,** Kazik Pazovski, M. Meibers • **301,** M. Meibers

10. • **302,** Grant Heilman • **303,** P. and S.Wheeler • **308,** University of Illinois • **310,** Susan Hyde (S. R. Aldrich) • **311,** Data from Zuber, University of Missouri • **314,315,** Susan Hyde

11. • **316,** Grant Heilman • **319,** USDA • **321,** Robert Nyvall, Iowa State University • **323,** Pfister Associated Growers, Inc. • **324,** V. W. Davis, USDA • **326,327,** P. and S. Wheeler • **328,** South Dakota State University • **329,** John Knoop; V. W. Davis, USDA • **332,333,** Information Canada, Publ. No. 1205 • **335,** Susan Hyde (T. A. Hieronymus) • **337,** L. F. Stice, University of Illinois

12. • **338,** Grant Heilman • **341,** P. and S. Wheeler (S. R. Aldrich) • **343,** P. and S. Wheeler (S. R. Aldrich); Illinois State Water Survey • **344,** W. R. Oschwald • **345,** S. R. Aldrich • **347,** University of Illinois • **349,** Grant Heilman

13. • **352,** Grant Heilman • **355,** John Siemens, Robert Hoeft, University of Illinois • **357,** H. P. Bateman • **359,** Grant Heilman

14. • **360,** J. C. Allen and Son • **363,364,** P. and S. Wheeler (S. R. Aldrich) • **366,** P. and S. Wheeler (S. R. Aldrich) • **367,** Grant Heilman